One Hundred Years
of Hill Farming

First published in 2014 on behalf of the author by
Scotforth Books, Carnegie House,
Chatsworth Road, Lancaster LA1 4SL

ISBN 13: 978-1-909817-10-4
Printed in the UK by Short Run Press, Exeter.

One Hundred Years of Hill Farming

G. H. Cole

CONTENTS

ACKNOWLEDGEMENTS

For our parents, for Ella, Paula and John and for our grandchildren, Reuben and Nathan.

A few words are necessary about the scope of this book. Based on a series of articles written by my father for the *Penrith Herald* after his retirement in the 1970s, these are interspersed with letters, records, descriptions and artefacts covering our lives in 'Cumberland' through a century. It should be emphasised that the opinions presented in this book are our own but on certain topics I have included appropriate quotations by notable writers which underline and tune with my arguments. The mistakes this book doubtless contains are all my own work; all opinions expressed are all our own.

The later chapters were written in response to Structure plans, Political Papers, disease epidemics and similar crises over the last sixty years.

We thank Mrs Phyllis Scott for her excellent typing, patience and suggestions in the preparation of the text, and Mrs Penny Hayashi for the excellent layout.

All the illustrations and drawings are our copyright except those specifically acknowledged. The photographs were reproduced from glass half-plate negatives in the twenties, and from Verichrome and Selochrome negatives (120 size) in roll-film cameras up to the nineties; from the very simple to secondhand models you 'traded up' to something better as or when you could afford to treat yourself. My early colour pictures in the fifties were taken with a Zeiss 'Tenax' camera (a model manufactured in 1938 and way ahead of its time), yielding superb transparencies, 24x24 mm on Kodachrome 25ASA film. These were stored for half a century and pressed in envelopes in books, etc. undisturbed, until I could afford the digital scanners and printer to reproduce them. It is indeed remarkable how well the colours have lasted all those years and how good were the colour emulsions.

I only changed over to digital SLRs since 2008, meaning that today I have thousands of historic slides to sort through, save and print as records for posterity…

A Spanish silver crown given to Mary Robinson – the Beauty of Buttermere – by Hatfield and inscribed with her name. He was hanged for bigamy. Later Mary married Richard Harrison of Todcrofts farm, Caldbeck. This coin has passed down the female line of the Harrison and Greenup families.

FOREWORD

The first time I saw my future father-in-law was on Border TV where he had a ten minute programme on antiques, bygones and collectables. My mother and I watched every time he was featured.

Sidney was the son of two ship owning families from Blyth in Northumberland. His father and grandfathers were seafarers; Captain John Cole ran away to sea aged 12 years. They owned collier brigs and traded with the Baltic countries during the upheavals of the Napoleonic wars taking out coal and returning with timber and general cargo. This meant as a boy my father-in-law heard many stories and was introduced to many ships' captains and their families.

Perhaps this background prepared him to become a prolific writer interested in reading, researching the ways, customs, traditions and artefacts of his adopted county. A man before his time, and skilled in so many crafts (he was a very practical man as revealed in the book), he constructed perhaps the first radio in the parish and built one of the very early and successful motor hay mowers. During the long winter evenings he crafted furniture from locally grown oak. With his many friends of the first world war, he played billiards and laid out a private golf course on Faulds Brow Common!

He was born a 'Geordie' but played a noteworthy part in the Cumberland Dialect Society which he and his wife loved. So the Northumbrian lad became a true Cumbrian, ably assisted by his wife Dora. Her relations on one side of a yeoman family go back to Mary, the beauty of Buttermere, and on the other, the woollen industry, manufacturing blankets and John Peel's coat so grey...

During a sort out amongst the vast archive he left us, my husband and I thought it would make interesting reading to combine his father's 50 years of farming with his own, into a book. We hope readers find this compilation of history and life on two hill farms as absorbing as we have in researching it.

Ella Cole M.B.E.

In my youth and up to the early sixties there were two butchers in Caldbeck – Pattison's in Mid-Town and Ashbridges at Heron Rigg, Upton. Sam Ashbridge and his father Edgar butchered sheep and cattle in the barn here and the meat was hung up in the shop (the right-hand small door). After September 1939 controls required all slaughter to be centralised. – in our area in Wigton at premises in Water Street. (The parish hall is in the background of this picture.)

ONE

FIFTY YEARS OF FELL FARMING

'S. H. C.' looks back to his early days

Mr S. H. Cole, Brownrigg, Caldbeck, who has written articles for the *Herald* for over forty years, many under the title of 'On t' Fellside Now', tells of his introduction to farming and how he came to Caldbeck over fifty years ago.

In 1919 my father bought me Brownrigg, Caldbeck, and I began farming on my own, and without a wife!

A prominent businessman in the village was heard to say, I was told, 'He won't be there 18 months'. That was 50 years ago and I'm still there! Perhaps a letter dated 7 March 1897, and written to my father by one of his close friends, a shoemaker in the village of Felton in Northumberland, congratulating him upon my birth, may shed some light upon my leaning to farming as a career.

The writer, like so many more country craftsmen of his time, was a versatile man, shoemaker, great reader, local preacher and smallholder.

The three-quarters of an acre almost kept him in food. In it he kept a dozen hives of bees, a sow and pigs, hens, grew all the vegetables he needed, and all the fruit. He also kept a cow and her calf and somehow managed to make enough hay to winter her. But to get back to the letter, he ended it like this, 'The little boy will never thrive until he is carried 6 times up and down our garden and the cow licks his hands and feet and his nose, so come quickly and give the young man a chance for maturity.'

As I grew up I was brought much into contact with shipping, coal-mining and railways throughout the Northumberland and Durham coalfields because my father was mineral agent to the North Eastern Railway.

A large part of his work involved visiting ships, mines and rail depots. I used to be taken with him whenever possible and perhaps this made me like an open air life. In any case it

A model of a family-owned collier brig, the *Vesper*.

was perhaps just as well because although I was sent to the Royal Grammar School, Newcastle, I was the perfect dunce. I was so hopeless that most of the masters there ignored me. The French monitor, a tall heavy man, like de Gaulle, who was very excitable, once got down on his knees behind the blackboard and prayed for me!

I left school in 1912 and went, as a daily worker, to a large farm near Consett to learn farming.

Starting Wage – Nothing!

The terms were that I paid nothing for being allowed to learn, and I got no wages. I had to carry my own meals, had to do as, and whatever, I was told, had to be there at 8.00 a.m. and had to cycle the three miles there and back each day. I was usually allowed to start for home at 5.00 p.m. in winter, but in hay harvest we worked until the dew came down.

My relatives, all shipping or business people who had never heard of a member of the family being a farmer, were rather sorry for me. Such a nasty, dirty, hard work sort of job. An old schoolmaster uncle, who was head of a big school in Gateshead perhaps summed the matter up for them when he said to me one day, 'Oh, any fool can be a farmer – you cannot stop the grass growing!'

Unfortunately this attitude is still at the back of the mind of a large section of the public today. Fortunately my father was behind me all the way. He had been a sailor

The Royal Grammar School in Newcastle. The building is still in use today.

but had always loved the country and its people. My mother had been in business on her own account and knew how to keep her own counsel and remained completely neutral. I don't remember feeling that it was strange that I should choose such a job, or that never having done a day's work on a farm mattered in the least. So I set off with an entirely open mind upon my first day's work.

I was an only child, and very shy. So when I arrived at Urpeth North Farm to be a farmer's boy on a cold and wet November day in 1912, the first job I was given might well have driven the whole idea from my head for good.

I was told to go into a draughty and cold barn to sort sticky and wet potatoes with a gang of girls employed on the farm. There were whispers and sniggers and sly glances at the new boy from the girls, and how I got through the day I don't know. It still ranks in my mind as the very worst job I ever had to do on a farm. But it didn't damp my enthusiasm.

Modern Farm

The farm was an amazingly modern one, even by today's standards. There were 300 acres of it, half reasonably flat, and the other half as hilly as any farm in Cumberland. It was about 15 miles from Newcastle and two miles from the nearest village.

The boss was a 'square hat' farmer who never worked manually himself. A just man, and a man of few words, a strong churchman and a bachelor. I never saw him lose his temper or be upset by any happening or the vilest weather, and no swearing was allowed on the farm.

The staff comprised a housekeeper, a housemaid, a foreman, Tom Pringle – a grand fellow – a head horseman and a second and third horseman, and three other men all able to handle horses, 12 girls, mostly pitmen's daughters, and two of the farm men's daughters and a 'gaffer' who was in charge of them. There was also a lad of about 14, one of the men's sons, whose ambition was to be a jockey.

One of my jobs each week was to be sent to the bank in Anfield to get the wages. These were, by today's standards, amazing. The foreman had 25s., the head horseman 22s., the second 21s. per week and their cottages. The other men had 18s. and no house and the lad had 7s. 6d. The girls had 1s. a day and their gaffer £1 per week. All had to take their own meals. In hay and harvest the boss paid overtime and 'laid on' as many miners as cared to turn up at 1s. an hour. I have seen 20 turn up on most days and this made haymaking a busy and satisfying time because it meant that good hay was made when the weather allowed and taught me that money spent at hay-time is always well worthwhile. The boss always met the foreman at 8.00 a.m. and gave his orders.

The stock pens at York Auction in 1960 to which droves of cattle came from Ireland and the North of Scotland. Cattle dealters offer their stock in the pens beneath the imposing city wall. The mart has long since been moved out of town and redeveloped.

During the two years I was there I never saw a hitch – the place ran like a good clock. It was, I suppose, one of the earliest 'specialist' farms. We had 14 work horses, mostly Shires, and it was almost a certainty that each Monday morning two or three of them had a 'shot of grease' in the legs. After a rub with homemade embrocation and work it was usually gone on Tuesday.

We also had a stud of 12 'blood' breeding mares and a 'blood' stallion. Of course, we had numerous foals and yearlings and two year olds. Tom, the foreman, looked after the 'blood' mares and the stallion. Bob Liddle, a Cumbrian, and we two lads, helped with any horse jobs. Tom never entered the stallion's box until he had thrown in his cap to see what sort of temper the old chap was in. If he came forward and trampled and muzzled it with his ears back, Tom took special precautions.

Tricky Horses

All the young horses and brood mares were to exercise every day and a hectic job it was. You had to learn fast to survive, for these horses had every trick off and were as quick as lightning.

One of the worst jobs we had to do was to accustom them to road traffic – motors were so rare then that every one was a menace – and to trains upon the railway which was about half a mile away. All long distance transport of cattle and horses was by rail in those days.

As the horses were for racing and hunting the boss insisted that they all be trained to stand under a certain railway arch while a train went overhead. This was quite a test for both horses and men.

Our other stock at Urpeth was two cows, two pigs, a few poultry and 40 Leicester sheep. Each back-end about 60 bullocks from Ireland were bought in and fed during the winter. We men never had anything to do with the cows, pigs, or poultry – these were looked after by the women in the house, except for cleaning out.

A strange stock, you will think, for a good 300-acre farm! Stranger still, 280 acres of it were ploughed in rotation all the time! The 20 acres of grass, with the fogs from the hay crops, were used for the horses and sheep.

Everything, excepting some of the hay and the straw and some threshed oats kept for the horses, was sold in Newcastle market.

I have said that the farm was amazingly modern. The bullocks were fed on the self feed system so much advocated today. They were housed in an open yard about 40 yards square with hay racks around the walls and with half roofs and open fronts and were allowed to eat their fill of hay and straw put into the racks daily.

Instead of wasting the straw, as is so often the case today, it was tipped into the cattle yard each week to a depth of about four feet for the cattle to tread into manure. It was emptied and carted to the fields once each week during winter and refilled with fresh straw. This was the primary purpose of the bullocks.

A picture taken in 1962 of a hay stacking gang on a large farm in Fife, Scotland, the same method used on the large farm in County Durham where my father began work as a farm lad. The block and tackle is used to lift the grabfuls of hay up to the mewers and swing into place on the stack. The Fordson Dexta has replaced the horse.

Nitrogen Frowned Upon

The huge ploughing acreage kept the six drafts of horses going every day, there was no carting to be done. We even had a proper artificial manure shed, covered in and with a loading and unloading platform like a railway station, for the handling of slag, superphosphate and potash. Nitrogen was hardly known then and was frowned upon.

To keep the land in good heart, since everything was being sold off, train loads of 'night manure' from the privvies in Newcastle and fish heads and guts from South Shields were bought and sent to our station whenever possible to get them. Leading it to the farm was a frightful job. Thank heaven, after about five minutes in a five-ton truck of it, you could hardly smell anything!

The farm belonged to the coal-owning Joycey family and their collieries bought nearly all our 120 acres of hay each year as they had hundreds of pit ponies to feed at that time. The colliery representative checked up on the date the hay was made on each farm contracting to sell to the colliery. All hay had to be piked and had to stand in a pike three weeks, and each farm was notified of the date they were allowed to lead it to the huge 500-ton stacks on the collieries. This was, of course, a precaution against 'firing' and poor quality musty hay. On leading day, with pike bogies, every load went over the weigh bridge and was then dumped at the foot of the hay stack mast and was hauled up by a pony with block and tackle, the arm of the mast allowing the hay to be swung to any part of the stack where it was levelled out.

The wheat and oats filled a stackyard with 50 or 60 very large stacks and required several weeks each winter to thresh them with a 'steamer'. Potatoes made up the rest of our cropping. Practically all of this was sold in Newcastle market.

Production entailed every type of horse-work. Whenever I could see an opportunity I used to ask to be allowed to go with Jack Strangeways, the head horseman.

He had a grand quiet way with his pair. He trusted them and they trusted him and would do anything for him.

The second horseman was a shouting bully who was really frightened of horses. His pair were always on edge and fidgeting, and he taught me what not to do with a pair of horses.

I used to take Jack an ounce of tobacco and a newspaper whenever I thought there was going to be something I wanted to try my hand at, and he used to allow me to have a go while he had a smoke and read in the dyke-back – always watching that I didn't spoil his work though.

Despite its situation in a high remote lakeland Valley, Caldbeck village posessed several notable houses. Midtown House in the center of the village was owned by the Jennings family and tenanted by Mr and Mrs Hewitson, and was where my father 'lived in' with other learners. Upton House was the home of the Greenup family, and was my mother's home. Ratten Row belonged to the Ivinson family. Others of note were Bridge End, Fellside Mansion, Hesket Hall and Brownrigg. Brownrigg was in poor shape when my father purchased it.

Moving On

By the time I had been on the farm two years I had been shown my horsework by Tom, Bob Liddle and Jack, and was able to do practically everything with them. War had, however, broken out and most of my friends had joined up. I wanted to do so, but my father would not agree. I was only 17 and, at that time, not eligible, and I knew he would get me out if I did join, so I felt I should go to some farm where I could really be needed as a horseman.

I advertised in the farming press. Many men had volunteered from farms and men were scarce, and I had the amazing experience of having 142 replies to the advertisement to go as a 'horseman improver'.

Hand milking – a pail between your legs, head pressed into the cow's belly to make her keep her leg back and stop her from kicking. The man sits on a typical three-legged 'copy', or stool, a meal 'kist' is to the right, and the typical shorthorn cow is feeding at a wooden trough.

Bucket feeding calves a portion of linseed gruel mixed with separated milk (a by product of buttermaking). This was a familiar scene on any Cumbrian livestock farm up to the 1980s.

These replies to my advertisement for a job were quite bewildering. They were from as far afield as Devon and Aberdeen. Many offered me my own terms, plus horseriding, shooting, fishing, fox hunting, otter hunting; some said they had a daughter but the one who capped the lot said he had two daughters and a piano!

Well, I certainly wasn't interested in girls at that time, so that one was out straight away. The hunting, fishing and shooting did not appeal to me either. What I wanted was to go as a horseman on some farm where I could gain experience with other livestock. So I chose Christopher Hewetson's at Midtown, Caldbeck, whose farm was very mixed and included a fell stock of sheep as well.

I realised immediately that Christopher knew his job because he met me at Wigton station with his fast trotting pony and American buggy (see picture on p. 132) and so the journey to Caldbeck did not look half as far as it really was, or often looked many times since.

The terms were that I was to live 'as the family' and receive 3s. 6d. a week. I wasn't interested in what money I got – I wanted to learn the job and was prepared to take anything so long as I got the knowledge. But I often wonder what modern young men would think if they had to start the same way.

Hours were not mentioned, but we were very short staffed on this (then) 160-acre farm, with a fairly large 'heafed' flock of sheep at least three miles over the fells to walk to get to them about twice a week. With foals and yearlings, about seven horses, 50 pedigree Shorthorn cattle and a bull, three or four sows and litters, and usually 15–20 calves to bucket morning and night, it was a 'thrang' place with only three of us and the servant girl to get through it.

The Daily Routine

It turned out that we started at 5.00 a.m. The routine was always the same. Tommy, the other young chap there, and I, turned out the horses from the stable to water. While they were out we cleaned out the stable and put up their bedding, brought them back in and gave them their corn and hay. The byres were next mucked out, the cows foddered and caked (if they were milking). The mistress, the servant girl, and usually Christopher, turned out next – the women to help with the milking while Christopher did the bull.

The others were excellent milkers, but I had never even tried it and even after six months the others could milk four while I milked one. I am convinced that unless you learn hand milking while a child you never do make a good milker. The milk was next separated by an old 'Diabolo' hand-turned separator and the cream taken to the dairy for butter making.

Linseed meal gruel was next mixed and fed to the calves with the separated milk. This was all expected to be done by 7.30 a.m. prompt, when we all went into the house for breakfast. This consisted of a bowl of thick porridge, a pint of skim milk, bread and butter and tea, and unless you were taking the bull cart to Wigton or Penrith, it never varied.

At 8.00 a.m. we turned out with our horses to the field work, 'loosed out' at ten minutes before noon for dinner and began again with field work at 1.00 p.m. until 5.00 p.m. Then came the routine of milking, calves, pigs, horses to do up for the night, and we were supposed to be finished at 6.00 p.m. These were pretty hefty hours for me, but I stuck it.

On top of our own work we did a lot of threshing, rolling oats, grinding wheat and even drying corn on our proper grain dryer (coal-fired in those days) for neighbouring farmers. Our threshing and milling was done by water wheel from the beck.

The fact that we were short staffed ensured that I got every job on a farm to do, and so much of it that I have been thankful for the experience ever since.

Christopher was an even tempered, shrewd, capable practical farmer who knew every twist and turn and trick of stock or the weather. He had also acted as assistant for many years to his brother, a veterinary surgeon at Brampton and was nearly as good as a vet himself – especially in those days of 'treacle and sulphur'. He was called in to all emergencies in our parish of Caldbeck and even further afield and I was often taken with him, a valuable experience indeed.

Important Experience

But the really important experience was, when living as the family, the 'crack' of farming folk, the boss and his wife and farming friends who dropped in either to take the advice of Christopher or to discuss markets, methods, weather, the mistakes of other farmers and the country lore. This cannot be learned in agricultural college.

In those days of 1914–15 there were no effective remedies for navel-ill and joint felling in foals; glanding in horses; white scour in calves; milk fever; mastitis (called garget then); or fluke in cattle and sheep; or black quarter and pulpy kidney in sheep.

Abortion was also a scourge. Christopher had all these upon his farm, as had a great many more farmers in the area, and it was just a matter of allowing them to run their courses and, as we know now, they did to a large extent inoculate the animals and their offspring in due course. Meanwhile, it was a question of who could last longer, the farmer or the disease.

Due to disease, the boss once told me he didn't know where to turn for his next penny. His farmhouse was a large Georgian one with about eight bedrooms and it was then, in 1912, that he told me his wife and he decided to take farm pupils. There were still two there when I arrived; the others, and one of these, all joined the forces. He took pupils after the war again and had quite a lot in 1918–19 and these saved the situation for him, but for many farmers in those days who earned their living from livestock, disease drove them out.

These young gentlemen paid high fees but very few indeed ever became successful farmers upon their own account. Christopher and his wife were an ideal pair for the pupil enterprise.

Through brothers who were a doctor, a vet, a clergyman and a lecturer at an agricultural college, he had ample contacts to get pupils and his even temperament and great experience made him an able teacher. He would go to endless trouble to show any of them who showed real interest in trying to learn the job, but if they were the idle playing type he ignored them and left them to their own devices.

An Excellent Cook

The 'mistress' was an excellent housekeeper. One of the best cooks I ever knew, she could make a 'tatie pot' an excellent and appetising meal with practically nothing but potatoes in it. Her rice puddings, with a lovely brown skin on them, could make your mouth water. And, again, her home-made cakes of the simplest kinds, were beautifully baked and shaped and a treat. Her meals had the great merit of always being dead on time; breakfast 7.30 a.m., dinner 12 noon, tea brought out to wherever we were working at 3.00 p.m. and supper 6.30 p.m.

The only time we saw bacon and eggs was when we had to get off to market with the bull cart to Penrith (17 miles) or Wigton (8 miles) at 5.30 a.m.

It was a long weary job with a heavy horse at walking pace all the way, and especially going there, for the horses were always to push when facing away from home. They came home at a good pace which improved the nearer they got to home. Hours were so long at Midtown – the only time we could call our own was on Sunday from 1.00 p.m. to 3.00 p.m. – and with half the young chaps off in the army there was little social life in Caldbeck and I saw little of the folk around me.

However, in March 1915, I was 18 and still anxious to join up. I shall never forget how guilty I felt when one day I was going home for a week-end and found myself sitting in the train at Carlisle station under the big Kitchener poster pointing at me and the caption 'Your King and Country need you'. I was thankful when the train moved out. As a farm worker I could have been deferred. That July I joined the army, much against the wishes of Christopher and my father.

Drilling bobbins at the Bobbin Mill in the Howk, Caldbeck.
Note the knee-deep shavings and saw dust - a perfect fire hazard.

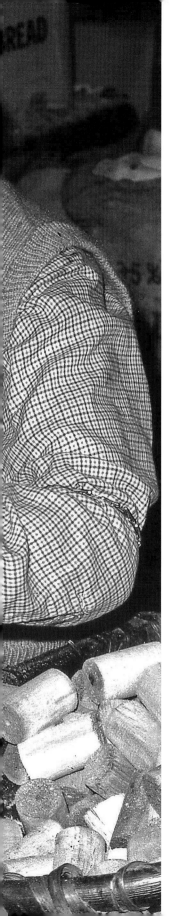

Two

FARMING ON MY OWN ACCOUNT AND LIFE IN THE VILLAGE

Fifty years of Fell Farming – 'S. H. C.' looks back to his early days

Mr S. H. Cole, Brownrigg, Caldbeck, who has written articles for the *Herald* for over forty years, many under the title of 'On t'Fellside Now,' told in an article last week of his introduction to farming in the days before the 1914–18 war. After serving in the army from 1915 to 1918 and gaining a commission, Mr Cole returned to Caldbeck in November 1918. In this article he describes life in the village and how he began farming on his own account.

My old farming job at Midtown, Caldbeck, was still open for me and I was glad to get back. While I had been in the army I had been able to see the hill farming of Wales, with its tiny and very poor holdings; the clever use of the rivers in the Dorset bottoms where they were made to irrigate the meadow lands to increase the hay crops. But French farming most interested me.

They did not waste an inch of ground. Even dykes and hedges were non-existent in most of the parts I was in, and cattle were 'hobbled' by a hind foot and made to eat up before they were moved. All their work seemed to be done by hand, and they were very clean farmers, so far as their land was concerned. Their farm yards and buildings were, however, literally dung heaps. But I had seen nothing better than Cumberland in my travels and preferred being a 'mud student', as folks like me were called in those days, to being an officer in the army.

In 1918 Caldeck was self-sufficient and self-contained. A few turners still worked at the Bobbin Mill, and one of the old workers at the woollen factory still worked one of the looms as a hobby for his retirement, making 'rag carpeting' for house

Inside the bobbin mill: note the depth of shavings on the floor. This picture was taken in 1966 before Stott Park closed. It was later re-opened as a tourist attraction.

mats. Two corn and flour mills were still in full work, and a saw mill was kept busy. The Barytes mine employed several men, including small farmers who carted the ore to Wigton by horse and cart.

Slowly the lads from the army filtered back. Unlike the town lads, who came back and could not find jobs, our lads were able to find work, for we had three blacksmiths in the parish, three joiners, four boot and clog makers, several masons and a large quarry supplying road stone to the Council. We even had a cycle shop, and the beginnings of a Post Office-cum-tailors'-shop-cum garage business. Three tailors and several milliners also flourished, and there were four butchers and five grocery and provision businesses.

A Model T Ford

The owner of one of these provision businesses, the late William Ivinson, was the possessor of our only motor car, an old model T Ford. There is little doubt that if he had been driving it today he would have had a daily crash, for he never expected to meet anyone else on the road or to have to pull up at a cross roads.

Our parson and doctor were friendly souls who had been with us long enough to be upon familiar terms with everyone from the smallest child to the oldest inhabitant. The school master declared a holiday whenever there was a hunt and joined in. If fights broke out among his boys he cleared a ring and refereed the fight and then made the contestants wash each others' faces and shake hands. Joe, the policeman, was a gem who would say a friendly 'good night' to a passing villager after dark without a light. He liked farming and used to get his coat off and help when supervising dipping. But if any of the children were caught stealing apples and the like small crimes, he gave them a hiding, and peace reigned in our village.

The strange thing is that, while wages were rarely more than 30/- a week, there was no stealing. You could leave your house open, or tools lying in a field for a week on end and they would be there when you went for them. We made our own amusements. There was the 'show' dance, dance at the terms and upon public holidays. Our own folks performed at the church, chapel and school concerts, and the bowling green had a 'smoking' get together (men only). See John Jackson's letter!

We also had the 'Lord's Supper', again, men only, given by the Lord of the Manor as a thanks offering to the farmers and shepherds for leaving his grouse alone! There was free beer and tobacco, and all the old songs. 'The old white mare', 'You never miss the water till the well goes dry', and, of course, 'John Peel', with clog dancing on the tables and 'apple splitting' by the odd bald-headed performer.

While Arthur Lawson was at Hesket Hall we even had a cricket club in our twin villages of Caldbeck and Hesket-new-Market, and in winter we had the rifle range in the old brewery and a billiard table in the bowling green hut, both well attended. Girls didn't get about half as much as they do today and while they made the most of the

The bobbin mill in the Howk, Caldbeck, as it was pre-war, before the mysterious and disastrous fire which destroyed the roof. The wonderful wheel, powered by the Ellerbeck and the second largest in Great Britain, went for scrap and armaments in 1940.

A Ford Model T like the one owned by William Ivinson, rattling past our gate during a Lakeland veterans' rally.

opportunities they had, fathers did keep a strict eye upon their daughters those days, and – as far as possible – after midnight was not allowed.

Not Many Honeymoons

Marriages were great events and usually the first night the happy couple came back from their honeymoon, or slept in their own house (for by no means all those who married did go for a honeymoon), it was customary for a few chaps who had guns to fire shots over the roof.

Towards the end of 1919, after I had been back at Mid-town nearly a year, Brownrigg came into the market. After having worked on farms only about four years, I marvel today at my audacity in wanting to make a start on my own. Christopher looked it over for me and considered it to be good land, so my father bought it for me.

Knowing the snags in starting farming – or in farming at all for that matter – I am, however, convinced that until you are actually farming on your own, and your mistakes have to come out of your own pocket, that no one can learn farming in any other way than on their own account.

I suppose this is why I have always taken such a dim view of all advisory services and of advisers who have not farmed successfully on their own account. So, in September 1919, I became the possessor of 77 acres of inside land and a heaf on the fell. The fences were in ribbons and quite unturnable, the house and buildings were in a mess, but in those days folks looked at the land first and put up with any other inconveniences.

Fortunately I was prepared to wait to put the house and buildings into better order, remembering the old Cumbrian advice 'Mind you don't build your head in and your backside out.' This is advice that is frowned upon today, but it may yet be better remembered.

The farm cost £1,850 in 1919. The man I took it over from in February 1920 told me that when he took it in 1912 he had not his first half-year's rent in his pocket. He had eked out a living by borrowing a horse and cart for a small sum each week from a neighbour and carting road stone for the County Council. He had gradually saved enough each year to buy a cow or two, a few Herdwick sheep a pig and some poultry, and had slowly built up his stock over eight years until, when I took over the farm, he had over 30 cattle, two horses, 100 fell ewes and gimmer lambs. Quite a nice stock for those days.

Immediately after the war, in 1920, stock were very dear indeed, practically the same price as they are today, with the difference that money then was worth four times as much. My father allowed me £650 to start with, and after I had bought a pair of horses, one at £90 and the other £100, a calving heifer at £80, and an old cow and calf for £60, and paid £3 a head for 100 Herdwick heafed sheep, my capital was gone.

Making Ends Meet

For the first three or four years, while building up a stock, I took cattle in both summer and winter and made ends meet by selling my wool and my tup lambs, and the odd foal. In those days borrowing money was the last thing anyone thought of, and thank God I didn't, or I would certainly not have survived much longer than the chap who gave me 18 months had prophesied.

Fortunately living was cheap in the countryside of Cumberland. We were still in the era of candles and oil lamps, to such an extent that we had a specialist distributor of paraffin called 'Paraffin Bell' who, with a tiny holding, made a living out of the job. We burnt a great deal of our own wood, and coal could be bought at Allhallows pit, near Mealsgate, seven miles away, for 12s. 6d. a load on a block cart with sideboards on. We took care to take the largest sideboards we had and the only snag was the amount our horses could pull up either Daleside and Thistlebottom brows, or up Brocklebank. Usually two loads sufficed for the winter.

Rates were only a pound or so and, if you paid any income tax at all, it was only levied upon twice the rent or annual value at about 3s. 6d. in the £. We had our own water supplies, and we used bicycles or a 'spring cart' for transport to market or visiting.

A suit of clothes cost from 35/- to £3 10s. and lasted us at least ten years. Clogs were 8s. 6d. a pair and we could caulker our own for 4d. The postman always worried if any newcomer thought of taking a daily paper, because it meant a journey to that farm every day. One family who came to Mosedale were townsfolk who had the habit

Brownrigg farmhouse from the farm yard. Note how the windows were blocked-up to avoid window tax.

of buying many things from the London stores and when asked what sort of folk they were, the postman said, 'Oh, they are all right but they get every b****y thing but their coals fra' London.'

Sound But Poor

The land at Brownrigg was sound but miserably poor and it was many years before I dared to spend money on that. Hay crops were so poor you could see the knife bar and fingers as you cut the grass, but until my stock had increased, the hay did me. I mended the fences with second-hand wire and posts from the dismantling of Gretna armaments depot.

Fortunately the farm was a healthy one and my stock losses, apart from sheep, were few indeed. Fluke among sheep was an incurable disease on the fells in those days and we just had to suffer the annual loss of from 15% to 20%. Low country farmers kept this disease down by keeping ducks to eat the fluke snails, but this was impossible on open hill grazings. Wages were low and I was able to get a housekeeper for £1 a week. I had some strange experiences with them; some were lazy, some couldn't cook, some liked cream and others liked gin. But eventually I got an excellent one who remained with me about four years until I got married.

Because we had the factory, the mills, mines and quarries still working in the parish, it was always possible to get ample help with hay making or dipping, and other jobs needing a bit of help (especially in the evening – the important time for hay) – and for turnip thinning or potato lifting, if one did these jobs on Saturday afternoons. This point is overlooked today when people are being allowed to drift away from the countryside everywhere, and has resulted in driving the farmers in the Midlands and South out of 'casual' crops like sugar beet, potatoes and turnips.

A tale of my father's was very amusing of those times in the 1930s. Autumn was often one of the periods for farm sales and it was usual to buy 'something' if it was a neighbour or someone in the district. Dad bought quite a few odds and ends at a particular sale and as it was wet the following day, he set Tommy off with the horse and cart down to somewhere around Mealsgate to collect the goods. It was the custom that buyers were given a ticket for a free tea – but there was always a load of food left over next day.

So imagine Tommy jogging steadily along on horse and cart on a wet afternoon – he was a bit simple but the truth would out. 'Did th' gey tha thee tea Tommy?' 'Oh aye – sec a gran' set oot … thu' wus breed an' jam, teaceaks, an scones – see a' eat aw' that! Than th' fetched some mair breed an some pleat ceaks – see a' eat that … Than th' fetched mair pleat ceaks – apple an' geusberry – an a' eat aw that lot! Thoo knaws some fuokes isn't suited if tha doesn't clean up!

Horse mowing haygrass July – August, 1934. I'm riding on the mower with my father before the adaptation to a motor mower using a cut down old car. See the length of the crop!

A picture of John Jackson – international chess player, Oxford research scholar and keen observer of village affairs. Here he is studying his next chess move.

Three

John Jackson

Life in Caldbeck, up to World War One

In this chapter I have collected together various descriptions of life in Caldbeck from the end of the nineteenth century and the first 30 years of the twentieth century. John Jackson (or J. J.) was an Oxford Don who lived in Caldbeck well into the 1960s. He was a research fellow in Latin and Greek, a brilliant man who represented Britain in International Chess matches – by postcard of course. As a student of languages (although he could never speak the writings of foreigners) he could work out the meaning of text. The story goes of one competition that his opponent replied a move – in French. So John replied in German and so these exchanges went on throughout the competition until John had to concede he was defeated by some obscure oriental language.

In the spring and summer months he used to walk up to Brownrigg on a Sunday evening for 'a crack' – he had an amazing memory of parishioners, affairs and events. Also he could discuss politics with my father. Thus, from a very early age, I was listening to a commentary and speculation about European politics and events – for example the British reaction when Herr Hitler re-occupied the Rhineland or the Anschluss in Austria, or the Chamberlain sell-out of the Sudetan lands and the butchery of Czechoslovakia. Interesting that today our good friend Peter in Bavaria was a descendent of one of those families kicked back into Germany by the Czechs at the end of World War II.

So from John Jackson and my father I have always been interested and fascinated by European affairs and today I feel just as much at ease in the European Community as I do here in England. John had an acute sense of affairs in the Parish and wrote frequently to 'Uncle Dick' with whom he was a great friend as well as many others from the parish serving in France, the Middle East and the Balkans. Beautifully written in his exquisite handwriting – a joy to read – I reproduce the complete newsletter of 5 February 1918.

Bridge End
Caldbeck
Wigton

5 Feb 1918

My dear Dick

I was extremely pleased to get your letter this morning. I have often wondered lately how you were faring in that eccentric part of the world which geographers call the Balkan Peninsula, and Ben Hind 'Sally-what-is-it'. The Sunday before last, I came across Percy and your sister going to Church, and got your new address from them; but as I never do today what I can put off till tomorrow, no immediate results followed. However, though I can't hold a candle to St Paul at writing epistles to 'the people of Thessalonica' and what I do in that way isn't half as edifying as his efforts, I'll see if I can produce anything for your spiritual benefit – it may help to send you to sleep, if the insect life of Macedonia is more than usually aggressive.

Well, Caldbeck is very much the same as it was when you left it – which, I suppose, is very much the same as when Julius Caesar landed. The end of Mrs Pattinson Bell's house has fallen in, and they are putting up a jigger and a jaw-breaker at the factory – one apparently jigs and the other jaw-breaks. That's all I know about them, but it sounds as if they would be rather vulgar machines. These, I think, are all the external changes of real consequence, though I believe there is a new gate somewhere, because Joseph Jennings asked me if I'd noticed it and seemed surprised when I hadn't. The population is very nearly unaltered, though unfortunately not quite so. Mrs Ivinson died on Friday night, and was buried today. It is a great pity – I always thought her an exceptionally kind woman, whom one was bound to like and respect. I am afraid it will be a great shock to Harrison in Mesopotamia, as well as to his father and sister. People thought on Saturday night that there might easily be another melancholy piece of work for the rector, as Jack Simpson – who had started from the mine near

The factory at Hodden Croft, Caldbeck, in which the Ivinson Mill operated and where Hodden Grey, made famous by the song 'John Peel', was manufactured. The mill also made coarse blankets which have warmed generations of the Cole family. They were very heavy, with a simple herring-bone pattern.

Swineside at 7.30 in the morning – had never turned up, and, though people had been out to look for him, no trace could be found. However, he landed at Fell Side next morning, after losing his way on the fell in the mist and spending the night under a rock. 'Those damned mountains', as you justly observe! However, it hasn't all been tragedy, or threatened tragedy, with us. We have had some quite cheerful episodes – for instance, when Tommy Milburn came home on leave. He called to see me one night – I was a little surprised, until he mentioned casually that Stamper had told him that Jos. Jennings and myself both wanted to see him! He is still the same Thomas, and, though he has been opening bully-beef tins in France for over a year, he hasn't quite got the Parisian manner yet. He seems pretty well satisfied with himself, and informed Barbara that, while he was only a civilian, the girls in Caldbeck wouldn't look at him, but now that he had a uniform, he was positively persecuted with their attentions – so he may cut out your namesake with Kathleen after all. He has been stationed at Rouen and has collected the following facts with regard to the place: (1) It stands on a river which 'has a lot of water in it', though it had never occurred to him to ask its name. (2) If Mary Thorburn was transplanted to Rouen, the natives would call her Madame Bezel – 'and if thoo was a bit younger, they'd call thou a filly'. (3) The girls at Rouen often look at him, but he is unable to improve the occasion properly, owing to the fact that he has not acquired the language perfectly. He shows very little animosity for the Germans, but much for a certain Corporal Smallwood, whom he suspects of 'wanting to have him on', though Tommy always baffles him very brainily. He thinks the war will end about September – so now you know. We are expecting another warrior shortly. Lally, the doctor's daughter, had a letter a week or two ago from Willie James, who has been in France about a year now. He said that he was hoping to get leave very soon – in time to be present at the concert for the Nursing Fund and hear Fanny Ashbridge sing 'O Willy, we have missed you'.

However, he will have to put a little more energy into his movements than he used to in his commercial days, if he is to be up to time, for the concert is due on Friday night, and so far I have not seen any announcement in the papers that William has landed at Southampton. We were expecting a cousin of mine – one of the famous (or, at least, notorious) Anzacs – from Flanders. I had never seen him, and shall apparently have to wait a little longer for that pleasure, as we had a postcard from him the other day, saying that he had had his leave, but had spent so much of it in London that he couldn't look us up this time, but would infallibly do so on the next occasion. If he has inherited the family tendencies, no doubt he divided his time pretty equally between St Paul's and the British Museum. Tommy Sanderson, you will no doubt know, is in Italy. There was quite an interesting letter from him in the Parish Magazine this month. He also is an optimist about the duration of the war. The famous Billiard Association is still going strong. The outstanding events since my last letter have been: (a) a masterly 56, compiled I leave you to guess by whom, which carried off the President's five bob for the first fifty on the new table; (b) a sensational 19 – of which none was played for – by the President himself; (c) the unanimous election of Harry Lamb as Secretary and Treasurer (unpaid) of the Association, in succession to S. Forsyth, retiring full of years and honours; (d) the New Year's Day competition. The prizes in the last named function were: (1) a pipe in a case, emanating from Rotten Row; (2) half a pound of Three Nuns presented by F. J. Ryland (Proprietor of the Potts Ghyll Barytes Mine and of the Caldbeck Crushing and Grinding Mills – we generally call him the Mineral Magnate for short); (3) 100 cigarettes, presented by the same philanthropist; (4) twelve cigars (probably stolen), presented by the new Secretary. This sounds all very simple, but the complications began when the President remarked incidentally to the doctor that 'his brother at the mansion' once owned a pipe, similar in every detail to that now offered for the first prize, for which he had paid 4d without the case. My colossal brain at once realized that the safest plan would be to win the first round (there were eight players), lose the second, and make a bid for the cigarettes in the play-off for third and fourth prizes. I carried out the first part of the programme with much adroitness and went off to supper at Midtown with an easy conscience. However, it was decided in my absence that the winners should have their choice of the prizes in rotation, and the result was that the Three Nuns found sanctuary with Stamper, the cigarettes with George Steadman (whom the Mineral Magnate terms Vulcan), and the Secretary's cigars with your obedient servant. The pipe and case I saw again on Sunday – they are employed by Jimmy Craven and his little sister, occasionally for blowing bubbles, and occasionally for surreptitious whiffs of brown paper.

To pass to the less sporting members of the community – the Rector is now a Grandfather, as Mrs Bob Ewbank has had a son. Immediately the cable arrived, the shepherd of souls took the right course for ensuring publicity by going across and informing Mrs Brew – though Robinson, by the way, used to consider Sarah Hayton a still better medium for disseminating news. Mr and Mrs Hewetson are both flourishing – still visible to the naked eye in spite of the food shortage. The food shortage, as a matter of fact, is not hitting these out-of-the-way places anything like so much as the towns. Ryland, for instance, on his last visit, was able to carry back with him two hams, fourteen pounds of butter, and a good few eggs, whereas in London, according to his account, he lives on a gill of rain-water and an acid-drop per diem, varied with a bran-mash on Sundays. However, some things are pretty scarce. Matches are almost worth their weight in sugar,

Carting muck at Forester Fold near Wigton. Dropped out in small heaps and later spread with gripes by hand – a practice on Cumbrian farms well into the 1950s.

and we've installed a little Kelly lamp in the pavilion to light our Havanas at. Bottled Bass, I believe is only procurable in Heaven, and decent coal in the other place. To return to Midtown, Mr Hewetson has now a godly pair working for him in the shape of Jimmy Graham and Jossy Monkhouse, both of Hesket. They are said to have a word of prayer before doing up the horses and to distribute farmyard manure to a hymn. However, there is a hardened sinner going to join them shortly – one Andrew Scott, whom you may remember. Crossing the road, Isaac Arnison has got a son and a motor car – one new, the other second-hand, but both apparently satisfactory so far. Proceeding to Brownrigg, Harry Lamb shows no signs of decrepitude. He was in the other night, and we were talking about you. I'll give him your regards the next time I see him – probably on Saturday night. He'll be interested to hear that you have a school-friend of his in your platoon. By the way, Ingledon is a lieutenant in the Borders, and someone told me lately that he had been wounded. Your worthy uncle on Ratten Row I have not seen for several weeks, but I believe that he is unchanged and that he still maintains his friendship with the proprietrix of Ginger the cat!

As it is working towards the small hours, I had better be furling my sails. Demi is now an interpreter in the British army. His address, as far as I can make out from Caryophylles, who writes Greek and English equally wretchedly, is:

> *C. A. Demetriades*
> *71 Church Buildings*
> *Saint Minas*
> *Salonica*

In the second word of the third line I have imitated Sophroni's handwriting. I never heard of a saint of that name, but I should think the address will find him all right. I should certainly drop him a line – I'm sure he will be delighted to hear from you. Tell him that he may expect a communication from me shortly and that I think of him every time I use his coffee-pan – which is every night. I am delighted to hear that you are still in the pink. Mind you keep in it – eschew mosquitoes and Vardar winds and all the kindred products of Macedonia. (By the way, what sort of a river is the Vardar to look at?) I never thought you would have a picnic in that part of the globe, but I confess I did not quite realize how unhealthy it is. Have you ever run across Jack Brew? He has been in hospital twice this autumn, once with malaria and once with a bad thumb. Well, to quote my favourite apostle again, 'behold how long a letter I have written to you with mine own hands'. Don't go and forget to answer it. I am the worst correspondent who ever lived, but, all being well, I will try to reply rather more punctually next time.

Yours ever
J. Jackson

Dora Cole's grandfather mounted on 'Jerry', the pony he rode and drove to market for years. He lived until he was a hundred.

Moira Hoddell.

Four

HODDEN GREY

A family manufacturing business

From a paper given by Mrs Dora A. Cole, Brownrigg, Caldbeck, to the Cumberland Dialect Society.

The tale of Hodden Grey has been told many times, but I'm going to tell it, as one of the family that made it.

Before I start about 'Hodden Grey' I think I'll have to tell you something about my Grandfather and his fore-elders.

Two young brothers came over from Ireland for harvest and tatie picking – they must have liked the look of England for they stopped.

As time went on, one went into the grocery and bacon curing business, and the other had a few jobs before he became landlord of the Oddfellows' Inn at Caldbeck. His son, John, started a small mill in Friar Row, before he took over the 'Factory' from John Woodcock Graves.

I thought a lot of my Grandfather – they never make any like him these days! He was a fine example of an old-fashioned Cumbrian. A bluff, hearty disposition with a word for everybody and always ready for a crack with anyone.

He was born at the Oddfellows Inn and wasn't christened until he was nearly a year old – they used to save up the christenings in those days until they had two or three dozen to do altogether.

He lived until he was a hundred, and had all his faculties (except his eyesight, which he lost in his eighties) until the end.

He had a marvellous memory and a fine dialect.

He was as hard as nails, and liked nothing better than a wash in ice cold water, before he set off at 5.00 a.m. for Carlisle Market, every Saturday morning.

Fancy going thirteen miles to Carlisle with a heavy cart, a small one no doubt, built for his Galloway pony.

I well remember 'Jerry', the bonnie dappled grey he both drove and rode for years, and I've heard many stories of Nannie,

One Hundred Years of Hill Farming 27

W. Ivinson wearing his bowler hat

Jerry's mother, the old grey mare who was also a faithful servant. My grandfather started his married life at a small farm near the Oddfellows' Arms called 'Gates Bridge'.

It was in this house the famous song 'John Peel' was written by Woodcock Graves, which immortalised Peel – and 'Hodden Grey'. Grandfather hunted with Peel in his young days and could tell many tales about him – drunken old faggot!

John Ivinson (his father), when an infant, was the subject of a practical joke played by John Peel. One evening in the kitchen of the Oddfellows Arms, the hunter – during the absence of Mistress Ivinson the hostess – quietly lifted the baby from the cradle into the drawer of the dresser.

There was consternation on the part of the mother when she discovered her loss and Peel got a clout o't lug, after the missing baby had been found.

Caldbeck was a 'thrang' spot in those days and Ivinsons and their relatives seemed to have more than their share in local industries.

Grandad's sister, Ellen, married John Emmerson who had the Brewery, made good old Caldbeck yal (ale) and local housewives declared nothing could beat their liquid yeast!

Another sister called Jane Cape, followed her folk as landlady at the Oddfellows. Her tatie pots and the standing pies she made for Rosley Fair were famous all over the County.

Grandfather seemed to have his finger in every pie. He was Rector's warden 26 years, Surveyor for Caldbeck Low 36 years, Overseer and Chairman of the Parish Council 32 years, Local School Board 33 years, Poor Law Guardian 35 years, R. D. C. 17 years. He was in the Cumberland and Westmorland yeomanry 17 years and was Sergeant and Quartermaster. He was the oldest Oddfellow in England, being a member of Manchester Unity for 79 years. He had the woollen mill for half a century. As Lord's Bailiff he represented Lord Leconfield for 35 years.

The 'Barney' Court was held at Hesket-New-Market pub and I don't know whether the business was half as important as the good feed and drink and the 'crack' after!

I've rambled a long way from the subject of my talk. The factory or woollen mill still stands at Caldbeck. It was set up by Captain Backhouse 175 years ago on his land and probably later sold by him to the Jennings family.

It consisted of three floors and a garret with a small dwelling house adjoining, and a rood of land surrounding it. The first tenant was John Woodcock Graves, who installed the machinery and carried on this work there until his departure for Tasmania about 1833. His home was at Gate House, Midtown. In a room there, the famous song John Peel was written.

In this mill was woven the grey cloth of which John Peel's hunting coat was made – hence the opening lines of the song 'D'ye ken John Peel with his cwoat so grey'.

John Ivinson followed Graves and carried on the business for twenty years . He in turn was succeeded by his son William (my Grandfather), who worked the mill for fifty years and was the last of the wool manufacturers in Caldbeck.

Large quantities of the grey homespun not now to be had for love or money was woven and used for making men's suits and overcoats. It was known by several names – Hodden Grey, Ivinson Grey and Skiddaw Grey. The last name was used in a verse describing Peel's hunting dress.

> 'No broadcloth of scarlet adorned him
> Nor buckskin that rivals the snow
> But a plain Skiddaw Grey wa' his raiment
> He wore it for work not for show.'

Hodden means hard; the rhyme goes:

> 'To wear a cwoat o' Hodden Grey
> In them old times was thought nea sin.'
> Skiddaw Grey fra' Skiddaw sheep.

Ivinson Grey explains itself. The cloth was made of natural undyed wool of the hardy Herdwick sheep which grazed the local fells. Their fleeces were a mixture of brown and grey – the lighter the fleece, the lighter was the colour of the cloth.

A small quantity of Leicester wool was mixed with the Herdwick. The cloth was noted for its extreme durability, lasting practically a lifetime. One account speaks of it as 'Tailors' aggravation'. It was warm and weather proof, the latter being accounted for by its being made of salved wool. Sheep were not dipped as they are today. They were salved and a gey slow job it was every autumn. The salve was made from rancid butter and tar melted together in a kale pot.

A good man could only do about twelve sheep in a day, because the wool had to be

Herdwick rams at Loweswater Show in 1966.

My great Uncle John Faulder demonstrates the method of salving sheep as practiced at the end of the 19th Century. Each sheep had to be handled on a stool.

parted, or 'shed' every two inches, and the salve smeared on by a push with the thumb and a flick of the forefinger. The job went on until late at night, by the aid of tallow dips and the salvers got threepence a sheep. Salving was used to combat scab and was even mentioned in the Bible.

This remedy for scab by applying tar gave rise to the proverb often misunderstood today, about the folly of 'losing a ship for a ha'porth o'tar' (farmers in the south and west of England talked not of their sheep, but their 'ship').

Salving was a communal job, and when it was finished there was merry making with a feast and butter sops were handed round. Wool staplers hated tar – they called it 'laid' wool, and it made a lower price, as the tar was so bad to get rid of and the wool wouldn't take the brighter dyes. Near the end of the reign of George III dipping began to replace salving, but many old farmers say that flocks were better protected from the weather with salving and the yield of wool was heavier.

I wonder if you have heard the verse:

'Oh! tarry wool, oh tarry wool
Tarry wool is ill t'spin
Oh! card it weel, oh! card it weel
Card it weel 'ere ye begin
When it's carded, wove and spun
The magic work is but half done;
But when it's woven, dressed and clean
It will be clothing for a Queen.'

My Grandfather's coat was in use for over sixty years and is still almost as sturdy as ever.

Other goods made were blankets, bed rugs (lappins) in a red herringbone pattern, pit flannel – known as Kersey, red and blue flannel for petticoats – wincey cloth, floor coverings, plaiding (used by saddlers for lining horse collars and cart saddles) and stocking yarn (natural and dyed).

Wool was bought from the neighbouring

Hodden Grey – The overcoat made for Joe Ivinson of Ratten Row around age 18 in the 1890s. Handed down from his sister Maria to my mother and my wife, who have looked after it for over a century. It is now on permanent loan in Tullie House, Carslisle.

farmers, from wool staplers at Bradford, and from Atkinsons, Carlisle tanners. Large quantities of wool came only to be carded for the owners to spin at home on hand spinning wheels. They then wove it on a loom, and brought it back to the factory to be scoured and milled (to raise the nap). This was done at the Fulling or Raise Mill where wire teeth were used.

The finer make of blankets were made of Leicester and Cheviot wool and were woven in one piece. Coarser blankets were of narrower width and colour, slightly darker. Blankets were stoved with brimstone to whiten, steeped in chamberly, and washed in warm water, then milled and hung on 'tenters' or sliding rails to stretch webs to required widths.

Some of the yarn used for other articles manufactured was either dyed in the factory dye house (the smithy now stands on the site), where there was a supply of running water, or sent to Brampton to be dyed.

In the walk mill were two large hammers, wooden ones in a sunken trough. These were called Fullers and were turned, like all the machines used, by water power.

On the first floor of the mill there was a machine known to the workers as 't'devil' and this teased the wool making it very light and fluffy before it proceeded to the winding wheel. From there it merged in a long loosely woven string, about finger thickness, and was spun into yarn and locally woven into cloth.

About twenty hands were employed when trade was at its greatest.
+ One carder to tease wool and make it ready for the engine.
+ Two feeders who fed the engine.
+ Two spinners with a spinning billy of sixty spindles each.
+ Two women, one winding for four weavers, and the other stocking trade.
+ One warper making warps ready for weaver to put into loom.
+ Four weavers.
+ Five children piecing and carding for the billies.

These boys and girls worked half time and attended school half a day. Trade was mostly retail and was carried on with many parts of the United Kingdom.

My grandfather attended weekly markets at Carlisle and Wigton. Penrith and Aspatria were visited quarterly, receiving wool for manufacturing and delivering completed materials.

Towards the end of my grandfather's time a finer cloth was made resembling Harris Tweed, and about thirty years ago the Herdwick Sheep Breeders' Association, with R. H. Lamb as the secretary, tried to revive a type of Herdwick Tweed, but this coarser wool is mostly used now for carpets, felts, etc.

Another branch of the industry was the weaving of rag carpets on a hand loom.

Women at home pieced together long narrow lengths of bright coloured cloth about one inch wide, wound into balls and sent them to the factory to be woven into carpets, some about one yard wide, others narrower for stair carpets and 'rat trods'. It needed great skill in weaving, both hands and feet being needed in rotation to send the shuttle to and fro and control the different strands and colours.

One of the old looms survived in an empty cottage, in Friar Row. I have the factory clock, a nice grandfather, with brass dial made by George Moss of Hesket-New-Market. These seem to be about the only relics left.

Changing times and fashions, old-fashioned machinery and transport difficulties, brought a once thriving industry to a close.

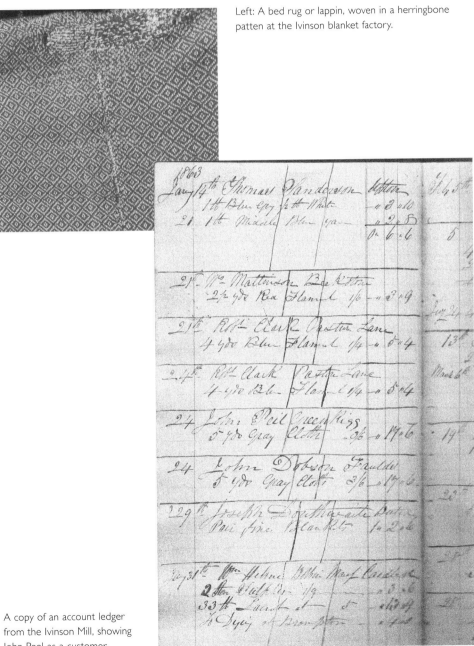

Left: A bed rug or lappin, woven in a herringbone patten at the Ivinson blanket factory.

A copy of an account ledger from the Ivinson Mill, showing John Peel as a customer.

Farmers mingle with servant lads and lasses on the Cocker Bridge in Cockermouth outside the Midland Bank. Two farmers discuss terms with a young lad maybe straight from school.

"Reet oot thee ne-ame an' address on a bit o'pyaper…"

FIVE

CUMBRIAN HIRINGS

From his earliest contact with farming in Durham and Cumberland, hired hands were part of the country scene. Village lads looked for a job in the district; farmers' daughters would seek to be 'in service' with neighbours, perhaps, whose families were very young, to move out of the home, make way for a brother's wife in the household or act as maids for those in the district who paid them a modest wage.

In his early days my father relied on a housekeeper and his cousin, who wrote this article and helped on every visit before losing his leg in a motorcycle accident.

I remember some of these chaps came from the mining areas of West Cumbria to escape the harsh days of unemployment up until about 1933, when poverty and disastrous prices forced farmers to ranch or 'do' on their own – holding on for grim death in conditions which drove American farmers westwards away from the dustbowl to California. Of my mother's brothers, one went to Australia in 1925 and the youngest became a quarryman up to 1935. The following writing by my uncle in 'Cumbria' magazine takes us up to 1950 with an illustration before 1939, and the outbreak of World War II.

The heyday of the Hiring was in the nineteenth century. A yeoman from the dales would offer a school-leaver £4 for the term.

'Whitsuntide and Martinmas are names no longer of importance to the majority of countryfolk, but in the old days before the 1939–45 war they could be the highlights of life when the half-yearly hirings and fairs were held in Lakeland towns.

A few years after the end of the 1914–18 war I drove down from Brownrigg, the hill farm of S. H. Cole, to the Whitsuntide hirings at Wigton. My companion had yoked 'Lady', the Clydesdale mare, between the wooden shafts of the farm-cart, intending to fetch up some linseed cake, a few rolls of fencing wire, some provisions and a few odds and ends you need on a farm.

The farm is in Caldbeck parish, nearly 1,000 feet above sea level. The land slopes down from the moor southwards to the beck that runs from Uldale Fells, through Caldbeck village to join up with the Caldew.

The cart rattled and bumped up the lonning that led to the moor and main road on the top. On our left was a panoramic view of the hills, Knott and Calva, with the crest of Skiddaw showing behind the green and purple skyline. A soft, but exhilarating south-west breeze from the direction of Bassenthwaite wafted in the tang of the fells.

A carpet of tufted grass and heather roots covered the moor outside the farm gate, and as we jogged along a pair of peewits, uttering plaintive, anxious cries, circled around hoping to lead us away from the nest they had built on the fell. The ground was dotted with Herdwick ewes and lambs, their fleeces displaying the red registration mark of the farm.

We reached the cross-roads where an ancient, weather-worn guide-post pointed a wooden finger to show that Wigton lay to the left. Reaching the breast of Brocklebank we could see far ahead the gleaming waters of the Solway, sunlit, with the purple skyline of the Scottish hills, dominated by the dark blue mass of Criffell. Down on the green chequered Cumberland plain a haze of chimney smoke advertised the presence of Wigton.

Our cart clattered along the street to the square space beside the church where we were near the auction mart owned by Willie Hope, a Wigton character of that age. Lady was unyoked, hitched to the cart, and given a nosebag of oats to munch as I followed my cousin to the mart office.

He had some sheep and bullocks to sell. They had been driven down earlier by a lad from the village. The streets of the old town were becoming busy. Other farm carts and traps, conveying farmers and their wives, were converging on the town.

Flocks of sheep and droves of cattle were pressing into the town and being crowded into pens near the mart. There was a cacophony of sound from baaing sheep, blaring bullocks, the stamp of hooves, the thud of drover's sticks and the hoarse voices of cursing men.

Few cars were being driven on the roads then, but occasionally you might see a Ford flivver, the driver hooting wildly as he attempted to steer through the press of animals, men, women and children packed in the cobbled streets.

Already farm workers, young men, middle-aged men and boys, were standing in groups along the street from the Kildare Hotel to the ornate fountain at the end of the street. All were waiting to be hired.

Brown-faced farmers from the hills and low country stood gossiping in twos and threes. Here and there were farmers' wives and daughters clad in black, voluminous skirts which extended down to their ankles. They had black bodices, and hats of black straw, with austere buns of hair at the back of their heads. Many of them were already around the stalls that street traders had set up near the fountain.

A farmer would spot a likely-looking lad, look him over and ask: 'Ist tha for hire, lad?'
'Aye maister.'

The man would size him up as he asked where he had worked. He wanted a man that knew sheep, could milk and knew something about the breeding and rearing of cattle. He must be a horseman able to plough, harrow and handle a mower or reaper.

Tractors had not yet reached the dales in those days, and cars and lorries, used only on very large farms, were often considered luxuries.

Cockermouth
Martinmas Hiring

The Town's Police Clauses Act, 1847

In consequence of the above Hiring to be held at Cockermouth on **Monday, the 12th day of NOVEMBER, 1951** the Urban District Council deem it necessary to make the following Regulations under the powers given to them by Section 21 of the Town's Police Clauses Act, 1847.

That between the hours of 11 a.m. on **SUNDAY, the 11th day of NOVEMBER, 1951**, and 10 a.m. on the following **TUESDAY**, no Carts, Carriages, Horses, Motors or Bicycles shall enter Main Street between Sullart Street and Castlegate.

The Council hereby prescribe as an alternative route Sullart Street, South Street, Lorton Street, Victoria Road and Kirkgate.

Any person committing a wilful breach of this Order renders himself (or herself) liable to a penalty of 40s.

Given under my hand this 6th day of **OCTOBER, 1951**

E. JENNINGS,
Clerk of the Urban District Council.

BAILEY, PRINTER, COCKERMOUTH.

If the man's replies satisfied him, the farmer might say: 'What's tha askin'?'

'Twenty-five pun'.'

'Naw.' The farmer shakes his head. 'Ah'll gie tha twenty.'

They would eventually settle half-way. The term was 24–26 weeks, and the wages included a week's holiday at the end of each term, agreed at the time.

At the fountain end of the street, traders had set up their wooden, canvas topped stalls, and the farm wives and girls were crowding around to examine the variety of goods laid out for sale.

Hiring fairs in the south of England were described by Thomas Hardy, the Victorian novelist. He wrote of carters and waggoners distinguished by having a piece of whip-cord twisted around their hats and shepherds holding their crooks in their hands.

These fairs died out many years before the hirings of Lakeland. The traditional way of agricultural life dies harder in such places as Carlisle, Cockermouth, Wigton and Keswick, and hirings took place between the two world wars.

Even as late as 1949 there was a fair in Carlisle when I visited it on Saturday of Whitsuntide of that year. It took place in the market-place before the modern congestion and one-way traffic systems altered the atmosphere which had existed for so long and which seemed to be watched over by the cross of stone with its sundial and curiously carved lion defiantly looking towards Scotland. Even this fair was a ghost of the former hirings which had taken place down the centuries since the break-up of the feudal system gave the worker the freedom to barter his labour for wages.

On that Whitsun Saturday there had been a few agreements made between farmers and workers. Labour was scarce, and few men and girls were seeking to be hired. Full employment in urban areas during the post-war period had stimulated the drift from the land that began after the war.

This encouraged farmers and their wives to pay higher rates for their hired men and girls so that they would not leave their employment. And the technical change in farming, with the increased use of machinery, especially tractors, was having its effect.

The Cumbrian farming community had poured into Carlisle to enjoy the fun of the fair, to shop and to see their friends; the hiring was in the background, and may have been the last to be held here.

The heyday of the hirings was in the nineteenth century. Many a lad left home aged 14 to earn his living. He looked forward to being hired. He would don a brand new suit, and wear a green and red tie, presents from his parents, and tramp to the nearest market town. There he would stick a straw in his mouth and stand in the market-place, often a shy, lonely lad.

A yeoman from the dales would offer him £4 for the term. If he liked his 'place' he might remain there two or three years and become a good all-round worker – a 'fine lad'. At 17 he would go to the hirings as a man and obtain £12 to £14 a year. He would 'live in', sleep in the farmhouse and have his meals with the family.

Later, in the better times, he got up to £45 a year. If he was ambitious he would aim to get his own dale farm and get a wife to help him. Many did so, for the cost of living was cheap then and the men were thrifty.

Charles R. Denton

The hirings in front of the Old Town Hall, Carlisle. The 'Ribble' bus passes through the centre with the "Crown and Mitre" hotel behind.

Hiring throng and farm hands at the Whitsun Fair in 1949 with Carlisle Cross and the Old Town Hall in the background.

The Caldbeck Boundary stone on Ellerbeck with the great boulder in the fell wall.

Six

Walking The Parish Boundaries

In the nineteenth century the age-old custom of walking the Parish boundary almost died out. It was undertaken usually every 21 years and is important in a district like Caldbeck as the lands stretch far out over the mountains and the common or unfenced areas. Although I haven't done the walk myself, never being at home in the years when it was due to take place, my mother undertook two walks in her lifetime. She always had plenty of training!

During the war and rationing she would regularly set out for Caldbeck from our farm three miles from the village to buy our ration of meat at the village butcher's, setting off at 7.00 a.m. and home by 9.30 a.m. – six miles in total. In her sixties she set out with friends to walk Styhead Pass from Wasdale to Seathwaite.

In 1953 – Coronation year – my mother wrote to a friend about her experiences walking the boundary 21 years previously in 1932. I must have been about 4 – too young – but as the press reporter on the actual day noted, there were a lot of very young as well as older participants on the 1953 walk.

20.01.1953
In this early spring of 1953 the thoughts of the whole country centre on the Coronation and while we in Caldbeck plan to prepare our celebrations, we also think of another celebration we hope to make in June – Caldbeck Boundary Riding.

We commoners keep alive this ancient custom every 21 years and though we may not do it with as much ceremony as our neighbours over the Border, nevertheless it is a red letter day to us. Caldbeck village lies in a valley almost surrounded by hills and to ride the Parish Boundary means making a sort of detour of those hills – a 24-mile ride through wild fell country taking 8 or 9 hours to accomplish.

It may interest you to know that this land is in the very core of the John Peel country where this famous huntsman used his ancient pack of hounds. His 'view halloo' echoed round the fells, dales and woodlands of our Boundary.

This letter will be completed before our 1953 Boundary Riding takes place, so I'll take you now down Memory Lane and I'll tell you something of the last one! We were up with the lark that brilliant June morning in 1932. What a scuffle to get 'done up'. Luckily the stock were all out to grass but chickens and pets had to have a day's rations doled out. Sandwiches were to make and at 8.30 a.m. my husband and I, with our small son, were on our way two miles over the fields to Caldbeck village.

Geoff was 'dumped' with his Grandma, and we joined the assembly at the Parish Hall. What a turn out! Of course more than half the crowd were there and 'set off' the riders and walkers.

About 40 riders were mounted on sturdy fell ponies, strong farm 'cobs' and a very few on more genteel hunters. The rest of the contingent – another 50 – were ready on foot, with stout walking sticks and haversacks on their backs. Not a Macintosh anywhere – surely all Caldbeck's barometers that morning pointed to 'set-fair'.

We moved off by the high road for Ellerbeck Common where we touched Thorney Stone, the first Boundary mark. Then on by the wall, round the old Roman Camp on Aughtertree Fell and over Uldale Fell. Here was no guiding stream. It would seem Caldbeck had drawn its line liberally round Uldale! Luckily we were doing the round in peaceful time and all we saw there were the Herdwick and Swaledale sheep grazing, and the odd shepherd amongst them, who gave us a friendly grin and doubtless in his mind, called us silly fools.

We aimed over towards Baggra Yeat and Sworley Farm, skirting the Uldale fells towards Brockle Crag. The road took us along by Longlands, Lowthwaite, Stockdale, all farms nestling in the shelter of the hills. Then by Overwater Tarn to Mirk Holme, a lovely farm mentioned by Denwood in 'Red Ike'.

We left the high road and started climbing. What a sight to see such a motley crowd wending its way on the lovely fells – what a day! We all agreed it was heavenly. Not a cloud in the sky. The air like wine!

The Boundary took us actually through the passage of a house on Brockle Crag. Yes, a rider determined to do it to the letter, led his horse through the farmhouse! Half an hour's halt after this, we made short work of our sandwiches and quenched our thirst with the crystal clear water of the 'Dash' beck. After lunch we aimed over Great Calva, the riders taking the path up a steep ghyll. I'll never forget watching from our height those horses, scrambling up that shelving slope of scree, the riders had to dismount. Our hearts were in our mouths as we watched them in single file get up that great almost perpendicular rocky hillside called, strangely, Horse Crag!

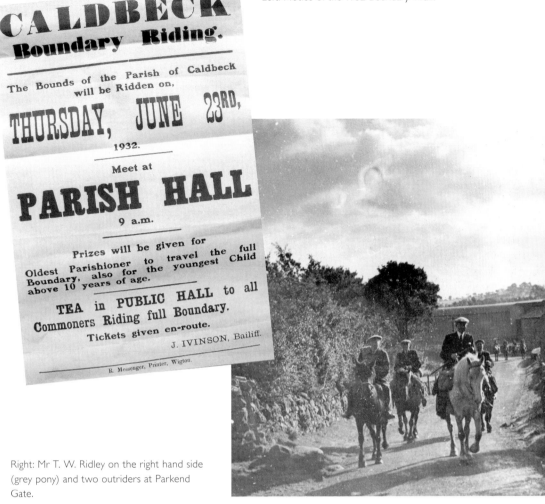

CALDBECK Boundary Riding.

The Bounds of the Parish of Caldbeck will be Ridden on,

THURSDAY, JUNE 23RD,

1932.

Meet at

PARISH HALL

9 a.m.

Prizes will be given for Oldest Parishioner to travel the full Boundary, also for the youngest Child above 10 years of age.

TEA in PUBLIC HALL to all Commoners Riding full Boundary.

Tickets given en-route.

J. IVINSON, Bailiff.

R. Messenger, Printer, Wigton.

Right: Mr T. W. Ridley on the right hand side (grey pony) and two outriders at Parkend Gate.

Riders and foot-folks joined forces again in 'Whylie Ghyll' where the river Caldew rises and forms a boundary by Mosedale, Haltcliffe, Hesket New Market, back to Caldbeck Church. I'd heard a lot of 'Whylie Ghyll' – the scene of many past and present shepherds' meets, but I had not been there before. I'll always remember the trek that day – the bogs were to many of us unexpected. We had no idea they were so dangerous till we saw one of the horses, carrying a girl at the time, quickly engulfed almost up to the neck. We women, I'm afraid, just watched, while the men rescued – struggling with ropes and halters, pushing and pulling. Two more horses went in though not so badly – they got one onto its legs and in it went again!

The old documents call this 'Scoy Bog by Dead Foot Beck'. We were glad to leave it and descend on hard ground by Swineside.

Whylie Ghyll Shepherds' Meet in 1945. A sheep fold where shepherds exchanged their 'ratches' or stray sheep at certain times in the farming year. Some of the flockmasters present: Two farmers with bottles having a noggin of whisky. Left: Wilfred Brown, Parkend farm – and unidentified. From extreme right – William Pears with his father Chris Pears, Fellside – and centre of group facing, Jimmy Winder.

We were back at the Parish Hall by 6.00 p.m. where we found a sumptuous meal ready (given by Lord Leconfield, the Lord of the Manor).

You need scarcely ask if we were hungry or did justice to such a spread! And tired? – well perhaps we were but all pronounced it one of the best days ever. One of the loveliest walks one could wish for. Previous Boundary Riders I knew had terminated in a Grand Dance, where even the stalwarts who had 'done the round' tripped the light fantastic till the 'sma hours'. My memory fails me as to whether there was a dance in 1932; all I remember is that after the feast and a prize-giving my husband and I had to do another climb – up the hill to Brownrigg to face the music of 'delayed action' on our farm. Milking two hours behind schedule, every animal on the place raising its voice in protest, asking to be fed! I had been determined to 'do' the Boundary Riding in 1932 – I thought I'd be too old in another 21 years! Now I'm wondering? If I do it again perhaps I'll tell you about it later!

Extract from the Herald, 26 September 1953

Twenty-four-mile Parish Boundary Walk: Time-honoured trek over Caldbeck Fells. Strenuous day for grandparents and children

Caldbeck was a deserted village for seven hours on Saturday, when there was scarcely an able-bodied man, woman or child to be seen in the village street. The solution to the mystery of its quietude was that a stalwart party of 73 parishioners were 'walking' the 24-mile parish boundary – a time-honoured custom which is observed every 21 years.

Shortly after 9.00 a.m. the concourse assembled outside the Parish Hall, fifteen people on horseback and the remainder on Shanks's pony. Sunshine brightened the scene as camera shutters clicked on the colourful cavalcade. There was a cry of 'Are we ready?' and by way of answer the village folk burst into song with the 'John Peel' chorus. The boundary walk was on again!

Leading the party out of the village on to the Uldale road was 72 years old veteran Mr T. W. Ridley, Chairman of this year's boundary walk committee, mounted on a dapple grey Dales cob. Three or four riders were in close attendance, followed by the first vigorous group of 'infantry support' – laughing and walking, they swung away down the road.

More riders followed, and then a larger party of walkers, waving merrily to those who were too young or too old to accompany them, or had other business to attend to. But neither 'too young' nor 'too old' was interpreted very strictly, for there were some participants, youngsters and veterans, who might well have been considered to quality for one category or the other. Grandparents, in fact, walked side by side with their grandchildren!

Born and brought up in 't' back o' Skiddaw' country, successive generations of Caldbeck people have jealously guarded their Common rights on the high moorland that climbs away to the south, observing the custom of boundary walking from the time when parishioners walked their own boundaries to preserve grazing and other rights. The landmarks are passed down from father to son, and so the custom has survived through the centuries.

Climb to over 2,000 feet

Following the road through Whelpo and Parkend, the walkers made their first halt at the Thorney Stone boundary mark on the side of Aughertree Fell, marking the 'frontier' with Bolton parish. The party then turned south, crossed the Uldale road on to the fell, and climbed up the side of Charlton Wath Beck, and so to the top of Great Sca Fell, 2150 feet above sea level.

Dark rain clouds blew overhead during the climb, and the sunshine vanished for the day, but there were no thoughts of turning back – not even when a cold grey mist swirled across the fell with accompanying rain squalls.

There were occasional glimpses of Bassenthwaite Lake and Overwater far below when the mist lifted briefly, but visibility was reduced almost to nil as the long column traversed The Knott, 2329 feet high.

Leaders were lost

For a few minutes, the leaders were at a loss as to their exact position, but their accumulated years of experience on the high fells stood them in good stead, and soon they were leading the way down to the Whylie Ghyll stream, where a welcome halt was called for lunch. Thus refreshed, the walkers followed the steam down until it joined the River Caldew, where they caught a glimpse of Skiddaw House away at the head of the valley, and agreed that it merited the title of 'Cumberland's loneliest farmhouse'.

From Whylie Ghyll there was a long trek down the Caldew valley to Mosedale, and it was here that the distance began to tell on the participants. In place of the two laughing groups that had left Caldbeck a few hours before, they straggled over a mile or more, but everyone was determined to keep on and receive their 'tatie pot' supper by way of reward at journey's end!

At Mosedale, the route turned north for Hesket-new-Market, where the villagers shouted encouragement as the boundary walkers found a new lease of life and energy. The walk was now as good as over; it had been a grand day, and they would not have missed it for worlds! The vanguard arrived back in Caldbeck by 4.00 p.m. and everyone had completed the circuit within the next hour.

Veteran's third Boundary Walk

While the veteran of the party was the committee chairman, Mr Ridley, a very close second was 'Willy' James, Caldbeck, the oldest to walk the boundary on foot. Admitting to being 'ower seventy', Mr James led the way with a brisk, spanking stride that "ud mak' a few young 'uns look up', and had the distinction of being the only person present to be walking the boundary for the third time.

The last occasion was in 1932, when eighty people turned out, and Mr James's first walk was 21 years before that – in 1911. He had three grandchildren on the walk this time – Stanley, Nora and Henry Bell – and 'grandpa' finished as fit as any of them!

Heroine of the day was Mrs S. H. Cole, Brownrigg, Caldbeck, who was rightly proud rather than bashful in acknowledging that she was the oldest lady on the walk – a very sprightly 57 year old! Mrs Cole told a *Herald* reporter afterwards that she had enjoyed every minute of the walk and was very keen that such old village customs should be continued down the years.

For the Rector of Caldbeck, the Rev. R. L. W. Jones, the boundary walk fulfilled a three year ambition, for he has been intending to do it ever since he came to live in the parish, and his subsequent comment was that it was 'a very interesting walk'.

Five members of one family

One of the largest family parties was led by Mr James Savage, Nether Row, Hesket-new-Market, with his sons Thomas, Alan and ten-year-old Arnold (the youngest boy to walk the course) and daughter Margaret, while two other energetic walkers were Arthur Evans (13) and Peter Scott (12) who went round together.

The youngest member of the entire party was eight-year-old Ian Todhunter, mounted on a grey Shetland pony. Ian, who had only ridden the pony for two days previous to the walk, was the most colourful member of the party wearing the traditional John Peel costume in which he won the Caldbeck Coronation pageant, complete with a hunting horn borrowed from the Blencathra Hunt. The horn was Ian's big worry, for it would not give its best performance in his hands and was finally passed over to his father to blow on the appropriate boundary lines!

A most pleasant feature of the day's program was the 'tatie-pot' supper served in the Parish Hall as soon as the boundary walkers returned to Caldbeck. Piping hot, and prepared from a prize heath-going Herdwick supplied by one of the generous patrons of the walk, it was given short shrift by fell-sharpened appetites. There were two helpings – 'and more if you want' – for everyone present, and one village worthy was heard to remark 'Man, the lads may be tired, but their eating mechanism is working all right!'

The 'tatie pot' was prepared by ladies of the village on their own stoves and hearths at home, and then carried in trays into the Hall to be distributed to the waiting plates. The ladies responsible for the catering preparation were Mesdames J. Graham, E. Strickland, R. Thornthwaite, F. Stanger, J. Bennett, G. Teasdale, V. Hill, J. Richardson, and D. Cowx, and the Misses L. Bell and M. Thomson, while those 'waiting on' included Mesdames W. Wallace, R. Grainger, E. Yeomans, J. Leech, J. Graham, T. Pearson, E. Sewell, and J. Scott, and Miss F. Ashbridge.

Later in the evening there was a whilst drive in the Parish Hall, and during an interval Miss E. Jennings presented special prizes to Mr Ridley and Mrs Cole, Ian Todhunter, Arnold Savage, Nora Bell and Joan Broatch – the oldest and youngest male and female participants – which brought a memorable day to a fittingly happy end.

A summer's morning and my father with Bute and Nell at the farm fell gate.

Seven

Fifty Years
Of Fell Farming

Financial struggles of the 1930s

Here my father talks about the financial struggles of the '30s, tree planting and the collie dogs of the sheep farmer.

In the early 1930s my own case was typical of hundreds in the counties in the North West. I had run up an overdraft of £650, a very large amount upon a farm with a total capital value, including the land, of (at prices in 1932) about £2,000 – for land values had dropped to very little indeed. I was thankful that I had not been tempted to borrow money to get a stock together when I had started, and had worked into a stock while taking in stock to summer and winter, or I would have been ruined.

I think those of us who went through that period never want to see an overdraft again. Until about 1935 there was practically no milk selling on the fellsides. Anyone who did sell it was considered to be very hard up indeed and in a bad way. Sheep did not conflict with stock rearing, so nearly everyone who had fell rights (and nearly all of us in the fell parishes had them) kept their flock of 'heafed' sheep.

'Stinted' Fells

The fells and commons were so heavily stocked in many areas that flockmasters were 'eating each other out' and, where the sheep could get off the commons or fells on to the highways, they did so to such an extent that many shepherds spent half their time collecting them back to their heaf. So I started a movement to have the fells and commons 'stinted' and grids placed at the road entrances.

While the 'Barney Courts' (Barons Courts) held sway, until about 1900, the custom was enforced that only as many sheep were to be placed upon the common grazings as their owner could winter 'inside' on his farm. The large landowners of that period were Lords of Manors and, because there was no security of tenure in force, they were able to enforce this ruling at the Barney Courts held about twice a year because any tenant who did not toe the line got his notice.

As death duties compelled the sales of large estates, the grip of these large landowners and the power of their courts gradually died until the 1914 war. After that the common grazings became a 'free for all' and 'off wintering' of gimmers and wether lambs became general and allowed flocks to grow to such a size that the grazings could not carry them without large losses from lack of food.

Men with large families of strong lads who were 'keen on fell work' could hound anyone off, and much harm was done. My effort to have stinting and grids had a mixed reception and folks were almost equally divided upon the matter. King's College, Newcastle, took up the idea and a committee was formed to further the idea.

However, very little was done about the commons until well into the 1960s. The Hill Sheep subsidy of the 1950s had enabled the hill farmers to cease milk production – the milk churn lorries collecting up and down the Lakeland valleys stopped. There was a period of 'calm' until governments, their advisors and 'cash flow' accountants with full bellies started to subvert the terms of the 1947 Agriculture Act. As I point out later, the war was forgotten, cheap food – the 'birthright' of the British people – became the policy.

As support for hill farming declined a 'living' was only possible by expanding acreage or increasing stock numbers on the fells – with predictable consequences for hill farmers and their lands. Flocks disappeared with farm amalgamations or acquisitions – so that the number of flock owners prepared to shepherd over miles of open fell has reached a crisis point and 'heafed' flocks were given the coup de grace by the Foot and Mouth disaster. There are very few on the staff of Natural England with experience of hill-farming life from childhood to carry through a programme to revitalise fell farming. One or two whom we know and whose fathers and families in the past encouraged them – 'if you can't beat 'em, join 'em' – are nearing retirement, to be replaced by staff with certificates/degrees galore, but these are all short-term contracts and what's worse is that they're attempting to tackle the problems with (always) inadequate long-term funding.

For many years the changes to the family farm structure in uplands (and lowlands) was almost imperceptible. It was dramatic in the arable areas resulting 'in extremes' with the prairies of East Anglia. Cash-flow accounting and profit have changed the population structure of Cumbria with creeping farm dereliction and the loss of heritage and tradition – the gardeners have gone.

'Bald' Brownrigg

While I could ill afford it in the early '30s, I did allow myself to indulge one long-term improvement. When I bought Brownrigg it was as bald as an egg. With the exception of the house and buildings there was no shelter at all in the land.

There were several areas of poor land, either rocky, damp, or *awkward corners*, impossible to get implements into, and others that 'drifted up' and buried sheep in storms – I had hoped to plant up with trees. So I planted my first acre of trees.

It is interesting to remember what this acre cost. The trees were Japanese Larch at 30s. 0d. per thousand (I planted 1,200 to the acre). There was a wall round one side of them, and the fencing of the other sides cost 120 posts at 1s. 0d. each – £6.00; three rolls of square mesh wire, £4 10s.; and half a roll of barb wire, 10s. 0d. Three of us did the job on one Saturday afternoon, wages 30s. 0d. A total of £14. 6s.

That plantation was remarkably successful. It has been twice thinned and, although it stands 1,000ft up and on the top of the farm without any shelter itself, it is now, 70 years after, 50ft high and affords magnificent shelter for my lambing ewes – and more than half of all my lambs are born in it, for the fences round it were removed about 15 years ago. One point I learnt from that wood was to always put a gatestead into a wood fence. I did not do this and when any stock got into the wood – as it inevitably will, no matter how good the fence – it did more damage in getting out than getting in. That wood was the beginning, over 20 years, of plantations now covering *10 acres*. Far from losing land the shelter given by them has saved me much cost in hay, etc., every spring, because I can get stock out much earlier. Some of my last plantations are of ash, elm, beech, etc. The costs of planting are now from five to ten times that of the first.

My Sheepdogs

Like all hill farmers, my constant companions have been my dogs. Our slape-haired, non-pedigree curs are among the best in the world, and are to be found all over the world where sheep are kept. I've had the good fortune to own a long line of them going back to Nap, a dog I bought from Isaac Pollock, Godferhead, Loweswater.

Nap had been trained on an enclosed fell, so when I put him round my flock on Faulds Brow, Caldbeck, an open common of about 1,300 acres but with walls here and there, I thought he had gone for good.

However, in about three-quarters of an hour he came back with four or five flocks he had gathered from far and wide, his tongue hanging out and nearly done.

He was a grand dog but had the fault of occasionally 'taking off' for no apparent reason, and this usually happened when I was most busy and anxious to have the sheep in. It was maddening, and I was young and used to give him a hiding when he came home.

This happened perhaps half a dozen times before we had a severe snow storm, and Nap took off that day. Usually he came back in an hour or two. This time he did not come in. The snow was a complete 'hap-up' (i.e. not a blade of grass showing) and deep drifts. For three days he stayed away, but barked round the farm each night. There was no food for him and he had none before he took off. On the third day I decided I would either have to get him or report to the police in case he began worrying.

A sunny summer morning's walk around the stock... SHC accompanied by Bright (left) and Nell (right) photographed in 1950 by his cousin Charles Denton.

Wendy came to us a puppy in 1940 and was one of our favourite sheepdogs. Very, very, shy – she didn't trust cameras but my Uncle caught her while I talked to her. Highly intelligent, she would nip over the wall into a neightbour's field to position herself to fetch errant sheep back down the lonning. An excellent ratter, she was nipped by a dirty rat and died of septicaemia in 1950. Penicillin was not readily avaliable then.

Took The Gun

A report to the police would have meant an organised shoot to kill him. I decided if anyone was to shoot him it would be myself, so I set off with my gun. I must have covered three or four miles without result when, as I neared home, I spotted him lying asleep on the top of a wall level with the top of a drift.

I got up to within 20 yards of him, put the safety catch up and covered him with the gun and said, 'Come in a hint, Nap.' He woke up, looked at me (and like most dogs he was afraid of a gun) he came to me wagging his tail.

I have rarely been more relieved in my life. We went home and I fed him without touching him. He made me review my treatment of him and I decided not to touch him again if he took off. He gradually dropped the habit and lived many years and he taught me that striking a dog is a mistake. I have never hit a dog from that day, and have never needed to.

Nearly all our dogs have work inbred and fall in naturally with the farm and fell work. 'Trials dogs' are a different matter, and to get them perfect needs years of patience and never passing a fault, but a stick is useless. Men like the late Joseph Relph, whom I knew well, never laid a hand on one of their dogs.

One of my dogs could sort off my sheep from my neighbours while I stood 200 yards away. Another bitch could capture a single stampeding sheep down a hill. She used to reach the sheep, run by its side for a few paces, click a front leg which threw the sheep and rolled it over, and place her front legs and paws over it, and sit on it until I got to it.

Tragedy Of Laddie

These Dogs are always ready to go, sunshine or snow, and they will risk their lives for us by tackling a bull or a mad tup, and all they ask is their supper each night. The tragedy is that they live such a short time.

When Uncle John retired as shepherd to Lord Leconfield, his oldest dog, Laddie, retired with him. His greatest interest in life was to shepherd my sheep with Laddie on Faulds Brow. After several years a motorist hit Laddie and knocked him out, but did not kill him. The motorist stopped and asked Uncle John how much he owed him. Uncle John said 'Mister, ah want nothing fra thaa, but ah wad rather thoo had hitten me 'er that dog.'

Laddie never properly recovered and after a few months he was in pain, so John felt he had to have him put down. He took him to Willie Coulthard, Biggards, who was a good shot, and asked him to shoot him for him. John said 'Ah can't do it mesel.' Willie promised to do the job for him. As John left him he turned to Willie with tears in his eyes and said 'Thoo won't miss, Willie, will ta.' Willie promised. But Uncle John was never the same man again. His pal and his interest in life had gone.

Wooden 'hands' for working up butter and the beautiful wooden moulds for attractive presentation patterns.

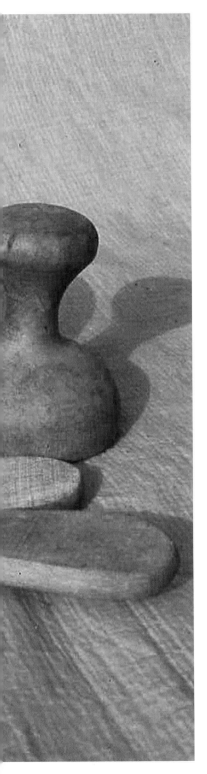

EIGHT

'BUTTER MAKING FOR PIN MONEY'

A regular milk cheque and drudgery

It is easy to forget that prior to 1940 there were no such things as a regular monthly milk cheque or 'cash flow'. Searching for some old pictures left by my father, I came across the annual livestock valuation for 1938. It was written on the back of an envelope and was probably for the bank manager because few farmers kept accounts in those days. (Eighty fell going ewes and lambs plus twelve cows and calves plus crop in hand came to £800.)

Hill farmers had to exist for very long periods by frugal living and careful budgeting – it was a hand-to-mouth existence, there was little 'slack' for any form of investment and those who started on the hills looked for a tenancy on a farm on the Solway plain as soon as they could, especially if their wives had bred any family! Even today upland farms are experiencing the same squeeze as in the 1930s – farms from which the dairy herd disappeared in the '90s thanks to tanker milk collection; the tradability of milk quotas in Britain which destroyed the very farmers it was designed to save, and the 'coup de grace' came when politicians used EU competition regulations to force the demise of the MMB.

Even today on the hill farm, 'income' comes in about five 'pay days' per year: the wool cheque (in August – but these days it costs more to shear the sheep than the fleece is worth so often it is burnt!), half-bred gimmer lambs, store lambs, draft ewes and suckler calves – in September, October and November respectively – and that's your lot. Little wonder the hill sheep and cow subsidies were so welcome in February and March when outgoings were highest!

World War Two and the drive to produce ever more milk for sale to the Milk Marketing Board, changed the whole face of farming in the uplands – and throughout the

One-gallon galvanised cream churns made in Denmark and sold by Robert Stoddart – plumber and ironmonger of Wigton. Each had a soldered on brass label of the farm and farmer. E.g. one of these belonged to E. Hird of Parkhead and the other to Cole, Brownrigg. (The Swan Vestas matchbox gives a feel for the size of the churns.)

country dairying earned that title 'the sheet anchor of British Farming'. The regular monthly milk cheque became at first a blessing and then a curse to livestock farming – security on which money could be borrowed to expand the farm business either in land, machinery or livestock.

My earliest recollections of butter making on our 80-acre hill farm at Caldbeck (900 ft a.s.l.) go back to 1936 when, as an eight year old, I was expected to turn the ALFA-LAVAL separator for 20 minutes morning and evening. In spring we had about eight cows and heifers and about twenty calves (or 'stirks' to use the dialect). They were bucket reared on the skimmed milk (separated) or on a mixture of separated milk and linseed gruel. In the '30s, sales of a little butter and some eggs provided the only meagre cash on the farm – often pin-money for the farmer's wife. But in 1937 a dramatic change took place. My father and a few others were persuaded to sell our cream to a firm of confectioners who had a chain of cafés in the north of England.

The company, Carricks, had a creamery on the Cumberland–Northumberland Border at a place 25 miles away called Low Row, on the railway line to Newcastle – their main base. There had to be sufficient farmers prepared to supply and justify collection

My father and mother photographed by his cousin on a 'day out' about 1928, starting the ascent of Honister Pass from Buttermere. Note the gravel road before tarmac was laid. The Rover 8 is in its coupé form with a canvas hood for summer. In winter it had an easily fitted 'saloon' top.

by a 30 cwt Ford van every two days; and the van travelled as far as Bassenthwaite in the west. The van collected the cream in a small one-and-a-half gallon churn every other day (I still have it as a keep-sake). It was never full but we were paid 10s. 0d. a gallon – a fortune in those days. Much more importantly, my mother was spared a hard day's work churning and making the butter once a week so the old end-over-end barrel churn was pensioned off.

In those days my birthday 'treat' was to be taken to Carlisle – (like going for a weekend in Paris today!) – and to have afternoon tea in Carrick's café and chocolate éclairs filled with real whipped cream! My father had an air-cooled 'Rover 8', with a flat twin engine bought for him as a wedding present by my grandfather in 1926, and only the second car in the parish!

However, by 1940 our dairy herd had been expanded to 15 dual-purpose Shorthorn dairy cows and we were into 'intensive' milk production in a big way. Our herd was awarded one of the ten 'Golden Churn Certificates' in the county for high milk production. We even had a Gascoigne portable milking machine which you pushed from one byre to the other. Yes, in those days up to 1945 a farmer could make a good living

A glass or 'blow' churn used on your knee or kitchen table to churn a pound of butter. Used from 1937 and all through the war years when all milk had to be sold to the Milk Marketing Board (MMB) after butter making was stopped.

Pats or lumps of butter float in the buttermilk/whey to be removed and worked using wooden 'hands'.

My wife's aunt working butter in the seventies – note the churns on the rack, brass scales, salt, etc.

from a herd of 15 cows … but of course we had no butter for the royal slice of bread!

Ever resourceful, my father bought a tabletop glass 'Blow Churn' and we were into butter making again. Terribly illegal but you skimmed off a small cupful of cream from the evening milk churn which had stood in the cooler house all night – before it went off on the lorry. This was set up in a very large glazed earthen bowl and by the end of the week you had enough to churn on the kitchen table and make about three quarters to one and a half pounds of butter.

For making larger quantities on the farm the cream was collected up for about a week in large earthenware bowls or a 'crockpot'. It was stirred every day with a large wooden spoon often called a thyval. This was made from an Ash tree. The cream was then emptied into the churn which had previously been rinsed with cold water (so that the cream would not stick to the barrel). You then proceeded to turn the churn until the cream turned to butter; this was obvious from the different 'noise' of the churn when the butter particles (globules) or 'pinheads' separated from the blue tinted butter milk. Next a large wooden bowl turned from an Ash tree trunk was scalded with boiling water to ensure good hygiene. The buttermilk was strained off and this was used to feed the calves or mixed with a fattening meal – (in this area usually ground oatmeal) – or potatoes etc. to feed to the pigs. Or, in our case, it was mixed with bran (unrationed), a poultry meal called 'layers mash' (coupons related to egg sales during the war), and coarse wheatmeal to a 'crowdy' (dialect) and fed to the hens. To eke out the meal my mother used to boil a huge pan containing about a half hundredweight of unpeeled potatoes on the 'Aga' each afternoon, to augment the scarce rationed feeding stuffs for the laying hens.

To about 10 lbs of butter 'pinheads' in the bowl you added a good handful of salt and then began to squeeze out the excess liquid like kneading bread dough. You then weighed out the butter into either pounds or half-pounds on the large brass scales. At this stage you might dip your hands in oatmeal from time to time and rub them to stop the butter sticking.

The mound of butter was shaped on a flat wooden board into oblongs using the 'Scotch Hands' and placed in neat rows in grease-proof paper. Or it might be pressed into moulds containing an exquisite woodcut pattern, e.g. of a thistle, a rose, or an ear of corn, to provide an attractive decorative presentation. It was taken into the local market town on market day where it was sold (even in the 1970s) for 1*s*. 0*d*. to 2*s*. 0*d*. a pound. Under the new Single Farm Payments regime farmers may well return to a modified system their grandfathers knew so well – thrift and self-sufficiency!

Although my father photographed many of the activities in a farming parish and work on the farms, he overlooked the introduction of the Gascoigne portable milker to our

More of the wooden hands and moulds used to shape and decorate pats of butter

Dual purpose shorthorns being machine-milked on a typical Cumbrain milk-producing farm from about 1938. The byre had a concrete floor and water drinking bowls. These Gascoyne two-unit portable milking machines were very popular, especially on hill farms with the cows often housed in separate byres around the farmyard. This photograph courtesy of the Library of the N.I.R.D. Reading University.

farm. Luckily from memory I was able to sketch the machine, but the National Dairy Archive came up with a picture reproduced here. Such machines are still very much in use today in the mountain farming areas of Austria, Slovenia and the Carpathian region. Essential on hill farms in those days – you could trundle the apparatus from byre to byre which might house from four or six to twenty cows. Concreted floors, feeding troughs and water bowls were all to come later as the war years advanced. The tap-water-connected milk cooler improved keeping quality, but the glass lined chilled bulk storage tank was a long way off and only really made a change on hill farms when most of us had freed ourselves of the drudgery of twice-a-day milking, 365 days in the year – slavery!

Willy Todhunter assists 'quack' vet Joe Benson to pull teeth from a heifer. Sometimes if an animal was not thriving it might be assumed the cause was a bad tooth.

NINE

FARMERS' NECESSARY ECONOMIES

Pre-1939–45 War

In this article my father describes the economies made by farmers to meet the difficulties in the days before the 1939–45 war.

During the long slump nearly all farmers, I among them, tried increasing our stocks of cattle, sheep and pigs. We very soon found out, however, that this only made matters worse and played into the hands of buyers; we only knocked the bottom further out of our market. This is why those of us who remember those days have no faith in the constant cry of the ministry of Food and Agriculture for more and ever more production to meet foreign competition.

What feeding stuffs we had to buy we made up ourselves from bran, pollards, Indian meal, and by rolling our own oats and growing turnips. We turned to doing our own joinery, masonry where necessary, and simple blacksmithing and plumbing, to keep costs down. We 'cold shod' our horses if they cast a shoe. Chaps like my old boss, Christopher, and other unqualified 'horse doctors' acted as parish vets (despite the fact that qualified veterinary surgeons only charged 7s. 6d. a visit and often did not send in a bill for years!)

Saving the 'Half-Croons'

To save expense of transport to Wigton or Penrith of half-a-crown or five shillings to take a beast to market, we used to meet on market days on the village greens and all walk our cattle to Wigton – Penrith was too far but we borrowed a bull cart to take them there with our own horse. As a chap said to me one day on our way walking cattle to Wigton 'Yan hez t' save oor bits o' half-croons these days'.

We had some struggles getting cattle up our hill, Ratten Row, and over the common for we were driving from 'home' and, as often as not, one or more would break away despite all of us and dogs, and we just had to abandon it and hope to get it to market the next week. Self-sufficiency saved us from bankruptcy and was the order of the day. I often think of today's costs and wonder what would happen if there was another slump of the same magnitude.

Some idea of prices can be gathered from my experience in 1931 when our wool was 2d per lb. I wanted a suit – I had not had one since I was married – so I went to a well-known tailor's in Carlisle where I saw a tweed I liked the look of.

It was priced £3 10s. 0d. I never wear a waistcoat so, having in mind the price of our wool and the waistcoat, I argued with the little man who was serving me about the price. I found later that his name was, very appropriately, Peacock.

Harker and Bell's, Gents' outfitters in Carlisle. Today it is a charity shop.

This little man pulled himself up to his full height and said to me 'My dear sir, we are not cheapjack tailors, we build quality and service into our suits. If you want a 'reach me down' you can go down Botchergate and get one for 30s. 0d.' In fact I got a lecture and liked his courage so much that I bought the suit and have dealt with the firm ever since.

In about 1932, Carrick's, Low Row, began buying cream from fellside farmers and had a round in my district. Their price for 50% cream (so thick that it would not run), was 10s. 0d. per gallon, and less for lower percentages. This was about twice as good a price as for butter and cut out much work in churning. As work began to relieve unemployment in the towns, our sheep and cattle prices rose until we were again on at least an even keel, and our overdrafts were stationary.

First Cattle Grids

As far as I can remember it was in 1932 that the first County Council cattle grid was placed at Lazonby Fell. Through the influence, and with the assistance of Charles Roberts, the Chairman of the County Council, I had been pressing for grids for some years. Plans were prepared for placing many others but, due to difficulties and the war scare that was developing, the plans were pigeonholed and did not emerge again until after the Second World War.

However, and again through the influence of Charles Roberts, a Hill Farming Committee was established at King's College, Newcastle, to go into the whole aspect of commons grazings in the North West. The Cumbrian members were Mr Roberts, Mr. J. H. Faulder, Newton Rigg; Mr J. F. Herdman, Garrigill; and myself. Mr Lyle-Stewart was the veterinary adviser to the Committee and the College too, and a very fine chap indeed.

February snow and Carrick's 30cwt Ford van collects our small churn of cream from the fell at Brownrigg, where it is destined for the Low Row Creamery and their shops in Newcastle, circa 1936.

Through the work of this Committee, the Royal Commission on Common Land, under the chairmanship of Earl de la Warr, was appointed to consider the whole question of Commons.

During the visit of the Committee to Cumberland, the late Mr T. Ridley, Wood Hall, entertained the Committee and acted as the chairman of a local committee set up to meet the Royal Commission. The report of this Committee was pigeonholed due to war preparations and nothing was done. But this Committee laid the foundations of the present Commons Registrations Act. In 1930 on Faulds Brow Common, where my sheep are heafed, there were 13 flocks numbering 1600 sheep on 1300 acres of the common. Today there are 7 flocks and 800 sheep. Milk selling caused the change – milk and sheep won't go together. Circumstances alter cases, and in my opinion the Registration Act can only cause harm now.

Soldier Farmers

When the army was demobilised in the 1920s many men had decided that they would not go back to a sedentary job after the open air life of soldiering. Farming attracted large numbers of these chaps, and especially if they had any capital or had been officers and had a gratuity. Unfortunately farming to those who spend summer holidays in the country always looks a silly-simple job. It was a tragedy of the slump that nearly all of these men lost their all.

The Colonies, and especially Australia and Canada, had the same experience with their returning troops. They did better than our government. They gave land on very long-term repayments and at very cheap rates, with ample acreages to be able to earn a living and capital with which to equip them.

But nearly all of those who took up these offers failed and the farms were left on their government's hands. These lands were offered to British farmers who wished to emigrate on the same generous terms as had been offered to their own men and very many of our fell farmers and farmers' sons took them and did well despite the slump. But it must be remembered that the colonial governments stood by these trained farmers from Britain during the slump. Many of my friends were among those who took advantage of the offers, and there is scarcely a village in our two counties that did not contribute these well trained men to those colonies.

VILLAGE LIFE AND THE JOHN PEEL BRANCH

In the '20s our village lads and lasses could usually find work in our villages and on our farms. The parson, doctor and local landowners employed the girls and some went as 'servant lasses' to farms. Their jobs were nearly always all hours from rising at 6.00 a.m. or 7.00 a.m. to bed-time at 10.00 p.m. with only one evening a week off from 6.00 p.m. to 10.00 p.m., and when there was nothing else to do in the way of hard work they had to knit.

Their wages were from 3s. 6d. to (in exceptional cases) £1 per week and 'all found'. The best girls did not need to stand in the hiring market – nor did the best lads – they were asked if they were staying on and if not there was some other farmer after them before the 'hirings'. Many preferred to go to the hirings to get all they could in wage. The lads stood at one side of the street and the girls either in the local market house or on the street. Better times and fuller employment and the 'minimum wage' killed hiring about the beginning of the last war in 1939.

The hirings were a lottery for both workers and masters unless you could get someone who you knew something about, and both tried to be in the market as early as possible to get both the servants and bosses that were the best. Fell farms were none too popular, very largely on account of the winters. One of the last lads I tried to hire, when we had agreed wages and conditions and I offered him his 'earl's penny', said to me: 'Where's it till?' When I told him Caldbeck, he said: 'Oh, Aas not garn up theer t' be blan away', and that was that.

Profitable Business

As we on the fellside watched low country farmers beginning to hit better times by milk selling, those fellsiders who were near enough to be able to join collecting routes did so and it was a profitable business with very small overheads in those days. I never liked milk selling and stuck to cream until the war made this impossible.

As milk caught on and monthly milk cheques began to come in, a change came over

Peacetime and a petrol ration allowed the public to buy motor cars once again. This was the Ford advertisement from 1945.

our way of living on the fellside. Until then a careful watch had to be kept upon bank balances and the accumulation of money we had received from the sale of wool, sheep and store cattle, and foals, at the end of the previous year had to meet all our outgoings until the back-end of the next year.

Milk made folks more venturesome and, unfortunately, they put all their eggs in one basket. Hill sheep were the first to go, horses and, in many cases, the rearing of bullock stirks followed. As poultry and pigs failed in the later years, milk became the be all and end all of existence for too many. To those who lived in the heart of the Lake District, the coming of the £100 family small car proved to be a lifeline to many, but we in Caldbeck got little benefit from that.

John Peel Branch

I had always taken a keen interest in the N. F. U. and I think it was in 1933 that I approached several friends and the late R. W. Bell, the County Secretary of the Union, with the idea of forming a local branch. Mr. Bell agreed and a branch was formed. The late T. W. Ridley of Wood Hall, Hesket-new-Market, was our first chairman and he suggested it be called John Peel Branch. The late R. H. Lamb was our secretary for several years until work in connection with the Herdwick Sheep Breeders' Association, which was formed about the same time, claimed his attention.

We soon had quite a large membership of about 120 and a very active branch. It was R. H. Lamb who, in an effort to find better outlets for Herdwick wool, had the very good idea of trying to have suitings made for ladies' and men's suits and costumes. He was assisted by a firm of woollen manufacturers at Otterburn and a firm of tailors at Wigton and the result was some very fine cloth. I had one of these suits and it was almost everlasting and almost waterproof. Unfortunately the colours had to be dark and they were heavy, but there was a good demand.

Another very good idea Harry tried out was to 'cure' Herdwick sides and legs like bacon, and he called this 'macon'. Unfortunately these ideas were launched when lighter cloths and imports of Danish bacon were coming in, in ever-increasing quantities, but they survived for many years. Caldbeck had, however, a reputation for the Herdwick 'Hodden' or 'Ivinson' grey, worn by John Peel and made at Woodcock's, and later at Ivinson's woollen mill at Caldbeck.

Paying Off The Debt

It was decided in 1936 to hold a 'John Peel' celebration to pay off the new Parish Hall debt and a committee, with R. H. L. as secretary, was formed. We knew John Peel was famous and had a great following, but that was as far as we could go in estimating how large a crowd to cater for.

Our new Parish Hall had just been built, very largely due to the gift of the land by Mr. N. Helme, and of a considerable sum of money given by the late Joseph Jennings, but we still had a considerable sum to raise to pay it off. We hired a large marquee and erected this in the field adjoining the hall. This was used for the singing contest for the best rendering of 'D' ye ken John Peel,' for 'gurning' contests, clog dancing and as a canteen.

The day began early in the morning with a meet of the hounds on the village green in front of the Oddfellows and in view of the house where Woodcock Graves wrote it. The hero was first 'toasted' then R. H. L. led the singing of the song, those of us on the committee doing our best to leave a small clearing in the middle of the huge crowd.

Masses of Peel enthusiasts turned up from all over the country. The daily newspapers had got hold of the story and we had journalists from London arriving in the old aeroplanes of the period. These were circling overhead looking for flat fields to land. By eleven o'clock it was obvious we were going to run out of both food and drink, so I and several others with any transport we could find, set off to Wigton and Carlisle to buy up all the pies and similar 'eats' we could get, and to order further supplies of drink.

Tattie Pots Saved The Day

Every oven in Caldbeck had been commissioned to produce tattie pots and these very largely saved the situation until we got the pies etc. By tea-time we reckoned we had some 2,000 people in the village but we had got over our surprise and could cope.

After the takings of the dance in the evening had been added, we of the committee found ourselves the custodians of between £400 and £500, so we took turns watching it until it was safely housed in a member's safe. Our profits went a long way to clearing off the hall debt, but we all realised that, had we known how many folk were going to turn up, we could have completely cleared the debt and perhaps had a bit of capital left.

Until after the 1939–45 war, we on the fellside had no water, gas or electricity supplies, but fortunately we had good springs or wells. Our struggles with 'American' ranges, oil stoves, pressure stoves, oil lamps, carbide and petrol and mantle lamps made us literally experts upon these subjects, and I often wonder just how much we spent upon them. The marvel is that I cannot remember a single serious fire during the twenty years while such makeshifts were used until electricity came – but not until about 1960!

Grace Teasdale assisting her father to thatch a typical Cumberland small round cornstack at 'Longlands' in 1946. Small stacks are still favoured on hill farms to allow 'crop' which may not be perfectly 'fit' when carted to dry out.

Ten

PERIOD OF DEPRESSION

Between The Two World Wars

In this section my father describes his struggle in the period of depression between the wars.

In 1920 there were still fields of hay-grass being mown with the 'Armstrong' mowing machine (scythe) and there was only one binder in the village. This belonged to Christopher H., and he cut quite a lot of corn with it for other people for a small charge, or they hired it from him to cut their corn.

We nearly all had mowing machines though, and cut our own hay with them, and some for other neighbours, if they would come and give a hand in making our own hay. These machines had reaping platforms and a second seat could be placed on them to allow the use of the machine for reaping corn with a 'putting off rake'. This device enabled the amount of cut corn for the making of one sheaf to be left in a nice handy pile ready for tying with a 'band' made from the cut corn.

Stacking Art

One of the most satisfying jobs I know used to be building our round stacks of corn in harvest time. Each one was a challenge. Time had not to be lost and yet every sheaf had to be put down properly with the right slope and angle, or the stack slipped and was to prop – not a pretty sight – or it rained in if the hang of the sheaves was not from the middle outwards. Thatching was also a grand job and a test of skill.

We all had our five or six acres of oats until milk selling came along and made it necessary to buy more concentrated – or are they? – feeds to get ever more milk from the same cows. We also had our two to three acres of turnips and an acre of potatoes but these have gone because of the difficulty of getting casual labour. These crops had the great merit of making us independent of bought winter foods for cattle, pigs and sheep.

Popular on hill and grassland farms – a single horse reaper. There are seats for two men but this horse is so well trained it is proceeding up the field with little guidance, leaving the man able to work the 'trip' of the corn carrier with his foot, at the same time pushing off the heads of corn with a special rake – an amount sufficient for a sheaf of corn.

A practice which has almost disappeared since the perfection of the spacer drill. Two workers illustrate two methods of 'singling' a root crop (turnips, cabbages, carrots, etc.). One man has sacking around his knees and is 'crawling' as he weeds and singles the plants; the second man is using a hoe.

Harry Dowthwaite of Plumpton was very proud of his steamer, here at work at Beckstones Farm, Caldbeck, in 1938. He worked from the Eden Valley across Cumberland to Ireby in the west.

Although the best cattle cakes could be bought then for £7 a ton, and pig and poultry foods for about £5 a ton, we could not have survived the depression of the 1930s without our own crops.

Until about 1923 there was a subsidy payment of 13s. 0d. an acre paid to farmers for wheat and oats. This was increased for the last year to £1 an acre in exchange for farmers accepting the national minimum wage.

After that payment, farmers were left with the wage to pay and the country washed its hands of 'the saviours of their country'. How the wheel runs full cycle!

Many farms had their own incubator and after hatching the chicks were transferred to a brooder and kept warm with a paraffin storm lamp.

Start of N. F. U.

In 1919–20 I joined the Wigton branch of the National Farmers' Union. The Union had been formed in 1916 from several small ones in Norfolk, Devon and elsewhere when these were grouped into one and given the title 'National'. It was quite active and succeeded in gaining several benefits, such as the de-rating of farm land and concessions from the railways for the transport of farm products. The attendance at meetings was as poor in those days in many branches as it is today and so, at a very badly attended annual meeting of the branch, I was elected delegate to the County Executive – at the age of 23.

From 1919 to 1924 my stock grew and I had 160 sheep, 30 cattle, 10 sows and 20 young pigs, and for those days a very large poultry unit of 600 birds with incubators giving me a capacity of 500 chicks a month.

Farming Pays!

I was able to dispense with taking in stock to summer or winter and began to build up a small bank balance of about £200.

I had 40–50 lbs of butter a fortnight at 3s. 6d. per pound. Decent year-old bullocks were making £20 to £30, foals up to £40 and our Herdwick wool was 1s. 6d. per pound. Looking at some of my old accounts I see that my stock in 1924 was worth about £1,200.

At that time it was quite possible to farm with such a stock in comfort, and put something by. I had no rent to pay and no mortgage. But in that year stock values began to fall, until in 1926 they had fallen to half. The colliery dispute which included the general strike caused mass unemployment and hardship and knocked the bottom out of the price of all meat – for once there is a lowering of income of industrial workers, food is the first thing to be cut. By 1930 cows had dropped to £20 a head, sheep to £1 a head, and pigs to £4 as baconers. I had 70 at the time and they nearly ruined me. I tried to feed them out and if I had buried them I would have been wise. I've never had a pig on my farm since!

Wool had dropped to 2d. a pound, and one neighbour refused to take that price and held it for a year, only to be offered one-and-a-half pence and had to take it. In that 'back end' I took 20 of the fattest Herdwick wether lambs I have ever had to Wigton and they were bid to 4s 9d. apiece. At that time the butchers were working 'rings' on the glutted markets. I refused the price, and like hundreds more farmers in the country, took them home and illegally butchered them one each week through the winter and sold the meat to people in the village. The butchers were nearly ruined in the country villages because of this practice. Many farmers were prosecuted in those 2–3 years of the early '30s for butchering on unlicensed premises, but still the practice went on.

Gradually my small balance at the bank ran out and I began to have an overdraft. I never gambled, or drank, or spent on clothes, or any sort of high living but, try as I would, I could not prevent the overdraft going up about £150 a year. I became so annoyed with it that one night I sat down and went through every item of expense I had with a fine tooth comb. I stopped smoking, cut out a daily paper, all magazines, all subscriptions to this and that. I even wrote to the District Council and asked to have the rates reduced (and got them down), but still the rot went on.

Fell Farm 'Slaves'

To return to the ladies. It's a marvel that girls would marry farmers in those days, and especially fell farmers. Even on low-country farms life was hard enough for women, but on a fell farm it was one long dedication to slavery.

Not only were most hill farmhouses dilapidated, as was mine, but the climate at 1,000 ft is rigorous indeed. The walls inside Brownrigg were white-washed, and old seventeenth-century stone fireplaces with carved mantels and pillars (very beautiful when clean stone) were tarred. The ceilings were nearly black and seventeenth-century 'rush' on the floors, beautiful sound oak beams were 'boxed'

A household mangle in common use throughout the countryside. Feeding in blankets or heavy sheets caused many injured fingers amongst the women folk.

and ugly. To achieve a decent standard of living and comfort under such conditions was a challenge to any woman.

In those days, clothes were to make, and stockings and woollens. Washing days with a dolly-tub and poss stick, and churning and baking with crude tackle, were bad enough, but there was milking night and morning, and calf feeding and the care of pigs, poultry and (in the days of Herdwicks) as many as a dozen pet lambs at a time to feed – and no 'convenience foods', fridges, or even running water until about the 1930s. So when I married in 1925 (or shall I say 'she agreed to marry me'), the daughter of a well-known Caldbeck family, who knew all the snags, including handling a husband, she must have seen something in me that I haven't discovered yet!

In 1930, I think it was, to make matters worse in Cumberland, there was an outbreak of scouring among the cattle in the county, both on the lowland and upland farms. Thousands of cattle were affected, and many hundreds died. Fortunately I had none affected myself, but one of my neighbours came to see me with tears in his eyes. He had seven affected out of 25 cattle and said if they died he would be ruined. I knew Lyle-Stewart, the veterinary adviser to King's College, Newcastle, and veterinarian to the Alan, Duke of Northumberland Fund for the advancement of research into animal diseases in the Borders.

With the help of John Faulder, the then Principal of Newton Rigg, I got Lyle-Stewart to come over to investigate. He did so, and several large stockowners in the county gave him permission to butcher one of their affected cattle, farmers in their areas were notified, and they attended in large numbers. He demonstrated the cause of the trouble (we call it nematrodirus worms today), and gave the remedy to their veterinary surgeons, and the disease was wiped out almost as quickly as it had begun.

He did a magnificent job for Border farmers and found remedies for very many of their diseases. Unfortunately he left the north when the Duke's Fund was incorporated in the N. A. A. S., preferring to work upon his own account.

Our other great enemy, liver fluke, was mastered about the same time when a simple cure was found in carbon-tetrachloride and our losses fell to almost nil from the disease. In fact, it can be said that losses after that discovery were due to neglect to take the precaution of dosing the sheep.

My parents and I turning hay by hand – 1936. If a crop was laid by bad weather the old swathe turners were not able to lift it effectively.

Mowing

Up to the mid-'20s, many farming cultivations and harvesting had changed little in 80 years on the hills and poorer lands. As my father noted, hay, grass and cereals were scythed by hand. Hay would be hand turned to kill it and dry it. Half dry, it would be protected from showers by lifting into small footcocks; these could be broken out and scaled about when a fine day came along.

Piking and Sweeping

My father had experienced 'piking' on the larger Northumberland farms for the pit pony trade, which demanded quality hay. In the '20s, he began piking to counter the wetter climate of Cumbria, to the curiosity and amusement of his neighbours.

You needed a 'sweep' which was a simple bit of kit with wooden teeth. These teeth were broad and flat on the top and underneath sides, fitted into a strong wooden beam about one foot apart. It looked like an oversized hair comb. The 'beam' had a pair of handles and chains from each end were attached to a swingletree taking the load to the single horse's collar.

Hayfield scene at Thornthwaite. The horse has been pulling the side-delivery rake and the tractor sweeping the rows to be piked.

A piking machine with a pick-up elevator behind the David Brown tractor taking up the crop to drop into the cradle forming the pike. The man has just got out of the cradle which has been tipped to discharge the pike. In some arrangements the piking machine was hitched behind the tractor with the elevator loading from behind but this meant the machine had to be uncoupled from the tractor to tip the pike.

On a fine day with a crop three-quarters made or in good fettle, a tipping hay rake collected the crop into rows. Then the wooden sweep collected the crop – as much as the horse could easily pull – usually using the slope downhill, into large heaps. When sufficient was collected, the horseman lifted the back of the sweep with the handles, causing the teeth of the sweep to dig in and the beam to ride up over the hay and hey presto, off you went back for another lot.

The sweeps would all be in a line across the field and from these you built your row of pikes. There had to be room below the line of pikes so that you could 'lead' them home on a pike bogey.

After three weeks you went to the field, backed up to the pike, tipped the bogey under the pike, unwound the chain (or rope) from the windlass and laid it round the base of the pike. Then you kicked the rope/chain right into the base of the pike which by now was fairly solid and had settled. You took up the tension on the windlass. 'Git up a step' was the command to the horse, and the pike bogey and pike broke the seal, as it were. So now you could wind the pike up the tipped bogey until it reached the tipping point, and down it crashed into the bogey chassis.

You put the safety hooks in the slots and off you went home to the barn or yard; child's work. I was doing it at age 8.

There was a secret to piking which for a time many of my father's 'copiers' did not know. If the hay was carted before three weeks you broke the 'sweat' of the maturing crop and the result – come winter time – was 'stourey' (i.e. very dusty) hay. Before that, at hay time, it could cause spontaneous combustion, i.e. a barn fire if carted before the three weeks 'sweat' was over. But dusty hay was the cause of a lot of 'farmers' lung' in those days.

As the years progressed, more machinery was involved. Especially on the farms on the Cumberland plain, the hay was picked up by an elevator towed behind the tractor, which delivered the grass into an upturned cone (like a jelly mould!) A man would be in it treading the crop into the frame as the cavalcade progressed across the field. When full, the cone-shaped cage was tipped upside down and there was your pike. Apart from a little tidying up the system didn't need so much brawn.

In Durham and the bigger farms of the North East, a simple crane and pulley arrangement with a large grab was used to lift the pike complete up onto the large rick, where there would be a gang of three or four spreading the hay about and consolidating the very large stack. I photographed this system back in the 1960s where a Fordson Dexta tractor provided the power for the grab and pulley.

Horse mowers were the 'tackle' for cutting grass but were hard on the horses and often could not deal with the crop.

The home-built grass mowers lasted up to the late '50s on the hill farms. Contraptions they were and came in all configurations. In Caldbeck George Steadman, the local

My father's modification mower on the chassis of a Morris Oxford.

Our Fordson 'Dexta' turning hay at Brownrigg, c.1960. In the distance the beautiful field pattern of the Caldbeck valley.

When he came to Caldbeck my father commented that many crops were still cut by 'armstrong' mowers, i.e. by hand with scythes! At Paddigill in 1940 Jack Watson scythes a heavy crop of oats while the family ties up the sheaves.

Blacksmith, built his with the mower under the car's back-axle, so the driver was looking down on the cutter bar and the front wheels were now at the back like castors – an arrangement which is the basic principle of the modern combine harvester and forage grass harvesters!

Harry Stoddart from Ireby made a 'bullnose' Morris Cowley into a tractor with cleated driving wheels which towed a horse mower, but this needed two men to operate it and it wasn't very 'nimble' at the row ends when you needed to manoeuvre back into the crop.

As the 'recession' receded and farming improved, upland farmers could consider liming their fields and applying basic slag which improved the crop yield, so it was important to relieve the strain on your horses. At that time you would have two or three Clydesdales on a hill farm and perhaps a strong fell pony capable of the lighter jobs. In the haymaking season the horses could only do so much and mowing was either an early morning or evening job.

So with the assistance of George Steadman the village blacksmith, a second-hand Morris Oxford was purchased and the saloon body removed. The shafts of the rear wheel transmission were fitted with two large cogwheels which drove a roller chain on each side to large cogwheels clamped on to the mower wheels, and the mower became part of the whole outfit, cast in Carlisle at Pratchitt's workshop. The levers which controlled the mower for lifting the cutter bar and its angle to the work were modified

Afternoon 'crowdy' feed (including potatoes) from my mother for the Black Leghorn hens kept in six hen houses around the top 5-acre field.

so that they could be operated from the driver's seat. It was a similar principle to the Ferguson Mounted mower of the 1950s. Because the drive was constant through the old car's differential, the mower had to be knocked out of drive when you reversed etc. to turn at the ends of a pass.

The final result lasted into the 1950s, until it was disposed of. By then the war had ended and we had reduced our full-time farming using contractors to cut the crop and the International B45 baler had arrived to bale the hay.

Baling

The Fordson continued to haul the Lister-Blackstone side-delivery rake, to sweep hay for piking and haul bales, pikes etc. home. Meanwhile I had gone to college and the army before I came back to Brownrigg in 1958. In that decade I'd had two new tractors in Yorkshire and machines such as the Vicon Acrobat, wufflers etc. had come onto the hill farm scene.

So in the 1970s the toil of bale loading had given way to elevators. In the 1990s grass crop preservation developed into big bales which shortly after could be wrapped in plastic – making them safe, weatherproof, and preserving the valuable nutritional juices which benefit our livestock today.

All these advances have taken place with the application of technology, and more *power* to operations. But even in 1950 it is sobering to think what a small tractor, the Ferguson TE20, could achieve – baling, mowing, ploughing, ridging and haulage – whereas today tractors have grown to mammoths of 150–200 horse power, with the average around 80. Such machinery is so expensive and costly to run and maintain, that crop contractors are increasingly employed to harvest the whole crop for you.

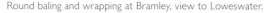

Round baling and wrapping at Bramley, view to Loweswater.

A horse pulling a pike bogey along the road, in the days before round baling and plastic wrapping were invented.

Square baling at Brownrigg with the Ferguson T20 and International B45 baler.

A 'picture postcard' image of the harvest scene into the late 1940s – a block cart complete with harvest ladders to extend the load area.

ELEVEN

SWALEDALE SHEEP, FARM HORSES, AND THE TRACTOR

In this article father talks about the introduction of the Swaledale sheep, farm horses and the coming of the tractor.

There were in the 1930s, as there are today, innovators who tried to improve our fell stocks of sheep by introducing new breeds. Cheviots, Blackfaced, Welsh and Dorset Horn were all tried, but they all faded out after three or four years. Our grazings were too poor and our winters too severe for them.

Our own fell breed from Westmorland had, however, been invading the ground of the Herdwicks slowly but surely, for several years. This was because they were rather more prolific breeders, better milkers and, if anything, they gave a slightly heavier fleece worth rather more per pound.

Most of us who have either cattle or sheep upon the fells know the very real danger of making changes. We know that if we make a mistake we may never be able to recover from it. So after watching the gradual change for some years I asked a well-known shepherd, who had made the change, what his experience of Swaledales was. 'Well,' he said, 'you'll lose half as many more Swaledales than you lose Herdwicks, but it will pay you to change.' So I did so in about 1932.

It took many years to breed out the Herdwick – and the odd sheep even to this day still shows Herdwick traces – but it was worthwhile. Nevertheless I feel sure that any of us who ever owned the hardy, fendy, little crafty Herdwicks have a warm spot for them. But the Herdwick can 'hold its ground' in the higher, drier, fells in mid- and south-west Lakeland, and it seems to me they always will.

We nearly all had Shorthorn cattle in those days, most of them non-pedigree, but strains that had been carefully bred by fellside families who were very expert stockmen and they were the fine types. With the spread of milk selling in the low country farms, a demand for good milkers arose and fell-bred heifers and third calf cows were in demand at better prices because they did so well when they went 'down the country'. Crossing our Shorthorns with black cattle produced the very fine 'blue greys' and created a demand we fell farmers tried to meet for white Shorthorn bulls.

Improved Incomes

These better outlets for our sheep and cattle helped to improve our incomes as the depression began to lift. But we had our laughs in the bad years too. My wife's uncle, the late John Faulder, was head shepherd to Lord Leconfield, on his farms in hand in Cumberland. John doted on sheep and considered it his duty to breed-up his Lordship's flock on Skiddaw Forest (a private enclosed fell heaf on Skiddaw). 'Lordy', as the staff knew him, was always a character to be reckoned with. One 'glorious 12th' he and his guests were out grouse shooting on Skiddaw. Lordy was a famous shot, but upon this occasion his 'eye' was out and he had several misses. He turned to the head keeper, who always walked with him and acted as loader, and said: 'Whose are all these sheep, Cockbain?' 'They're yours, my Lord' said the keeper. 'Well tell that chap Faulder to breed no more – you can't see grouse for sheep.'

About this time a new agent took over Lordy's estates and brought with him some new ideas. One of them (quite a good one that has become the fashion) was to buy about 30 pedigree Galloway heifers and cows to be run on Thistlebottom and Hill Top, two of the farms in hand and for which John Faulder was responsible. About a week after these cattle had arrived at Thistlebottom the agent arrived with a bundle of papers in his hand – their pedigrees.

In those days the only way of marking pedigree cattle was with black ink tattoos in the ear and, of course, it was almost impossible to find or identify these in a black ear. After a bit of fumbling he thought he had one identified and said to John: 'This is Lady Jane.' 'Well,' said John, 'Ah divvn't kna what she is on paper, but we call 'er "Bushey Tail".' Nevertheless, they were amongst the earliest 'sucklers' brought into Cumberland.

Until the invasion of tractors into our farming, the North West was a famous breeding ground for horses and each 'back-end' Wigton horse sales were the largest in the world, with the exception of Nishni Novogrod in Russia. When I began, I bought two Clydesdale mares, Tib and Lady. Lady was so quiet you could crawl under her belly with safety, but Tib was rather wicked and I had to warn anyone who handled her. If they forgot and 'loosed her out' without keeping hold of the reins, she almost invariably took off and I was the only one she would allow to catch her. Strangely enough, when she was yolked up she was always quiet. On one occasion a lad threw a loaded cart and

'Dinah' was one of the mares at Mid-Town Farm, Caldbeck. One day she began to give birth while my father was ploughing. Very fond of her, he drew this sketch of her in 1915. It was 'discovered' and we had it framed in 2000! Although he never had training as an artist, wood carver, joiner, model maker or radio ham, he perfected these skills during the long winter evenings of the inter-war years before radio or television invaded our spare time.

her over a side hill. The lad panicked and left her lying while he ran nearly half a mile to tell me. When I got there she had never stirred and I was able to undo her gear, loose the latch on the shafts and get her up, and not a thing was broken. I think her wickedness was probably due to her having been ill used, perhaps, in a timber-felling business, because to see her put herself into her collar and tense every muscle to move a heavy load was an education in exerting every ounce of physical strength. She was a great horse and I thought the world of her.

Once, a few years before I began on my own and while I was at Mid-Town, I was ploughing with Bloss and Dinah. Dinah was due to foal and the boss, very rightly, believed in working his mares – with common sense – until the day they foaled. My tea had been brought to the field and I was sitting in the dyke back when I heard Dinah begin to rumble.

Just In Time

I knew what that meant, so dropped my tea, loosed out and made off for home, Dinah as anxious as me to get there and fairly pulling Bloss by the head cord between them. As I entered the village, two front feet and then a head appeared and still we pressed on with 400 yards to go. The late Jack Brew saw what was happening and ran out of his shop, and running by the side of us unloosed her harness and what ploughing gear he could and someone – I forget who now – turned her collar over ready to take off. We just made it to her box and the foal was born in another couple of minutes. It was the only time I ever saw Christopher Hewetson run – he was a most imperturbable man!

The late Joe Teasdale of the Faulds, Caldbeck, told me that when he was a lad at home at Hudscales, he was walking through the fields one wild and dark night, and in getting over a stile he landed on the back of a fell pony which was sheltering behind the wall. It jumped up and took off with him and he said it was a most hair-raising experience.

Tractors Take Over

By the 1930s tractors began to take over from horses as the income of the low country farmers began to pick up because of milk selling We, on the fells, could not afford them but many of us, I among them, tried using old motor cars and lorries adapted for use on the land.

I bought an old Morris Oxford saloon for £10, removed the body, back wheels and mudguards and had two cog wheel plates cast at the foundry in Carlisle. Then by clamping the mower under the chassis of the car I had a chain driven mowing machine that lasted me for seven years until I eventually bought a works reconditioned Fordson Standard tractor in 1937. It cost £60 and had a factory guarantee for six months. The old motor mower was a very good job and saved me much valuable time in hay time by leaving the horses fresh to tackle the turning, raking and leading.

Before very long there were dozens and dozens of these converted old cars mowing and doing other work.

Not In Favour

By the time my tractor arrived, Uncle John was retired and spent most of his time at Brownrigg which was only a thousand yards from his retired home. He came across to see the new arrival and I knew he didn't favour it. It was a hot day and after he had walked round it, and obviously not wishing to be too outspoken about the tractor, he said: 'Well, there's ya thing – t' flees won't bother 'er.'

My pair of mares were getting old in 1937 and I felt that there was going to be war, so I decided to buy the tractor, one or two implements to go with it, and I also had the whole of the wire fences on the farm renewed. I had, when I first began, just 'fettled them up' with second-hand wire from Gretna.

By the time I had slagged and limed the land and the response was immediate, I had laid out all the money I dared to do. I also bought Thomas Pearson's pony Bess in case the tractor let me down. It never did, for those old Fordsons were the best tractors ever built and have not been improved upon today. So Bess had an easy time.

With old 'Tib' retired black 'Bess' enjoyed a very easy war. Friendly always and often a nuisance because of idleness, she was in the habit of following my mother to the hens at afternoon feed time to steal a few mouthfuls of the 'crowdy' – a mixture of warm boiled potatoes, oatmeal, wheatmeal and 'layers mash'. All very tasty!

Remember our fields were about 400 feet higher than the village – a good mile away with two other farms in between. One day mother scolded 'Bess' angrily and tapped her on the nose with the mixing stick. Whereupon the pony kicked up her heels – farted – and took off at a fast gallop. She ended up snorting and panting, proud of her escapade, a hundred yards from the village green, defeated in her gallop by a six foot high stone wall. She was eventually returned by a neighbour.

'Battling Bertha' turning hay with a Lister Blackstone side delivery rake in Yorkshire, July 1957.

'Three Shorthorn Cows' painted by B. C. Norton in 1876.
The cattle belonged to Samuel Foster, a wealthy businessman who farmed at Kill Howe, Bolton Gate near Wigton, Cumberland. The mansion has gone but you can still look at the view today across Ellenbank farmland to the village of Ireby – Binsey Hill and Skiddaw on the skyline. Foster was one of the first to introduce shorthorns into an area previously stocked with longhorns, black Galloway type cattle and stores from Ireland. Compare these animals with my photograph of the group of beautiful heifers near Greystoke in the 1980s.

Twelve

Life On The Fellside

During the 1939–45 war

Now, he tells the story of life on the fellside during the 1939–45 war.

Remote as we were on our fell farms as the 1930s drew to a close, much began to happen. The President of the N. F. U., Dorman-Smith, was made Minister of Agriculture and farmers became, once more, important people.

To encourage us to grow wheat and oats for human and cattle food, a subsidy of £2 an acre was offered and many of us ploughed out some of our grassland. A subsidy was also paid upon 'liming' and most of us were glad to give our land this much needed help.

The sale of cream came to an abrupt end and, since the government very properly gave first preference to milk production to ensure the best health food for young and old, a milk collection round was started. While I have never agreed with milk production on fell farms, the severe rationing of animal foodstuffs made it compulsory to sell milk if you wished to rear calves. So I began milk selling.

'Victory Churn' Contest

Strangely enough, I think it was in 1942–3, Mr J. F. Herdman of Garrigill, Alston, and I, were amongst the fourteen winners of the government sponsored 'Victory Churn' contest for the highest milk producers in the county. His farm was 1200 ft high and mine 1000 ft. To do it the sheep had to take a back seat and the cows had 'first bite' at everything.

I think my plan of growing kale for eatage until Christmas, and mangolds to follow until spring, did it. I also used one of the first electric fences in the county to give the cows their cut each day and thus save the very objectionable job of cutting and carting it. The War Agricultural Executive Committee ran a

The 'Victory Churn Certificate', awarded for large increases in milk output from individual farms in the war time. Brownrigg and Mr Herdman's farm at Garrigill near Alston – both above the 1000 ft contour – received this distinction.

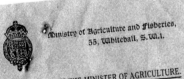

Ministry of Agriculture and Fisheries,
55, Whitehall, S.W.1.

A MESSAGE FROM THE MINISTER OF AGRICULTURE.

Victory Churn Contest for 1942/43.

It gives me great pleasure to send you the enclosed Certificate of Merit awarded to you and your workers in the above competition. Please accept, and convey to your workers, my hearty congratulations on the performance of your farm, and my grateful thanks for the contribution you have made to the great task of supplying the Nation with milk.

I know very well the many problems which milk producers have to face in these days. I am confident that, having overcome them in 1942-43, you and your people will continue to show this fine spirit of enterprise and energy.

COUNTY OF CUMBERLAND
WAR AGRICULTURAL EXECUTIVE COMMITTEE

Phone: Carlisle 2220

All communications should be addressed to
THE EXECUTIVE OFFICER,
OR THE SECRETARY
as the case may be

Postage MUST be prepaid

Our ref. 66/0/2/WH/IP

Your ref. ....

6, BRUNSWICK STREET,
CARLISLE.

6th, August, 1943.

S. H. Cole, Esq.,
"Brownrigg",
Caldbeck,
WIGTON.

Dear Sir,

VICTORY CHURN CONTEST.

The Ministry of Agriculture & Fisheries have recently sent us a list of farmers in the County who have increased their milk sales by 10% or more, for the period March 1942 - March 1943, over the corresponding period of the previous years.

It is noted that you have increased your milk sales by over 20%, and I am directed by my Executive Committee to congratulate you on this magnificient achievement obtained under difficult war time conditions.

Milk is now priority number one, and with the results you have obtained you have certainly proved that the County's Milk Sales can be considerably increased.

Yours faithfully,
John H. Faulder.
EXECUTIVE OFFICER.

The crew of the Royal Observer Corp's Post 'Easy One'. *Back Row* – Jimmy Boyle, Willie Todhunter, Arthur Brownrigg, Syd Tyson, Hugh Rigby, Jackson Hellon, Jack Lancaster. *Middle Row* – Mary Chope, Mary Wilkinson, Mary Tyson (wife of Syd), Sarah Lennon. *Front Row* – Ben Lennon, John Dalton, John Mellish, S. H. Cole, One missing – on duty at lookout. I presume Jimmy Elliott.

demonstration at Brownrigg to popularise the idea and they filmed it for the Ministry of Information

The week war broke out, I was asked to get an Observer post built on Faulds Brow (my sheep heaf) and to get a crew together to start training for the Royal Observer Corps. The 'post' consisted, in those days, of a butt of turf for our instruments – open to the sky for spotting – and a wooden hut for eating and sleeping. Two observers were to be on duty at a time and, unless there were enemy raiders notified from the coast posts, one could rest for an hour while the other held the fort.

Our post, E.1., was 1050 ft high and one mile north of the village. There were 16 of us, four full time, and the rest of us part-time, some farmers, others builders, quarrymen, and other trades. The full timers did 40 hours and the rest of us 12 to 24 hours according to what time we could spare. My job was to plot the duty register, keep accounts, and arrange training, and to keep the post manned night and day no matter what happened.

The Royal Observer Corp's Post 'Easy One', a sketch from memory as it was 1940 to 1945. Sited on a hummock at Blue Gate, Caldbeck, it had a super view across the Cumberland Plain and into Scotland. Note the wooden sleeping hut: inside were a plotting table, two bunks in case observers were snowed up, a barrel stove etc. The sod built butt had an observation platform with all round glass panels, stove and an old couch for one observer to relax – one hour on, one hour off. Note also the 'Khasi' in the old bell pit and the bicycles!

Bombs on Tyneside

Posts were spaced at about 10-mile intervals all over Britain so that 'planes could be tracked anywhere while they were in the air. As the war developed and enemy raids intensified, we could see from our post, bomb 'flashes' when the Hartlepools and Newcastle were attacked. As our night fighter shield developed, the enemy began quite regularly coming inland over Cumberland and Westmorland to go back to their bases over the Scottish coast or the Wash to evade these fighters and it was our job to keep track of them so that the fighters could intercept them.

Our other very important job was to guide our bombers returning from raids over enemy territory having either lost their bearings due to casualties in their crews, or been diverted to other airfields on account of fog. Because of the risk of enemy spies being parachuted into wild areas such as ours, we were armed. Which reminds me that one night when Jimmy Boyle, an ex-regular soldier, was on duty, a youth from the village (no names – he is a man now) stalked the post and jumped up shouting 'Hands up' at Jimmy. Jimmy never batted an eyelid but said quietly 'what would you have thought if I had shot at you!'

First Women Observers

Our post was the first in Northern Command to have women observers. The centres in the towns were largely staffed by ladies but the isolation and wildness of the posts were a different matter. I was asked to try the idea out and I persuaded Mrs S. Tyson, Mrs B. Lennon and Misses M. Chope, M. Wilkinson and A. Younghusband to enrol. It was the best thing we ever tried. They never let me down for a single day during the 2–3 years until the end of the war and proved to be such good 'spotters' that they made all of us pull our socks up. I admired their courage in getting to and from such an isolated spot in all weather and all times of day and night.

Two other members of our crew brought honour to our village by volunteering to go overseas with the invasion fleet to the Normandy beaches. They were Hugh Rigby and the late John Dalton, a veteran of the First World War. Every vessel carrying our landing troops had an observer of the R. O. C. on the bridge and it was his responsibility to order the anti-aircraft crew to fire or not to fire at any aircraft approaching the ship. A hair-raising responsibility

A few weeks before the invasion these volunteers were taken to R. O. C. Headquarters in the South and put through a most rigorous test. This consisted of being shown for not more than one second, a cinema 'shot' of a tail, wing, head-on or tail-on view of a plane little bigger than a fly. Those accepted had to have full marks. John Dalton passed and went over with the invasion and came back safely. Hugh Rigby failed the test but is nonetheless to be honoured for trying.

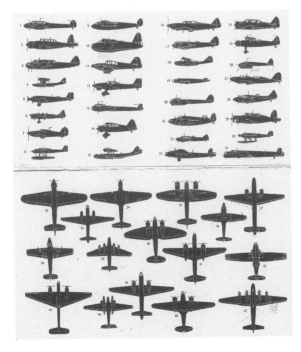

The 1940 issue Aircraft Identification sheets used by the Observer Crew.

The long frosty winter of 1963; visits twice per day with two milk churns to a supply in Mockerkin for weeks and weeks on end.

THIRTEEN

EARLY YEARS
OF THE NATIONAL
FARMERS' UNION

In this article father talks about the early years of the National Farmers' Union.

Those war years must have been hell for people cooped up in town or evacuated to the country – a few of them loved it, but most of them hated our isolated villages and farms. The few have been our friends to this day, but most saw enough of it to make them shun it for all time, and those war years must have been like a lifetime to them.

I, and I feel sure, all the other folks in the countryside, were so fully occupied that the years were hectic, and passed quickly. Most of us were very short of labour and we had extra ploughing and milk selling. Practically everyone of us had some other war-time job. Our wives and families had to help us out, and did so wholeheartedly.

In these days of safety regulations it is amazing to remember that my son, aged 9, and hundreds of other farmers' sons and daughters, could handle our horses or tractors as well as we could. Most of the children did an hour's work before setting off to walk to school and after walking home, often 2–3 miles in all weathers, they did an hour or more of work at night.

I was a member of Wigton Rural Council, a member of the County War Agricultural Executive Committee's (C. W. A. E. C) Transport, Labour and Machinery sub-committees and secretary of John Peel Branch of the N. F. U. These committees involved attendance at various places about twice a week for some 3–4 hours each, and the observer job usually entailed three 8-hour shifts on duty. But I don't think it did any of us men, women, or children, any harm. We never had a breather of a holiday. We still had none of those things called today 'mod-cons' on the fellside and this meant that we spent very little.

If you have a long memory you may have had clothes bearing the 'Utility' CC 41 mark. To maintain an acceptable value-for-money quality, the government introduced standards for clothes, bedding, shoes and blankets, and later as demobilization arrived, for furniture and 'demob' suits as servicemen returned from war – to protect the population from exploitation as civil production resumed in a period of shortage.

Rationing

Inflation was held securely by the rationing system and hire purchase was not with us. Prices did not outstrip incomes so we had no overdrafts either and could save for a rainy day – as most farmers do if ever they can. In the bad '30s we had adopted 'self-sufficiency' to save ourselves from ruin. In the war we adopted it to save the country. The 'standard bread' and 'utility' clothes were of excellent quality, and the Ministry of Agriculture's 'Grow More' leaflets were the best, simplest, practical instructions ever produced for information and instructions on growing unusual crops for war-time healthy feeding in either a dug up lawn or on a farm. They enabled us to have healthy foods and salads and proved that, if we tried, we could feed ourselves.

These measures gave us a purpose in life and we felt we were achieving something, the finest of all feelings, and it worked, and enabled us to win through!

As soon as the war ended I resigned from the W. A. E. C. and the Observer Corps. Until 1945 the N. F. U. had been staffed by many single branch secretaries and it was decided to group the branches into full-time jobs with approximately 1,000 members each.

The late J. J. Fiddler was secretary of Keswick, Cockermouth and Wigton branches and he felt he was too old to carry on so resigned abruptly when

Advice from the Ministry of Food during the war on how to make your rations go further.

My wartime ration book.

the new 'set-up' proposals were announced. Almost in a weekend this faced me with making a decision whether to try to take on one of these jobs.

N. F. U. Work

I knew I could do the work and liked it, and I also realised that if I did not take it on I would not get another opportunity because I was 47 then. My farm was earning me £600 net, not a bad income in those days for an 80-acre fell farm – or today for that matter! I thought I could possibly retain my farm for I had no wish to let it go.

My very good friend, Alfred Hall, and I were chosen for the short list. Alfred was interviewed first, and refused to handle the insurance business that was part of the job. In accepting the job I made a condition that I kept my farm and my writing. At that time the job wasn't worth having. The Union 'salary' was £120 per annum and £50 travelling allowance – I to find the transport. The insurance was supposed to be worth £135, but turned out to be less than £130. I dare not tell you what my wife thought of the job, but I thought I could see a future in it!

I believe I was either the first, or one of the very first, group secretaries appointed in England. My group included Keswick, Cockermouth, John Peel and Torpenhow, with a combined membership of about 400. I sold my milk cattle and concentrated on sheep and rearing young cattle, and writing was, as always, a hobby. I could easily keep going. A year or so after I took over, the Agricultural Acts 1947–48 became law.

Weapons Against Farmers

During the first years of the Acts, when food rationing was still necessary, we got a fair settlement from the Price Reviews and I thought the Acts were going to be a benefit to farmers. But as soon as food imports began to flow in, in 1950, it became obvious to me that the Act, and Price Review system, were going to be used as weapons against farmers.

The 'cap in hand' approach of the leadership of the headquarters team of the N. F. U. always struck me as stupid and I have always written against it. But my job as a secretary was to give the membership service and, until the lack of enthusiasm engendered by the effete efforts of the Union's leadership and headquarters costs made subscription increases necessary every few years, the membership of the groups increased considerably; for instance, the Penrith branch (begun with 400 members) increased to nearly 1,000, and my group to just over 950.

These increases, and much greater costs of insuring the mounting mechanisation, buildings and increased stocking to try to overtake slipping incomes, built up the insurance income of secretaries. I used to enjoy canvassing for members and it was very often highly amusing – if you could see a joke against yourself.

Canvassing

Some experiences as a canvasser when I began, taught me some smart lessons. One day a tall lady came to the door. When I asked if I could 'see the boss', she drew herself up to her full height and, without uttering a word, pointed to herself! I never again asked a lady who came to the door for the 'Boss'.

Not long afterwards, I called at a farm and a lady came to the door. I explained myself and she said: 'Oh, it's t'Union yer on for is't! Well, they're asleep!' I think I managed to persuade her that if 'they' were, I wasn't, for I managed to give her quite a lot of help.

Don't imagine for one moment I am running down the ladies. Time and again it has been my experience that they realise the value of unionism better than men. In the very few cases where the women have been against the Union, I have found it most difficult to get the men to join, and have felt when I succeeded that a rough domestic situation had been left behind. Some men were quite candid and many times I have been told, 'Well, we've talked it over and I'm willing to join, but you'd better have a word with her (the Missus). She's boss.' I never liked to bother folks when they were busy so one very wet day I felt sure a man whose subscription I had to get would not be busy.

The morning had been fine, however, and he had got his sheep in and started to dip when the weather caught him. And it was pouring when I arrived. He would have been better not dipping, for it was washing it off and, of course, he knew this as well as me, and was in none too good a temper. He saw me before I saw the sheep or I would have left the matter until another time. But I had to go on and mentioned what I had come for. He said: 'Ah's dipping ... and Ah's not gan intil 't hoose t' get me cheque book. Thoo mun just wait – er thoo can scrat me oot.' I waited and got it the next time I saw him!

Examples of the 'Bradbury' pound, and a ten shilling note.

Come 1941 and this was a very modern kitchen! The black leaded 'prairie' range burning coal has gone; in its place is the economical Aga heat-storage cooker with a boiler and tap. A stainless steel sink unit with hot water from a back boiler to the lounge fire – and electric lights. Notice the very large pan on the cooker which boiled about 15 kgs of 'stock feed' potatoes each afternoon to mix with the hen food.

Fourteen

Houses, Lights, Lamps, Stoves and Home Comforts,

Black Out Etc.

My wife's great grandfather was always accompanied to the Auction by either his wife or one of the children, who were charged with taking hold of the money (in those days up to World War One) usually sovereigns, before the husband had a chance to visit a pub and drink the cash or 'treat' his neighbours or cronies etc.

Imports after World War One, especially Australian and New Zealand mutton, or Argentine beef, made farming difficult and following the depression, Cumbrian farming families lived from hand to mouth. Many were saved by local grocers, storekeepers and merchants who allowed goods to be put 'on the slate'. Indeed, Harrison Ivinson – whose business in Caldbeck included a pig butchery, seed and fertilisers, groceries and all household and farming requisites – confided to my father in the middle of the war that many of these accounts were never paid off or settled despite the prosperity of the 1939 war. At the time Ivinsons had a very comprehensive business stretching from Caldbeck right over to the Eden Valley.

Grocers' shops had several assistants usually, who weighed out tea and coffee from bulk bags or plywood tea chests.

Later, Messrs Tate and Lyle made available lump sugar in oblong boxes weighing about 2lbs for genteel people – otherwise white cane sugar was weighed up from hundred-weight sacks into 'blue' bags of 1lb or 2lb, the top folded over neatly and tied with string. Every counter had a string cutter!

When the second World War started in September 1939, I remember my father went down to Wigton specially to purchase 2 x 1cwt Hessian sacks of sugar at West Cumberland Farmers, located at the 'Old Jam Works'. He had to haggle and plead with the manager that he had ordered it weeks before, because the imposition of controls and rationing were but days away. He also bought a 'box' of 50 or 60 bars of 'Sunlight' soap. The bars were about 2ft long by 3x3" – we had a supply all through the war. Because my mother was vegetarian we used to exchange a lump of soap for a lump of cheese from neighbours and friends!

The groceries – delivered in a wooden box or old tea chest – came fortnightly by Ivinson's lorry, usually on a Thursday on our round. The 'traveller' (John Richardson, who was eventually called up and served in Burma in the battle of the notorious 'Imphal box') called on the Monday and took/wrote down your order. After the staples – flour, treacle, sugar, currants, bacon, tea – he'd ask, 'How are you fixed Mrs Cole? For: shoe polish/matches/baccy/soap/thread/'Camp' coffee' (cheap substitute)/etc. etc. etc. Also on the order would be, say, 4 cwts of Layers Mash, and perhaps a bag of linseed calf gruel powder.

Remember, Heinz 57 salad cream was almost unknown. When we had salad my mother made salad dressing herself – eggs, vinegar, mustard etc. beaten to a cream by hand.

The advent and impact of the West Cumberland Farmers' Co-operative in 1926 dealt a severe blow to the 'provender' merchants who had taken their pounds of flesh from farmers since the nineteenth century. In Wigton there was a row of sheds with open let-down fronts from which these merchants plied their trade, long since gone, it was somewhere behind the Kildare Hotel.

My father was a founder member of West Cumberland Farmers. When it opened – financed by co-operatively minded farmers – the Manager, Mr John Wade, used to go to Liverpool docks and buy a ship load of Argentine linseed, for example, and this halved the price to members. Within a month many of the original merchants went out of business – two shot themselves!

But I digress. There were no detergents then – caustic soda, scrubbing brushes and maybe panscrubs of coarse metal chain link pads were the means available to wash

Collection of irons, tongs and heaters with clip-on Aga iron (given as a gift from the manufacturer to the customer).

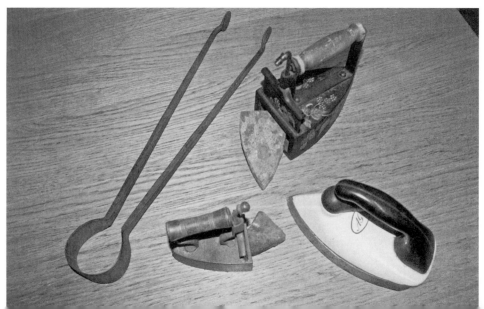

Left: examples of tin baths or wash tubs in which many of us country children were cleaned up before bedtime. Right: the Cumberland farmhouse kitchen which gave way to the Aga. The photo shows a black leaded grate, side oven with dampers and large set pot for boiling clothes. This example had a single brass tap in the window bringing water from a collection tank in the beck.

dishes, pots and pans etc., usually in a large tin tub or bath. Also used to bath the baby and me, even up to age 4, in front of the fire!

Clothes and bed sheets were boiled in a set pot fired by wooden faggots, mangled (many ladies suffered champed fingers feeding heavy sheets, shirts etc. into the rollers), and then hung out in the field on a line to dry, you hoped – if the cows didn't have fun and pull them down!

We had a 'petrol' iron, which was one of the first attempts to provide the housewife with 'flexibility' – it is in Tullie House now. It worked on the same principle as a primus stove but it is a wonder it never exploded or caught fire! Of course, later on the 'Aga' flat iron with two flats was a huge improvement but remember few of us had mains electricity until 1950.

In our house, as my father describes, in the kitchen you prepared and cooked food – it was a living room and in the evenings, a sitting room. Original black leaded grates with 'cranes' and side boiler and side oven provided the heat. Yes, the side boiler had water from the well bucketed into it, and usually ladled out with a 'lifter'. Some models – the very latest – had a brass tap!

My father used to go once every month or six weeks from Brownrigg to Bolton Gate (six miles to the station with horse and cart) to fetch a load of coals – about half a ton. Perhaps in autumn an additional supply was accumulated in case of hard weather. Where farmers had access to peat, the fire would stay on all night, but we were always collecting sticks and blown timber. There were no chain saws then, but a trestle, a hand saw or a cross cut. I bought my first chain saw in 1955, an American made 'Clinton' with a 28" blade; it was clumsy and weighed a half hundredweight – a dangerous brute.

At first our water came from a well in the back garden, about 30 metres from the house. Drawn by the bucketful these stood in a corner of the kitchen with a ladle.

Later Dad found a spring up on the fell which was piped 500 yards down to a large 5000 gallon tank located in the lonning, and down to the farm. It would last about five weeks before we went into milk production in 1939 and the ten dual-purpose shorthorns needed to drink. Gradually my parents improved the house.

A kitchen 'range' – a prairie type coal-fired range – went into the back kitchen and in the former kitchen/living room a new fireplace was installed with a back boiler!

The war caused a huge change to hill farms which had for over a century been livestock rearing enterprises, relying on about five pay cheques a year. Cash flow had not been heard of then. Over-wintered 'stirks' sold to grazers down in the Lowlands to grow and fatten on better pastures. Perhaps a few Wether sheep in spring, then wool in mid-August. The last of the five pay days came when you sold your surplus gimmer and tip lambs and perhaps a pen or two of strong store bullocks – October to December.

The drive for self-sufficiency and maximum production enabled us to go in for milk, and for the first time milk collection lorries rattled up and down our valleys, and the regular monthly milk cheque put a degree of confidence into farming.

Labour was short so we mechanised as much as we could, and to ease the housework and bring a little comfort to a hard life. We actually had hot water from a tap in the kitchen and cold as well. Of course, from 1936 to 1940 my mother had to light the fire first thing in the morning for the hot water, which was essential to prepare the calf gruel and wash up the dairy utensils, separator and milk cooler.

But in 1941 we really went 'modern' and installed an 'Aga'. No plumbed in water but a useful boiler and heat 24 hours a day – it was heaven. Luckily coke was unrationed (most households got a bag of coal a week in towns and villages) so Dad used to buy a railway wagon load at a time, and Willy Tyson hauled it to the farm, all 10–12 tons of it. This was a year's supply plus, so one railway wagon load would see us safe for a couple of years.

Such was the need to encourage farmers to produce, that very many farms installed Agas as fast as they could and many are still operating today. *Note*: the Aga, or heat storage cooker, was the invention of a Swedish engineer and as I was to discover when in 1948 I went to work on a Swedish farm, the initials stand for 'Aktiebolag Gas Accumulator'. That cooker installed in 1941 was still operating and went with my parents when they moved to a cottage in 1965 and it ran up to 1989.

My generation came into a world of candles 'to light you to bed' and 'Kelly' lamps (see picture in colour section). In later years the little Kelly lamp used to burn day and night in the toilet to stop the pipes freezing. You only get frozen up once in a lifetime! It is still used to this day to keep the air warm in our downstairs toilet. Today paraffin lamps with one or two wicks are much prized as antique collectables. However, they were smelly, could be dangerous, could flare up and were a regular chore for the womenfolk – to fill with paraffin, trim the wick, and clean and polish the glass with rolled up newspaper.

After all this performance, although softer on the eyes to read, you almost had to sit over them or a few of you had to all sit around the table. But then came along the 'Aladdin' lamp which, with its delicate 'mantel', gave a wonderful good even light. And today we still have ours ready for action in case of a power failure.

During the war we were all supposed to be blacked out at night time! So we had two frames covered with black roofing felt to fit up against the outside of the windows. They worked well but in a storm on a windy night they'd blow down onto the garden. My father's response was that 'Jerry' was unlikely to waste a bomb on us and as our house was well screened with trees on top of a hill, and miles from any neighbours, we didn't worry about the Police. Indeed one night – PC Dixon called with some message – one of the two windows was glaring into the night, but he said nowt! He was probably glad of the windows to find his way to the front door!

Then in 1942 my father found a 50-volt generator with a Lister engine; it supplied 50 volts DC to a battery of twenty-six 2-volt very large accumulators. We were allowed one gallon of petrol a week for charging and it used to pop-pop-pop all day once a week. No power plugs you realise, but instant light at the click of a switch through the house and the buildings. No longer any need to 'feed up' on winter evenings carrying a storm lantern and poking about, tripping over things etc. When I began farming in Yorkshire fifteen years later I had to rely on torches or storm lanterns to fodder up, until I had the place wired. And woe betide any sales 'rep' who turned up at 4.30 in winter to hold me up – because feeding up was a precisely timed operation. If I didn't start on time I was benighted, and groping about in barns and loose boxes.

Ploughing one winter afternoon, I spied a van pull up on the road and the rep. start to walk over the field. Pretending not to notice him, at the end of the furrow I lifted the implement and off home. Tough!

Another occasion I saw one drive up, so I nipped through the back door of the barn and said to Ulf – the Swedish student who worked for me – just politely say I wasn't home! Answering the rep, said Ulf looking very puzzled and pretending not to understand, 'Mr Cole – oh! He died months ago!'

The 50 volt D.C. generator ran for a whole day once a week to provide lights only for the farm from 24 large 2-volt accumulators.

One Hundred Years of Hill Farming   107

My father and mother digging out hay from the snow on a winter's morning after a blizzard of 1943.

FIFTEEN

CONDITIONS AFTER THE 1939–45 WAR

Here my father describes conditions after the war.

For some reason I cannot remember, I was in London in August 1946. It must have been a good reason, for I hate all towns and especially London. On the way back to Cumberland on the train, I was carried through flood water almost from the outskirts of London to Preston.

Hay lay in every conceivable condition in the water, and harvest tackle was bogged down in uncut corn fields. While this was the disastrous 'summer' of 1946 I thought then, and still think today, that the drains in all that land had been in since 1700–1750 and were done, or all that water would not have been there. But the job, even with grants, is too big for either landowners or farmers to take on today with taxation and death duties as they are.

Weather, disease and, on the family farm, illness, are the hazards we always have to face, and especially on fell farms.

In 1946 hay crops were poor in quantity which made many hold back cutting and by that time the weather never let up at all, and possibly half of the crop was lost, and what was got was bad hay, and our harvest was the same.

For several years I had been cutting early and I got my hay and, fortunately, I had a little left from the previous year. A blizzard blew in the first week of January and from that time until 13 March we never saw another blade of grass.

My fell is about 400 yards up my lonning and immediately through the gate, but it is hard to believe that it used to take me 20 minutes to get through the five to six foot drifts with sheets of hay.

Foddering our fell flock on Faulds Brow Common (1000 ft asl) – Paddigill Farm, Ellerbeck Common and Binsey Fell in the background.

Emergency Footwear

The snow was powder and it kept like that throughout the whole of the 9–10 weeks it was with us. You sank into it up to your middle, and sometimes your armpits. About every 2–3 days there was another blizzard which blew up any clearance you had been able to do and we all had to give up trying to clear our lonnings and roads. Some folks filled bags with hay or straw and put their feet in, and tied the bags round their legs to stop them sinking in the beastly stuff.

My sheep were on the fell, and very few were buried, and soon got out. But the frosts were vicious all the time and one of our first jobs every morning was to go up on the fell and pull the sheep off the ground where they were securely fastened by frost. This gradually pulled the wool off them, but it had to be done so that they could get exercise and feed. As time went on the next problem was water. It was no use feeding hay without it, and everything was so frozen up that snow was bad for them. The only way to get it up was in buckets and even when I set off with hot water it was solid before I could reach the sheep. The solution was a small amount of salt in it but even if this was not immediately drunk by the sheep it froze. (That year the shore was frozen at Allonby.)

It was useless to try to get the sheep inside – for one thing it couldn't be done for drifts and, when the wind settled, the sheep on the fell used to try to scratch the snow to get the heather, and this was at least something and gave them exercise. But they reached the stage when, if the wind blew at all, they were terrified and ran for the fell walls for shelter.

Big Losses

I started the winter with 123 ewes and ended the period with 73 ewes; practically all my hoggs (1946 lambs) died. I was fairly lucky, many men lost nearly all their flocks when they were on heafs two or three miles from their farms, as many are, and they could not get hay to them. The sheep were one item, but our cattle had to be watered and keeping our pipes and taps running was a daily struggle and battle of wits.

By the time the thaw came on the 13 March the sheep had reached the stage where they didn't care whether they lived or died and took little notice of anything. I am certain that if the frost had held a week longer every sheep in the county would have died and, of course, despite imports of what hay south country farmers could send us, very many cattle died and all stocks of hay were at an end.

I had a remarkable experience that year. Out of my 73 ewes that survived I got 66 lambs, had none to bottle and never had to take one away. It is usually said, on the fellside, that any man who tells you he hasn't lost a lamb is a liar. I did not lose one lamb that year.

We were issued with ewe cob coupons (rationing was still in force) and I was issued 10 cwts. I got these in about the first week of March. Every fell farmer who had a fell stock got them. Many used them to keep their cows fit but I poured them into my ewes and they got the lot in about three weeks.

I'm convinced this saved my ewes and lambs (for I lost no more ewes after the thaw, and many other chaps lost very many after the thaw), and ever since I have given my ewes in lambing time a good supply of nuts.

The Effects Of Wireless

In 1945 wireless began to affect more than the professionals who had very largely entertained the public during the war. For one thing transport was easier and petrol more plentiful. Perhaps because of my writing upon farming, trees, John Peel, etc., I was invited to take part in several programs from Leeds and Newcastle, and to make home recordings.

One very amusing programme in the *Country Magazine* series from Newcastle, with Mary Benn (great great granddaughter of John Peel), C. N. (Norman) de Courcy Parry (M. F. H.), the late Tom Taylor (shepherd to Lord Leconfield, after J. Faulder), and I, did upon Peel country in 1945 stands out in my memory.

During the programme, Parry had to blow John Peel's horn, brought by Mary Benn. So that he did not 'blast' the microphone he was placed behind a screen. At the critical moment there was a silence and Norman's face, very red, popped round the screen and he said in a dangerously audible voice: 'It's the hardest b***h I've ever tried to blow', and the face vanished, and a very good blast followed. (He could blow any horn at full stretch gallop and it must have been a hard one!)

Forerunner of 'The Archers' – the broadcasting team in the Leeds studio in 1945 (Right to left, Harry Wood from Yorkshire, Mrs Cole, the late Alfred Hall and a BBC producer).

Then Tom Taylor described our Herdwick lambing and, talking in dialect, he said 'in sna, thoo knaws, t' poor laal beggars hez a gey hard time.' Within ten minutes of the end of the programme the telephone was ringing at the broadcasting station (the item was done on a Sunday) and complaints were being received that we had been swearing on the radio – 'beggars' had been confused for another word barred at that time (unless they had heard Parry's remark!)

Regular Broadcasts

In the 1945–48 period my wife, Dora, did a great deal of broadcasting. She and Alfred Hall, and a Teeside farmer, Harry Wood, did a fortnightly broadcast from Leeds for two and a half years. This was the 'Kitchen Table Conference' and was the forerunner of the Archers programme. She also took part in the national programme from London in *Country Magazine* with the late A. G. Street, Ralph Whiteman and others. When the late Graham Sutton's play, 'Mary Robinson, the Beauty of Buttermere' was broadcast, he invited my wife (a relative of Mary) to introduce the programme.

Our amusements on the fellside were not much affected through the years until the coming of television for all in the late 1950s. They were simple and home made, and all the better for it.

A whist drive, supper (of home made delicacies) and dance, rarely cost more than 7s. 6d. and many were only 5s. 0d. Whist drives alone were 1s. 6d. to 2s. 6d. and were full houses. Children's concerts and pantomimes for Christmas were organised by energetic and dedicated teachers at our village schools and were very popular, and the proceeds were used for the village school outings (no continental holidays in those days!)

Favourite Band

Before the 1939–45 war our bands for dances were comprised of concertina, violins and sometimes a base violin, and brass instruments. In our district, Hewetson's band of Ireby did a lot of the playing, and many a time Jack has beaten the time on my back with his foot, if I was sitting under him when the band was on the stage. That foot acted as his baton and never stopped.

JOHN PEEL BRANCH
NATIONAL FARMERS' UNION
SOCIAL
CALDBECK PARISH HALL
FRIDAY, 6th JANUARY, 1961
Supper at 6-45 p.m.
Mr D. Bates' Variety Concert at 8 p.m.
Dancing 9-30 p.m. to 1 a.m.   Bowman's Band
TICKETS 7/6 EACH
SUPPER

Jackson's of Stybeck, Thirlmere, and Billy Bowman's bands were the other favourites. After 1950 Syd Jackson, Hilltop, started his own band and later called it the 'Blencathra' and it was a great favourite.

They all had marvellous tunes that made us 'hop' and, in those days the more we put into it the more they played us up until we were having a rollicking time. Coats came off, and sometimes waistcoats too. It was both work and play and great fun. And they were hard working chaps who, like us, turned out the next day and did a real day's work. There was no 'standing down' for an hour every hour, and their pay was as little as £1 apiece until the mid-'50s. Sophistication came with television. Until that era our girls did their own or each other's hair. It may be nostalgia on my part, but they managed to look every bit as pretty – and certainly more natural than they do today!

Film Shows And Whist

At N. F. U. meetings in those years, I used to run whist drives and 'Brains Trusts', or take an old silent 16 mm cinema round giving shows including Charlie Chaplin and Laurel and Hardy. One night I turned up at Stybeck to give a cinema show. After trying everything to get the machine to do its bit, I discovered we were on D. C. instead of A. C. current, so we had to run round the village and gathered enough cards to hold a whist drive.

Another night in about 1946 we had the Ministry of Information mobile cinema (talkies by this time) coming to give our N. F. U. meeting a talk and show. After waiting a quarter of an hour we sent out scouts in every direction and eventually found him a mile away in a gutter. We got him out and had our show, holding our meeting until he got himself organised. It was all good fun.

Our 4x4 in the drifted side round to our farm.

Sixteen

Those Winters

1939–47

We had to be tougher then ... but I sometimes wonder when I watch shoppers in our towns wearing cotton denims (short skirts) bare midriffs and acrylic or cotton jerseys etc. – kidney problems in the future? As children in the 1940s our mothers had to muffle us up in lots of layers, for even in our houses the doors were draughty and going from kitchen to pantry was often a breath-taking experience from the comparative warmth of the living room or kitchen, to the cold of the lobby or passage.

Caldbeck school had no central heating – instead there was a large open fire in each room, and if you went out to the toilet, 50 yards away across the yard, you didn't linger! No trouble then, with frost – sometimes winter provided the ultimate in hygiene because the buckets got frozen!

Fortunately most of us wore clogs which were warm and kept your feet dry. Rubber soled shoes or Wellingtons in hard weather were an invitation to develop chilblains, because they kept the damp and cold in the shoe/boot. Clogs were good except in deep wet snow, where the corkers built up coggins – quite dangerous but you either kicked them off or tapped your feet against a wall.

Stockings and socks were either cotton or wool – nylon was unheard of. Our mothers knitted and darned most of the winter. Indeed it was only on joining the army in 1950 that I encountered machine knitted stockings. I remember in the winter of 1941–42 being almost crippled with chilblains. My father bought me a larger size of clog and lined them with straw – great! The straw was dry, clean, and absorbed any perspiration. As my wife commented, the era 1945–50 saw the changeover in the Secondary schools where country lasses wore thick knitted woollen socks and felt fashion disadvantage compared with the town girls, who came decked out in white cotton socks.

In Wigton this clog-maker fashions the soles from blocks of ash. He used this simple adze and shaver mounted on a stool. He worked up to the outbreak of the war.

We in the countryside had never seen radiators until we went to the Secondary school – or perhaps only in the larger village churches.

Chilblains were awful, and if untreated became painful. They could crack and bleed too. Treatment of all kinds were tried – our favourite seemed to be camphorated oil, so your socks stank of camphor all day. In bad cases one used goose grease and kept your feet off the stone hot water bottle in bed at night. Remember Japan had occupied Malaya, so rubber products were valuable and scarce.

In winter and spring it was a common sight to see girls with pink blemishes up their legs (right up until summer) – a result of sitting close to the fire grate, reading, studying etc. Remember, too, that the boys were all in short pants at Primary school and often to the age of 12 at the Secondary school.

In the autumn we would visit Harker and Bell's outfitters in Carlisle, or Binns, Redmayne's, or Penrice in Wigton, to be togged up in warm woollen underwear. The brand name was 'Chillprufe' and I suppose I was lucky to be given 'combinations' – talk about being sown in or buttoned in for the winter!

My mother spent most evenings in autumn and winter knitting; pullovers, jerseys, short trousers etc. The farmers' stockings which would take no more darning, would be cut off at the ankles and re-footed. Because of rationing, shirts had to last as long as possible, so our mothers would 'turn' the collars and sew them back into the shirt again, prolonging the life of the shirt so that it didn't look threadbare, or she would cut a bit off the shirt-tail and sew it into the worn part of the collar.

Farming families would buy flour for baking in one-hundred-weight cotton bags, stamped with the logo of Carrs Flourmill at Silloth, Pattinson's Mill at Whitehaven, or Beacon Mill at Penrith. These bags were carefully opened with the draw thread, the flour put in a bin or 'kist', then the excellent cotton bag was washed as many times as needed to remove the blue maker's name dye. Then applying tapes at the open end, you had a very serviceable new pillowcase.

My overcoat, up to January 1939, was a lady's woollen overcoat (my mother's), with a nice red and brown pattern, cut down to fit me. Being sent to the Nelson Secondary school you were expected, on reaching Form II, to buy a cap and dark blue serge raincoat at Redmayne's in Wigton High Street. As clothes went on ration in 1940, the garment had to last – so mine was so long it came down to my ankles and often touched the ground. I was still wearing it as a good fit in 1946! As soon as you got home from school, mothers insisted you change into your old clothes for play, or messing about – we couldn't afford either the coupons or the money if a garment wouldn't last.

In Secondary school we all sat in rows of desks where your valuable books were kept – plus a rough work book and one ring file. The books were passed from form to form as you progressed up the school – writing your name in each year. 'This book belongs to … Nelson School, Wigton.' Writing ink was mixed up weekly from powder and put in an ink well (pot) on each desk. It was nasty stuff – made a mess on your fingers if you overdipped your pen. Time to time splashes would get on your book but there was little 'louting about' with it in case of a cuff around the ear from Mum or Dad when you came home.

Books were scarce and valuable – usually borrowed for a week from the Library, or in Primary schools reliance was mostly on the Library box sent out/exchanged about the county from the Education Department.

On most fellside farms, you would find a kind of calendar with a pouch hanging on the kitchen wall. It told you the basics – day of the week, date of the month, etc. In the wallet/pouch were placed the bills and any letters which came by post. On Sunday evenings the farmer would remove it from the wall, along with the spike on which the

A visit to the Roman wall in 1939.

After a 'snowblow' – a little boy (me) on an eight foot drift at the bottom of the farmyard, 1940.

receipted bills were impaled. The cheques were paid out, licences applied for dipping papers (red, yellow and blue in triplicate!) ready to deliver to the policeman … and if you weren't fiddling about with pedigree livestock, that was about it. Farm business management, alias bureaucracy, changed very little up until about 1960. Husbandry, not cash flow, was the business of farmers. My father wrote his stock valuations on the back of an envelope and his 'cash flow' on another.

Bank managers were 'managers' – not 'investment package' sales persons. If you wanted a loan or overdraft extension, anxious indeed to ensure their customers did not overspend beyond possible income, he would very often see you on the farm, assess the proposals, and size up the new wife – to see whether she was a worker/good manager/able cook etc. As my wife has commented up to the 1970s, if your bank manager met you on the street he raised his hat. For the farmer if you were in credit it would be 'morning, nice day' etc., but if you had an overdraft the conversation would be more *inquisitive*, to put it neatly – and perhaps in his office!

Winters in the 1940s always seemed to grow harder. The winter of 1939–40 was memorable for the hard frosts. The Clay Dubs was frozen for weeks on end it seemed, and I suspect the ice was almost solid. I remember one day someone came with a little terrier and put it down a hole in the ice – you could see it running about on the pond floor below. It was the phoney wartime and one day a convoy of army

Winter 1963. The severe frosts meant water had to be drawn from old wells. Ella's mother sets up a few buckets for the next day.

An outing in 1940 on the last days of the 'basic' petrol ration when we used a motor cycle and side car to make the ration go as far as we could. I'm looking at the Roman milestone at Vindolanda, the only one in England still in position on the *Stanegate* after two thousand years. The broken-off stump of another is located a Roman mile to the west on this road, which serviced the camps and garrisons to the south of the wall. Note my over-sized school overcoat, which lasted until 1946.

lorries with drivers in training stopped to enjoy the sliding, skating and sledging. You could still buy those crude clamp-on skates at Stodarts, the iron mongers, in Wigton, which some of us managed on quite inadequate boots – often they flew off, so you ended up in a heap on the ice or you had very sore ankles for days, but the army lads that day must have had very sore sides and bums from falling about all over the place.

We often had to clear the blown snow off the hay to get at the fodder. I recall a week in either '42 or '43 when it snowed lightly but steadily for four days – thank goodness it didn't blow.

Each day there was an almost continuous task of drawing buckets of water from an old well below the house, which mercifully never freezes. By 1942 the newer cow house for the ten milkers had water bowls and so long as a tap was left dripping and the supply held up, the main 'consumers' were okay. Funny thing though – when every drop has to be drawn and carried – the blighters seemed to develop insatiable thirsts!

The late Norman Parry out with his footpack of hounds, hunting across John Peel country against the magnificent backdrop of Mirkholme, the Whitewater Dash Falls and the Skiddaw fells to the right. Photo: SHC

Seventeen

Farming Life to March 1970

Mr S. H. Cole, Brownrigg, Caldbeck, who has written articles for the *Herald* for over forty years, many under the title of 'On t'Fellside Now', has described in previous articles his introduction to farming in the days before the 1914–18 war, how he began farming on his own account at Caldbeck, the financial struggles of the '30s, and life during the 1939–45 war. In this article he brings his account of farming life up to the present day, March 1970.

In 1954, upon the anniversary of John Peel's death, we held a 'commemoration' day in the village. It followed practically the same lines of the first event. The number of Peel enthusiasts who came was as large as on the first occasion, and we were prepared for them this time.

After drinking a glass to the memory of the great hunter and singing the song, the hunt moved off led by Norman Parry on one of his favourite horses.

Within the hour news was brought back to the village that this horse had been destroyed. In following the hounds in land above Parson's Park, one of its front feet had struck the head of a 5 ft post lying in a field. This had tipped up the post which had disembowelled the animal. It was a serious blow to Norman and cast a cloud over all of us.

As the day wore on it became one of the wettest days we have ever had. The visitors packed into every available shelter they could find, as well as the Oddfellows Arms, the Parish Hall, and a large marquee. This time we had an exhibition of John Peel relics and bygones collected from friends and our village people, and some of my collection. This was held in the Men's Club room, a room about 50 ft by 30 ft and with a large 12 ft billiards table in the centre, but with no windows.

This room was packed tight on account of the rain as well as interest in the exhibits, and I was supposed to give talks upon the items. The BBC was on the go this time, with television, and when they switched on their powerful lighting our fuses, not used to such activities, blew, and we were plunged into total darkness.

My friend, the late Graham Sutton, was in charge of the very valuable John Peel relics at a small table at one end of the show. Another friend, the late Joe Bennett, was in charge of the items on the billiards table. This was also loaded with such things as gold £5 pieces, guineas, silver items and vinaigrettes, and chatelaines, and a hundred other valuables, many unique. When the lighting failed Graham Sutton gathered hunting horns, stirrups, 'fox' drinking cup, and a deed with Peel's signature upon it into his hands, as well as he could, and held them. Joe Bennett did the same with as much as he could remember where they were.

I had a couple of tallow dips in old candle holders on the table and after a couple of minutes we managed to light these, and after about 10 minutes the fuses were replaced and we could have a look round. When we checked up at night we had not lost a single item!

One of my wife's and my interests is our Cumbrian and Westmorland dialect. My wife was born into it. I have known many dialects, Northumbrian and Durham, Norfolk, Dorset and Cockney, but have found none I like as well as ours. It is more apt and humorous than any, other than Cockney, and Cockney is too much froth and bubble for me. I think it was Gilpin, in 1792, when he visited the Lake District, said 'There was (in Cumberland and Westmorland) an uncouth (but nobly savage) peasantry, whose speech was extremely difficult to interpret.' I have learnt it by living and working among the folk, who speak it fluently.

Richardson, in 'Cumberland Talk', says:

The'r fine refinet language I know laal aboot,
The'r south country accent wi' t' 'Hs' left oot;
Fwok tell me 'at meanin' on' 't's baddish to know,
'At 'white' oft means 'black,' an' 'aye' sometimes means 'no'.
Bit Cummerland dialect issent that way,
Fwok say what they mean, an' mean what they say;
It's raider auld-fashin't, an' broadish an' aw,
Bit plain as a pikestaff, an' easy to know.

In my opinion no poet or English scholar can express themselves better than the ordinary fellside man or woman. Time and again when the going has been hard, or the road rough, a dialect witticism or apt description has lightened the job and the road for me.

It is a direct link with our Saxon and Scandinavian ancestors whose spirit and enterprise we inherit and which enabled us to tackle and subdue (according to Gilpin again) 'a very dangerous region, abounding in awful heights, yawning gulphs, frightful precipices, chasms, abysses, torrents and convulsions.'

One of the numerous local villages, hamlets, farms, fields and fells that reveal Norse origins of the Viking expeditions across Cumbria.

In 1965 I retired from the N. F. U. job. In one way and another I had served the Union since joining in 1919. Then there was some excuse for a tentative approach by farmers. Before 1934 ours was a 'horse' powered industry and we were poor customers of the industrial parts of our economy and had a poor claim upon the country for consideration excepting in war time.

During the first and last wars of this century, like everyone else, we forgot about incomes and prices and just got on with the job. But after 1944 and mechanisation on a massive scale by farmers, we rapidly became industry's best customer, a buttress against dumpers raising prices against us, and the support of our manufacturers' export efforts because of our demands upon their output, thus keeping their factory assembly lines running at full capacity and at competitive costs with foreign manufacturers. In consequence, there has been no valid reason for our accepting under-recoupment until it has become a public scandal.

This has been allowed to happen because of feeble leadership and the inability of farmers to stick together upon the cardinal issue of demanding that every farmer, large or small, shall have a fair deal based upon comparable payment for his work when measured by skill, investment of capital, hours of work and the ardour of that work, and that redundancy shall not be allowed to happen.

I have been saddened by this failure of farmers and their Union. It is, however, good to see that at last farmers themselves are realising the danger of their position and I feel sure that now this has been realised, like all Britons in crises, they will not be beaten. Ever since I saw the danger in 1951 I have done my best to warn my fellow farmers of the danger of apathy.

Meanwhile, after the 18 months I was given at Brownrigg – plus 50 years – I am still at Brownrigg and I haven't much inclination to give it up 'till A'hs touped!

I hope they won't be touped off their fell farms either – and they won't if they just keep hold of their brass until the conservationists and 'rationalists', and all the other 'ists' see that they are barking up the wrong tree. After all, it is a long time since James I tried to oust his tenants from their Westmorland farms, and had to pack it up, or have we to thank Sir Francis Bacon (Lord Verulam), his Lord Chancellor, who saw the red light?

Evidence of ridge and furrow ploughing on the higher fells away from the Cumberland plain. Note the 'dew-pond' in the foreground, one of the very few left in Cumbria. Artificially made, it provides water for livestock on high ground.

Eighteen

Various Snippets Of Farming Interest

When snow is thawing off our fell farms we still see the evidence, one hundred years later, of the 'six times about' ploughing of our ancestors.

To this day there are fields on this and other farms of ridge and furrow, or 'six times about' ploughing. As you climb out of Uldale village towards Caldbeck, you pass a notable example of a 'dew pond' on the dry limestone grazing land. But the whole field in the view towards Skiddaw reveals a strong pattern of ridge and furrow ploughing. Such cultivation reaching high up our Lakeland hills goes back to the blockades of the Napoleonic wars when it was said that 'farmers would even plough the sods on the roof'.

Today there are examples to be seen high above the Wythop valley – now covered with heather – along the flanks of the Mosser fells where those pairs of strong fell ponies cultivated and improved the land.

Much of this evidence was destroyed by the mistake of ploughing up the grasslands of the fell areas during the two wars. This is evident from the beautiful turf of the rig and furrow fields as compared with those which were ploughed.

There was sense in ploughing on fell farms in the eighteenth and nineteenth centuries. In those days, before transport was freely available, self-sufficiency was essential and compulsory, but mixed farming maintained the health of the soil. The men who evolved the system of rig and furrow (six times about) knew nothing of science, and their 'technology' was called 'craft' – a noble word when used in its proper sense.

Those chaps of two hundred years ago knew all about the things scientists of today are still investigating. They had learnt that if land was ploughed anywhere near straight up and down a hill, erosion took place in heavy rains, and that after light rain the water left it too quickly and it 'droughted'.

Plough team of fell ponies near Grasmere in 1890. Courtesy of Garnett's *Westmorland Agriculture* (1895).

Perfect Work

So you'll see that they always tried to plough across the contours, with a slight fall for drainage. Despite the fact that their ploughs were of wood, or at best 'ironclads', i.e. wood mouldboard with an iron sock, their work was perfect. Measure any example of rig and furrow and you will be amazed at the immaculate measurements of it.

The idea behind the system was to 'set up' the furrows from 'steep' in the centre of the rigs to a gradually less angle at the sixth time about.

The work was 'set out' at a spacing that allowed adjacent rigs to leave a furrow width between them. This furrow took the place of drains before stone or tile drainage became an accepted practice. It was magnificently effective and, even today, where the land has not been disturbed by later ploughing, these furrows still carry off heavy downpours of rain.

But the craft embodied in their ploughing was not all. Their work would have been futile had they not harrowed-in their seed with 'hinged-back' harrows. These harrows spanned the twelve furrows exactly and the hinges allowed them to fit the furrows without flattening the work as the seed was harrowed.

The fell ponies, with which all this work was done, walked, while harrowing, up the furrows left as drains and so did not damage the well set-up work of the plough.

Satisfactory Craft

When iron ploughs replaced wooden ones 80 years ago, our local blacksmiths and ironfounders in the North West evolved the very beautiful 'ley' mouldboard that has not been improved upon to this day for beautiful work. In the days of horses, and as late as 1920, many of us were still using these splendid 'swing' ploughs made by our local craftsmen. They were so beautifully balanced that, with a pair of sturdy fell ponies, ploughing with them was a satisfying craft.

Those who have not experienced the thrill of handling a nice pair of horses with a well-set swing or wheeled plough on a fine winter's day have missed one of the joys of life, and I know that those of us who knew this pleasure regret its passing.

Instead of clatter and noise there was peace and the companionship of horses and clean air to breathe, plus healthy exercise.

When our ancestors wrested the hill fields from the moorlands with their 'six times about' they must have been happy men indeed.

Threshing Days

Before 1939 hill farmers grew but a few acres of cereal – mainly oats or barley – for the immediate requirements of their own livestock. Sheaves of poor quality oats, probably weathered in a bad harvest, would be given to the cattle as a last foddering at night to save the hay. Some farms like this one when I came in 1960 had a small threshing machine in a barn often powered by a stationary 'oil' engine. Otherwise our parishes were visited by a threshing contractor – once in about November and a second visit about Martinmas (February).

George Steadman's mower – the Austin motor was mounted at the back over the twin steered wheels and the driver looked over the cutter bar similar to the forage harvester of today.

Willy Stoddart's 'tractor': a cut down Morris 'Cowley' motor car with shortened chassis, cleats on the back wheels and a concrete block to improve traction.

One Hundred Years of Hill Farming   127

The 'steamer' would come to those farms with relatively easy access or where there was a beck close by to give the engine a drink! Or rather the boiler and water tank could be replenished with water pumped from the beck. So farms like Upton House, the Wath, Biggards, Branthwaite, Wood Hall and Whelpo had threshing days and all the neighbours would come to help and a 'tatie pot' dinner at mid-day. Harry Dowthwaite's steamer and drum worked the Eden Valley, the Penrith area and as far west as Caldbeck from his farm at Plumpton.

One November day he was working at Branthwaite near Fellside – straw and chaff flying all over in the wind making conditions miserable; the gang were having their ten o'clocks when a local farmer said, 'Well, 'Arry, there'll nut be many spots thoo'll come till as wild as this?' (But if you know the Eden Valley and the force of the 'Helm' wind you'll appreciate Harry's reply.) 'Nay man – there's some o' them spots alang t'east fellsides where t'wind's see strang even t'crows hesta to walk yam!'

Despite Depression And Competition – Steady Improvement

Farmers in Cumberland and Westmorland have been notable for their enterprise, innovation and agricultural progress. We have been aided by wealthy landowners and industrialists who used their fortunes to improve animal and crop husbandry on their estates across the north of England. John Christian Curwen of Workington Hall founded the Workington Agricultural Society and developed the Schoose farm

A portrait of John Christian Curwen at Workington Hall by the well-known Cumbrian artist Joseph Simpson. Curwen's Schooze farm was justly famous and the Workington Agricultural Society which he founded continues today as the World Ploughing Association.

Tile kilns were quite common in the Borders until the Depression, making horse-shoe shaped land drainage tiles before the mass production of cylindrical pipes began. This kiln had just been abandoned at Ponteland, Northumberland in 1952.

to demonstrate the latest 'improved' breeds, husbandry and cropping methods. In the annual report of the society for 1809 it was noted that Mr Curwen was very impressed and pleased with the progress at the new 'Moor Enclosure', a couple of miles south of Schoose Farm; at that time much of the ground between Workington and Whitehaven was 'common'. But the Society eventually, in the 1940s, became the World Ploughing Association under the Secretarial direction of the late Alfred Hall MBE. He was a family friend from the start of the war, and the ploughing out campaigns. He took over the Society when my father became the first N. F. U. Group Secretary in the country in 1945.

The Schoose was a model 'demonstration' farm (an idea taken up by ADAS in that period of food and dollar shortage between 1945 and 1960); the annual show was the farming event of the year – new breeds to see, shown off in those pens arranged around the grand ring where the crowd could stand to watch events.

All over the north much land drainage work was carried out with horse-shoe shaped tiles manufactured locally in tile works. This one was still in excellent condition at Ponteland when I photographed it during my off duty hours in the army in 1952.

There was a small tile kiln at Bleabank, Brandlingill – a mile from here. (I know of another at Distington.) On this farm drainage of an area of peat moss for tree planting, ploughed with very deep furrows using a Cuthbertson plough, revealed that it had been very thoroughly drained with horse shoe tiles in the nineteenth century.

Nothing new under the sun? Away ahead of his time Lawson at 'Mechi farm',

The 'shop' windows have been removed and the property has become a private house. However it was originally established as a co-operative venture by Lawson from which his workers and villagers could purchase farm produce and groceries at favourable prices. The inscription over the door (inset) remains.

Blennerhasset, built a gas digester – using the byre and stable manure. It has since been demolished and replaced by more modern farm buildings. Visitors to Blennerhasset often wonder why there are two old gas lamps (preserved) around the village green? The gas plant at Mechi supplied the gas to light the village street piped up from the farm. As one of that great band of Agricultural improvers he demonstrated steam powered ploughing and cultivation on the farm and heavier soils.

Using two steam engines each with a windlass, the plough or cultivator passed up and down the field slightly guided by two operators. The Mechi farm range of buildings were based on the design of an Essex farm by Alderman Mechi. Atop the main building was a clock visible from most of the fields for workers to have their breaks etc.

Very aware of the wellbeing of his staff, Lawson built a 'co-operative shop' in the village so that his workers and villagers could purchase fresh farm produce almost at

cost. The shop has alas gone but the stone above the door can be seen, and today 'organic' grows in popularity with the discerning public.

Wilfred Lawson's farm at Mechi near Blennerhasset was important to Cumbrian farming in several respects. This picture of the buildings shows the clock tower (which could be seen from most parts of the farm) and opposite the separate building housed the gas digester, seen to the right in the picture, which produced gas and supplied the street lamps of the village.

Droving cattle along a country road with wide verges, towards the main road at Moota.

Just along the road is another 'milestone' monument to the improvers, at Whitehall, built alongside an original 'Pele' tower by a Victorian philanthropist and local boy made good, George Moore. His fortune improved the schools and education provision in and around Aspatria. His vision made available the 'school' library boxes distributed/carted around the whole county up to 1960.

At the opening of the new school at Bothel, he noted with considerable pride in his biography, '... he was much pleased to hear the children read – and with the newly appointed teacher', because as far as he could ascertain the only qualification the previous teacher had for the job was 'that he had a wooden leg'!

Droving

In his review of the harsh market conditions of the 1930s, my father mentions that farmers in a parish like Caldbeck would work together to 'drove' their stock to the auction – perhaps locally to Hesket pre-1930, or in our case, mostly to Wigton. So it is not uncommon to note that many of our roads have very wide verges – so as to accommodate a 'drove' of cattle, sheep, or geese.

To avoid paying tolls on the long droves from the Scottish Highlands down into Yorkshire, the drovers would hug the routes along the sides/lower slopes of the Pennines so the cattle could ford the becks and avoid paying the 'shire' tolls at places like the Bridge at Brougham, where they would be forced to cross the Eamont by a toll bridge.

Come 1940 and the huge 'plough out' campaign, our Cumbrian farms in lowland and valley imposed a dramatic change in the landscape and farming policies. On Brownrigg the ploughing out orders increased our acreage under cultivated crops to

25% of our total area. Thus the demands for threshing throughout the county increased to an extent that new contractors came in to cope with demand. John and Fred Brown from Parkend acquired a thresher and two standard Fordson tractors to handle these heavy machines down farm roads to isolated holdings. One of their tractors had a heavy winch so that the thresher could be let down into the farm yard or hauled out onto the public road; the tractor itself could not pull them, for a Fordson had not the weight to grip on road tyres.

These two men and many others equipped themselves with trailer ploughs and became full-time contractors; after the war the improving productivity of farms encouraged the growth in contracting for drainage, lime and slag spreading, timber extraction and eventually haulage.

Snapshots Of Farm Life Around North West Cumberland

There were few specialised buildings on average farms in Cumberland up to the establishment of the MMB in 1933 and the steady income to be made from milk sales. The interior of this 'byre' from an etching in a local journal is typical of the situation most of us knew as children. Rather scraggy horned cows with thick coats and

Up to the First World War the well-to-do land owners and gentleman farmers in the Cumbrian countryside had a pony and trap to attend auctions, social events, visit friends, the required attendance at church on Sundays, garden parties and generally as a status symbol. In my father's case his new boss, Mr Hewitson, met him at Wigton station six miles from Caldbeck. This fine scale model shows the village doctor looking at his watch as he prepares to attend church with his wife.

horns complete with muck buttons on their backsides. It was only in 1940 and the push for 'milk' that concrete replaced the cobbled floors – so difficult to sweep clean. Stalls could be washed down and the cows each had a water bowl. The middenstead was usually handy just out in the yard and foddering was by the armful from the nearby barn.

This etching of a cow byre or 'mistal' illustrates a scene typical to many Cumbrian hill farms right up until the 1940s.

In 1912 when my father came to Caldbeck I doubt if anyone had a car and he was met at the Wigton Station six miles away by his future boss, Mr Christopher Hewetson, with his fast pony and trap. The picture shows a model of a similar pony and trap acquired and superbly restored by him and Mr Graham Leach. It depicts the village doctor preparing to take his wife to church. She has the book of Common Prayer on the seat beside her and he is looking at his watch – 'Time to be off my dear.'

In Tullie House Museum you'll find a similar model made by a local joiner of the standard 'blockcart' complete with hay racks but made by a local joiner as a toy for a young lad.

Attending meetings, dances, whist drives, courting before World War I, you either walked (i.e. Shank's Pony) or rode a bicycle. Ben Graham who, with Les Reay ran the village garage up to the '60s, had a 'Penny Farthing' bicycle. My father had this Dursley Pedersen cycle with 3-speed gears! Way ahead of its time it was as light as a feather and very comfortable. It is now in Tullie House.

Well into the 1950s almost every farm kept a pig and there was a pig butchering day if a local butcher was available in the parish. These

The Dursley Pederson bicycle used by my father from his first days in Caldbeck up to the end of World War Two. Constructed of lightweight aluminium tube, celluloid mudguards, Sturmey-Archer 3-speed gears and downswept handlebars, it was years ahead of its time and as light as a feather.

well-preserved pig sties are at Lowfield near Isel but most have disappeared, demolished or converted to dog kennels, wood stores and so on.

In many parishes in the limestone areas of Cumberland, roadstone quarries worked well into the 1950s – Moota, Greystoke, Fauld's Brow, Deanscales, Eaglesfield, Plumbland, and dozens more along that great arc of carboniferous limestone from Pardshaw to the Eden Valley provided much material associated with lime burning or gravel production. On Fauld's Brow a couple of hundred metres from our fell gate, I remember the quarry working – the stone crusher, driven by a stationary engine similar to the one shown here.

There was a light railway incline down into the quarry and the engine man, Jimmy, operated the winch which would haul up about two small tipper wagons to the turntable above the crusher to feed the brute. The stationary steam engine and machinery were in a large shed like a steel barn open to the elements on the leeward or north side. We used to spend many hours there when it was working – a good place to warm your backside beside the furnace on a cold day. The crushed stone was fed into a cylindrical grader to hoppers for the various types. Operated by the Cumberland County Council the stone/gravel etc. was hauled to a highway gang by a family haulage firm, Stricklands of Ireby, who also owned or extracted limestone gravel at the Seeut (or Soot) quarry near the western end of the Fauld's Brow common, but they did not have a crusher. There was also a large well built cabin for tool storage, the manager's desk (or high stool), Martin Watson, and another room for the men to eat their bait, boil a kettle etc. Further along the escarpment located in a much earlier working was a strong concrete bunker-like building – the dynamite store.

Many farms had a few pigsties which have now been turned to other uses. This range is at Low Field, Bassenthwaite.

The county council stone quarry at the summit of the road from 'blue gate' to Keswick as it appeared up to the outbreak of World War Two. The engine house had a stationary engine like this to power the crusher and winch up the wagons from the quarry. The cabin for the foreman – Martin Watson – and tool store are nearest the road.

Post Box At 'Blue Gate'

The post box was used until March 2012 when it was removed after 72 years. It was originally attached to the telegraph post in 1940 so that my father, as chief observer, could post the time sheets for the crew of the nearby Royal Observer Post without going down to the village.

Talking of rural postmen reminds me of Christmas 65 years ago. I don't remember how many souls ran the post across the Parish in those days but Mattinson's post car with a large locked box on the back bumper, brought the post from Wigton. Every so often it suffered mysterious fires at remote places along the route – at the top of Wath Brow for instance! Very strange but a replacement appeared almost at once – to maintain the contract! In our case Bert Wood walked up the rough Parson's Park to Hirds at Parkhead on to Hodgsons, Bainbridges (Ryelands), and the 'Height' – half-way. Most of the trudge was across fields – come hail or shine, carrying his load in the large standard brown mail bag. The round then took in Knocker House, Lowthwaite Green, Low Brownrigg and was officially due at our place at 10.00 a.m. In the season

The origin of the name Mosser is pure Norse meaning the 'seter (or pasture) on the moss'. Looking north from our tiny listed fell church towards Criffel the drier gravel ground stands out against the wet boggy land surrounding it. In Viking times the bog would probably be impenetrable alder.

the postman would be 'loaded' with those small parcels which children imagined had come from Santa, but were stored by parents out of sight until 25 December, as well as the letters (not many at that time when next day delivery was guaranteed anywhere in mainland Britain for one-and-a-half pence (old money!)

Bert went on to Paddigill, Whelpo Head, Whelpo, and finally 'Beckstones' – in all a six-mile trail. It was a marvellous service. As war began Jimmy Boyle became a full-time observer at 'Easyone' and Lizzie Adams in her forties took over – these people tramped that round in all weathers right up to the post vans in the '50s. For the summer months to ease your feet from the strain of heavy clumsy clogs, my father used to buy a pair of cheap shoes which he wore for the season in reasonable weather, then threw away. At that time there were two principal 'mail order' companies in the business – Gamages of High Holborn, London, or the Army and Navy Stores. The shoes cost 5s. 0d. plus a few pennies postage – and they came by post!

A Name With A History

The address of this farm has strong Viking associations. Rising to 750 feet above sea level, from 500 feet in the farmyard is a feature, a small rocky hummock called Bramley 'Seat'. A glance at the topography and you realise that in Viking days that area would be very sparsely wooded for it is exposed to wind, rain and sun – an ideal clearing in the woodlands, it would be our 'seter' or summer pasture, hence 'seat'. Just along the road

For many years this postbox survived on a sawn-off telegraph pole. Fortunately it has been recently replaced. Observer Post 'Easy One' was located just behind and to the left of the photographer. Note the 'drove' road past the modern cattle grid to Wigton.

The type of stationary engine which powered the crusher at the County Council Faulds Brow quarry close to Brownrigg. .

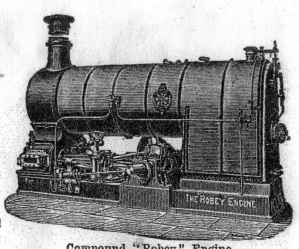

ROBEY & Co.,
LINCOLN,
MANUFACTURERS OF THE
"ROBEY"
FIXED ENGINES,
Specially adapted for driving
Stamps, Stone Breakers,
Ore Crushers, Pumps,
and all descriptions of Fixed
Machinery.

THE ROBEY ENGINE

Compound "Robey" Engine.

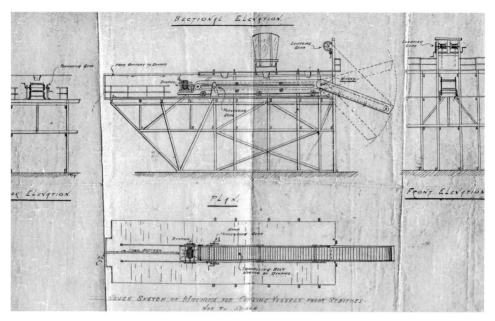

Scale drawings of mechanised coal loading staithes, from my grandfather's plans.

to Mosser as you look Northwards over the wetter lands in the valley bottom, there is an area of good cultivable ground around 20 acres (actually a glacial feature on gravel etc). The picture shows it looking down just when the first silage cut has been made which defines the feature perfectly. It is within a couple of hundred metres of Mosser hamlet. It is indeed 'Moss-er' or the 'seter' or clearing in the moss better for cultivation or grazing.

A Railway Connection!

After my Grandfather retired from the sea in his forties, he had a 'shore' job – being appointed operations manager by the North Eastern Railway Company for the whole of the Northumberland coalfield. His home was Blyth which had become one of the principal ports for the coal sent to London and to the Baltic Ports.

In the early days the chaldron wagons from the pits were pushed and trundled along a jetty which projected over the holds of the berthed ship and manually tipped. 'Trimming' the cargo must have been a dangerous and hellish job. So my grandfather designed and had constructed a moving belt conveyor to speed up the work. The drawing came from his papers; it was an important improvement although he never patented it.

The picture shows a wooden type of jetty on Tyneside at North Shields photographed by my father in the 1930s. It was to Blyth that the Westergren family came for a couple of years about 1908. The men folk were both seafarers and ex-captains, and along with their children my father and Signa were playmates. This was the lady pushing her bicycle as manager of the Hörby Farmers' Slaughterhouse in July 1946, who came to meet me during the YFC tour.

The railway connection has also had an important bearing on both my father's life and my own. Often teased by mother about his visits to 'the' resorts of the Edwardian Age, the family could visit places such as Buxton, Torquay, Keswick, Bournemouth and Cheltenham on a regular basis, for in those days all railway workers were given annual passes and for managers it was always first class. So to this day travelling by train for us is a pleasure – especially on the continent. I have been fortunate to have travelled with the driver on five European networks. And surprise, surprise – the view from the cab of the ICE at 186 mph is impressive. You only notice the speed if you look out across the countryside. See the colour section for another picture, taken through the rock guards of the cab on the famous Norwegian Flam line, as we entered a tunnel.

My Grandfather's design for a 'moving belt conveyor' at Blyth harbour to replace the coaling staithes which were a feature of the ports along the north east coast. This wooden structure, photographed by my father in the 'thirties, includes the typical 'chaldron' wagons used in the pits. They were often winched down to the dock on inclines and drawn back to the colliery by horses or simple locomotives.

Hesket Newmarket today.

NINETEEN

MISCELLANY

Hobbies and Pastimes – Furniture and Bygones

Here and there in my father's life story he comments on aspects of life in a hill-farming village. For those born in the last decades of the nineteenth century during the reign of Queen Victoria and the Edwardian period, living was for many a struggle for existence – far removed from the romantic images painted of the rural idyll or photographs posed of farm workers at their tasks, often with glum faces lined up with the 'master'.

This section reveals just a few glances at life backstage … suffered by our parents who shielded us in our childhood following the recessions of the '90s and the Great Depression of the 1930s.

In 1906 the road at the top end of Hesket Newmarket was at best a metalled track – cobbled around the market cross and in front of the cottages. It is winter and there has been a snowfall. I'm intrigued by the steps up to the second floors – were these bedrooms, storerooms, or crude flats? When my uncle John retired to bed he was 'garn on't loft'. On my farm here, there was a cottage, but you could only go upstairs by going outside and up the stone stairs! I demolished the building in 1974, alas.

The main street and village green of Hesket is tidy and gentrified today, but it had a livestock market once a week and my father sold some stock there. Cattle were tied to rings on the cottages all the way up, as you could see in Ireland in 1960. The view looks up towards the 'Temperance Hall' and the gates of Hesket Hall farm.

The lady 'darning' shows her sitting very close to the fire, wearing a knitted shawl and dust cap, with an apron over her heavy skirt. There is a soot-blackened kettle on the crane as well as a fairly modern looking pan on the hob. Some of us remember Mrs Brew who had the shop opposite the church gates in Caldbeck. She sat there day after day close to the fire,

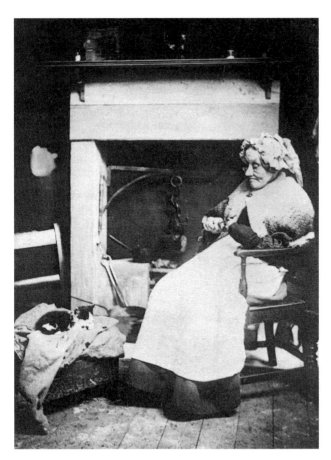

A lady darning seated by her firegate and the cat enjoying the warmth of her kitchen.

This building had two mullioned windows and outside stairs round the back. There was a large fireplace upstairs in the loft. It had been joined to another building (left) and had the remains of a fireplace on the ground floor. Before World War One there were three families at Bramley with thirteen children … today there's one family and one child.

similarly attired, shawl over head and shoulders, usually as black as a crow and you wondered when she washed – if ever! Cannot remember ever seeing her rise from her chair to serve a customer but never mind, she had all the parish gossip as quoted in John Jackson's letter to my uncle serving in Salonica in 1918.

Perhaps you don't remember bath night? Often, a working man's family would spend time together on a Saturday night – Husband relaxing with either a news sheet or an 'almanac'. A real bathtub which later gave way to a zinc-coated steel version in which I was scrubbed down in front of the kitchen fire – one asks the question, 'is the boy's mother looking for 'nits' in his hair?'

The washing is airing on a clothes horse but many farm/country kitchens had that useful aid – the clothes rack on a pulley. Notice the girls' bootees being cleaned and a few extra metal 'segs' being knocked into the toes and heels to prolong the life of the soles. Note the large teapot and paraffin lamp on the mantelpiece.

The kitchen pulley for drying and airing clothes is still a valued asset in a large farm kitchen.

A Victorian 'bath night' in front of the fire.

Winter snow in Hesket Newmarket, just before the First World War, looking up towards the Temperance Hall, with the Market Cross on the left and the site of the bull baiting ring..

Laundry Chores

How many remember the clothes irons and lifting the red hot 'heaters' out of the fire with tongs and dropping them into the body of the iron? In the '40s before the AGA came to the farmer's wife, with its clip-on handles which allowed you to use the two heaters alternately, this was a great improvement to a routine chore.

Clothes were dried on a line outside if you had space – bedding, shirts, vests etc. were all mangled resulting in many champed fingers for the women folk.

A regular dish was a herb pudding made with various vegetables in season – with nettles, dockings, dandelion leaves, sour docks, Easter Mergients etc., barley and spices. Some dried leaves were ground to a powder in a mortar with a wooden pestle. The example illustrated in the colour section – a bowl hollowed out of solid oak – dates back in history. The beautiful pestle was rescued by my father on a farm where it had ended its days working up a crowdie of coarse meal and pig swill.

Village shop keepers and their assistants were busy weighing up tea, coffee beans, sugar, etc. into one-pound blue bags neatly tied with string. Quite a skill. Until his retirement Mounsey's shop in Main Street, Cockermouth, was a jewel of history. Complete with the 'Tea Signs' outside (preserved!), my picture in the colour section shows the old man at work, batteries of drawers, tea and coffee caddies, scales both on the counter and in the back store for weighing sacks of coffee, and loose tea from large plywood tea chests (much prized before the war by do-it-yourself joiners).

Ivinson's in Upton Caldbeck was the only 'large' shop in the district that operated regular 'rounds' of the remoter parts of the Parish. Because they also supplied poultry and wheat meal, UVECO cooked maize plus linseed meal for calf rearing gruel, these items and your grocery order came about once a week. Ted Yeomans was the 3-ton lorry driver. In the shop, John Richardson had a dual role as 'traveller' and counter assistant. As children we remember 'old Bob' Dodd who came to take his place. He had

The boat deck of the White Star liner *Olympic* at the breaker's yard on Tyneside in the 1930s. She was the sister ship of the ill-fated *Titanic*.

worked in one of the very large 'posh' grocer shops of the cities before he came to Caldbeck. It was a treat to watch him weigh out a pound of tea, coffee etc. into a blue bag, neatly fold over the corners, put string around the package and stack on the shelves (no Sellotape then); he was one who had served his time to the grocery trade.

Another speciality of Ivinson's was sausage making, curing hams and sides of bacon, black puddings and potted meat. I cannot remember what happened to the 'trotters' and the pig cheeks. The unfortunates were slaughtered in the barn – now a house – and the hams, sides etc. were hung up to cure. And Cumberland Ham as cured then was 'rich' to say the very least. Two good slices and you were 'store fed' even if perhaps the rancid green bits had been scraped off perhaps with a few maggots in high summer. You could for years enjoy such a treat in the 'Oddfellows Inn' at Caldbeck, or in the 'Wasdale Head Hotel' in Wasdale up to 1970.

The recipes for sausage making varied and were closely guarded secrets. When businesses were sold or the owners retired, others acquired them, so today for example, Haigh's in Workington produce sausage which is well-known and much sought after by connoisseurs. Stoddart's at Ireby had their own special flavour and I remember Ivinson's was rather peppery. Most of our butchers had their own specialties in 'potted meat'.

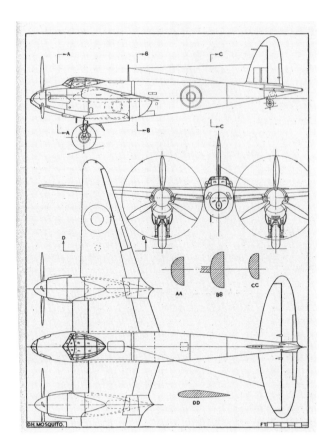

I have mentioned the 'Aga' during the war years with the very large cauldron of stock feed potatoes boiled all afternoon to augment the hen feed. On other days you would see on the cover of the cooker simmering plate a very large tin basin of dough warming as the yeast made the bread rise prior to being cut up into lumps for the bread tins to go into the oven. Then we made all our own bread – no easy run into the local town bakery as most take for granted. Even today our Lakeland towns are blessed with many bakeries – often family owned. The sliced packed loaf had not appeared! Only in the army did one experience sliced bread … in chunks as big as doorsteps!

From a ship-owning sea-faring family my father was fascinated by ships, steam and sailing. I remember being taken – no doubt to visit relations in the North East – to a Wallsend breakers yard where the White Star liner 'Olympic' was berthed prior to the breakers torch. My picture from 1933/34 was taken on the boat-deck of the four-funnel sister ship of the ill-fated 'Titanic'. We explored the ship which was open to the public – and lost ourselves, so Dad had to look out of a porthole to see where we were on her. We ended the visit with lunch in the grand restaurant – 1*s*. 6*d*. for me, 2*s*. 6*d*. for my father!

So among the four models he constructed was the 'Vesper', one of two collier brigs owned and sailed by my Grandfather. Then he built a 5ft model 'packet' steamer which was displayed in the children's room of Tullie House library up to 1939. Although prepared for an engine, one was never fitted because the war came along. In the splutter to store valuables on the outbreak of war, someone dropped it and wrecked the handrails. Pity, because it destroyed the old man's trust in museums for ages even though the late Tom Gray was one of his best friends. As curator of Tullie House Museum and also Librarian of the Carlisle City Library, the late Tom Gray was almost unique. His knowledge of Cumbrian and Border history was comprehensive and deep. He would have a word with everyone and anyone – a 5-year-old curious child or 80-year-old knowledgeable citizen. And he just loved a good 'crack'. Upon his retirement a far-sighted County Council charged him with the creation of the County Archives and its base in the castle.

For many years he wrote the background histories of all the Border personalities whose portraits appeared on Messrs Thurnhams calendars issued to schools throughout the area. The pictures were all painted by a notable Cumbrian artist, Joseph Simpson (he painted John Christian Curwen of Workington Hall).

Model Making

One of my father's finest efforts was of a Viking Ship – a beautiful craft. Its shallow draft and beautiful lines helps you to realise how the Norsemen ranged far and wide and could sail well inland from Ravenglass, for example, to establish their settlements.

The outbreak of war in 1939 resulted in the imposition of 33% purchase tax on all luxury goods. We had bought a kit of parts from Bassett-Lowke of Northampton to build an L.M.S. '0' gauge 'Crab' 2-6-0 steam locomotive. It cost £5. We could not afford the £12 for the factory completed model. From 1939 and the introduction of Hornby '00' DUBLO train sets, I had always craved an '0' gauge LMS *Princess Elizabeth*, but that could never be, for we had no electricity … so that 'Crab' steam locomotive was my substitute. The model is now part of the Tullie House collection.

For my own part as described previously I amused myself in the war building model aircraft from a book of plans entitled *Aircraft of The Fighting Powers*. They were all used to display 'Savings Week Campaigns' to encourage the populace to invest in war savings. As time went on and the war came to an end I'm afraid many of my models – an FW190, Dornier 26, Lancaster bomber, Mosquito, Boston, Spitfire – all disappeared and never came back to me. (See reprint of advert for a National Savings week in Carlisle to raise £500,000 for 25 bombers, etc.!)

In later years – 35 years to be exact – my only claim to joinery was to build a caravan body on a VW pick-up. It took me two and a half years to build, but gave us much pleasure during our son's adolescence when we could take off across Europe with our 'henhouse' on wheels. Equipped for Arctic chill to Mediterranean heat it saved us

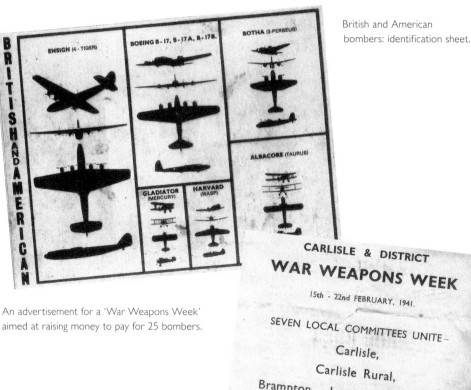

British and American bombers: identification sheet.

An advertisement for a 'War Weapons Week' aimed at raising money to pay for 25 bombers.

CARLISLE & DISTRICT

WAR WEAPONS WEEK

15th - 22nd FEBRUARY, 1941.

SEVEN LOCAL COMMITTEES UNITE –

Carlisle,

Carlisle Rural,

Brampton, Longtown, Wigton,

Aspatria, Silloth,–

TO RAISE A MINIMUM

OF

£500,000

THE COST

OF

25 BOMBERS

much in hotel costs. We crossed the 'Iron Curtain' several times, which in the 'Cold War' years was an experience in itself convincing us of our common European inheritance and the futility of war and division.

Living in a remote hill-farming area the winter nights began early and a family had to share the Aladdin paraffin lamp for whatever they were doing. Our mothers seemed to knit incessantly. At other times they would make 'rag' rugs on a stretcher frame – very often assisted by their menfolk as there was little else to do except listen to the news bulletins on a battery radio. I mention elsewhere the fortnightly task of taking into Wigton and collecting the 'wet' 2-volt battery. You could never afford to leave the radio playing away to itself or you would not be able to listen to your favourite programmes: 'ITMA' (30–40 minutes) and 'Ray's a laugh', towards the end of the war, and of course, 'The Palm Court of Grand Hotel' – one hour on Sunday night; your one weekly 'dose' of culture!

Rug Making

Well into the 1970s my wife and I made 'Readicut' rugs for the fireside or bedside. These were quite expensive 'kits' – a pattern printed on canvas base and a prodding needle. Simple pastimes.

In 'digs' my wife passed her evenings stitching a beautiful woollen bedside rug (for her bottom drawer, as was the fashion in those days). The work involved choosing your own coloured wool and following a pattern – as for example a knitting pattern – onto a canvas. Each row took about an hour to the accompaniment of records on an 'EKCO' record player much valued in those days before the tape recorder of the '60s.

In the 1960s, as I travelled about the country, I carried my 'hobby' with me – a simple 2' x 2' glass printing frame and two plastic jugs, one for the developer, the other the fixer. So I could print my snaps in a hotel bedroom! A very far cry from today's 'instant' digital picture making and printing on computer controlled equipment. In the wartime years our enlarger was upstairs in a back boxroom The light source was a 50-volt bulb and the gadget was four feet long – largely made of wood. It had a huge optical condenser weighing 5 or 6 pounds and you pinned the photo paper on an easel – exposure up to 5 minutes sometimes! We used to work in our overcoats and had to keep the developer warm atop a paraffin stove.

As peacetime normality returned to village and countryside, the village halls, schools and institutes, evening classes became popular provided in the relatively new Secondary Modern schools by the County Education department and that other excellent organisation – the W. E. A. (Workers' Education Association).

For us children in the '30s, the BBC provided 'Children's Hour' or we amused ourselves with the simplest of games – 'Snap', jigsaw puzzles, 'Beetle', Dominoes, perhaps; whist if there were four in the household, or maybe Chess.

My wife Ella making a 'Readicut' Rug on printed canvas.

For the decade of the '50s, Cumberland was quite isolated from the rest of the country by geography, topography and communications. The 1953 Coronation was viewed by the odd homestead in the area with almost a 'freak' TV signal. The building of the BBC Sandale mast enabled us to connect with the rest of the country and it was a decade later that the M6 extended into Cumbria.

Reception on TV when it came was patchy in many Lakeland valleys and our farm was virtually under the mast. But on this farm and in the Lorton Valley our programmes came from Shotts up in the Border, right up to the digital age and satellite dish. Certain programmes stand out – the corny 'What's my Line?' For children – the cartoon of 1965, 'Pinky and Perky'. Older readers will remember the classic April Fools' day leg pull of Richard Dimbleby about the 'Italian Spaghetti' harvest. It is easy to forget that in the '60s, package holidays were in their infancy and a visit to London was a major expedition, never mind going abroad!

Furniture

Where he learnt it I do not know, but one of my father's hobbies/skills was wood carving and furniture making. In the '20s he bought some sawn board and timber of oak from Parson's Park and put it away to 'season' for about five years under the haymews. A beautiful Monk's Bench he made had a carving under the lid 'A candle while consuming itself gives light to others'. A small black cupboard gave him considerable satisfaction. The hinges for this and the Monk's Bench, and the handles for the drawers he fashioned out of brass. He was friendly with a Mr Allan – a notable antique dealer from Aspatria – who called for tea one day. I remember the old chap running his fingers over it, and declaring it 'genuine – a nice piece'. Luckily I must have kept 'mum' and the maker was thus kept secret. I could not use it so eventually when my father moved from 'Brownrigg' it was sold.

4 September 1939, and spare time for hobbies in the farm household rapidly declined. My father, very much aware that an almost timeless way of life was drawing to a close, began collecting rural bygones, artefacts, furniture etc. The modest improvements after 1936 in farming caused farmers and their wives to seek rather more comfort in their homes. The hard chairs went out – the feather beds were gradually replaced by spring (uncomfortable) mattresses, and so on. Very well aware that bodies like the National Trust were rather too keen to preserve the homes of the wealthy, Dad became a collector of rural antiques rather than making furniture himself. Our farmhouse was relatively large, rambling and cool, so an ideal place for robust oak furniture. My mother also became interested in restoring oak pieces which had frequently been 'clarted up' with varnish etc.

How her hands survived I do not know but the 'treatment' involved scrubbing down with mild caustic soda, then vinegar, and real bees-wax/turpentine with elbow grease!

In 1940 they got their eyes on a 'robe' in a well-known Keswick antique shop – it cost £30. The piece measured eight feet by six feet by three feet and weighed goodness knows! The 'treatment' lasted most of the winter but revealed a most exquisite simple pattern of barley heads inlaid on the doors in bog oak. Such a piece I understand was carted around by army officers in the eighteenth century from camp to camp. It was complete with drawers – a pull out writing drawer (i.e. a desk) and secret compartments. When the dealer saw it restored he tried – but couldn't – to buy it back, despite a vastly enhanced offer. Today it is displayed in a Scottish National Trust house as with many other items from his collection, because I do not like to think that such relics should end up exported out of the homeland. Thus, the artefacts and antiques my father saved are to be seen and on long-term loan to Tullie House, Abbott Hall and Beamish.

The carving on the underside of the lid of a Monk's bench made by my father, of Caldbeck-grown oak and seasoned in the hay mews. 'A candle while consuming itself gives light to others'.

Channelling the waters of the powerful Caldew into the mill was this weir and its sluices; it was badly damaged in a storm and this photograph was taken before its demolition.

TWENTY

'TAKEN FOR GRANTED'

It should be remembered that up to the late 1950s many villages had their own 'local' water supply. As conditions improved after the war, more and more settlements were put on a 'main' by the water companies. In 1938 a study/report to the CCC of Water Resources in Cumberland reveals the extent of village supply schemes. It was planned to build a dam in Wylie Ghyll and the road up Swineside was improved up to the Wolfram mine, and on roads over a bridge (still there today) leading to the dam site.

Our own supply came from a spring on the fell about 500 yards away above the farm, where my father and some workmen built and laid a one inch galvanised pipe to a 5000 gallon header tank in the farm drive above the house.

At last, water in a tap! It was planned to hold enough to outlast around a month's drought, which it did, until we went 'on the milk' in 1940. Thereafter twelve milking cows severely stretched the system. So, beasts had to be grazed overnight in a field with a spring lower down the farm, and spout water had to be channelled into a drinking trough in the yard, at which the young stock drank when they were let out twice a day – while their stalls, pens, and byres were cleaned out and rebedded.

So if you had a freeze up in the winter, or a long cold dry spell, watering the livestock with buckets drawn from a well was a very time-consuming task, as a cow in calf will drink her fill of around 4 to 6 gallons!

In the early days of Brownrigg, there was a well close to the back door – it never froze – and if perchance the piped supply failed, as it was sure to do in hard times, then we had to draw water from it. Indeed, in the 1990s my father used it for his main source of supply. Water supply is even now a problem on Cumbrian farms. My farm today, like many others in this valley, takes its water from a spring, through a filter into a collecting tank. Water is now expensive from the mains, and for us connection to the public supply would cost many thousands of pounds and render dairying or beef production uneconomic.

Being responsible for our own supply involves regular maintenance of the filter, holding tank, and keeping the gutter from the spring to the collection point clean, fenced and safe.

To protect the spring, we have a fenced-off area of around an acre, on which a wood has been established. In autumn and some other times of year, pine needles and leaves build up and block the filter. Although it is a relatively simple job to rectify, the water cuts off usually without warning, and often decides to stop at 10.00 p.m. – or after dark on Christmas Eve – to much cursing by all and sundry. However, it is good pure spring water and the cost is minimal. Despite the floods which Cumbria suffers from time to time, water is scarce and quite an industry has grown up for companies who will sink bore-holes on your farm, or try to find you a supply on your own land. The acquifer along the Eden Valley is a blessing to dairy and beef producers there, not only as the principal supply, but often to augment water provision in off-lying fields.

Difficulties with water supply persisted into the 1960s for us, long after milk production ceased in 1945. Matters improved remarkably as a spin off from the spread of television transmission across Britain. The Sandale BBC television transmitter had to have a secure electricity power supply. One line came along the valley from Caldbeck, onto Ellerbeck Common and then up to Sandale Fell. As it happened, the line was to pass through our lowest fields along the beckside, towards Whelpo. At this juncture, no farms or properties were to be connected to the line. However, it was discovered that with a bit of arm twisting and 'no way leave without a supply' we were able to receive power to a small pumphouse fed from one of the best springs in the valley. It was a long and steep 'lift' but it worked until the mains came to the farm over Fauld's Brow tops. The water was pumped to a tank above the steading and a back feed operated down the line, and supplied field drinking troughs. It was, however, an expensive solution, and needed much maintenance and no leaks!

Here on this Loweswater farm, the prolonged drought of 1976 caused me to revise my thinking and planning about the wet areas on the land. On the higher fields where there was a slope, it would have appeared sensible to have drained the water away downhill. Good farming practice would have encouraged plastic drain pipes, the water taken away into a guttered stream then ploughing or reseeding and improved pasture. These places were often covered with rushes and the soil swampy, so that a tractor or even a large animal would sink. Unsightly, but the severe drought showed they were caused by springs which could be tapped and collected in simple tanks, and distributed in proper alkathene water pipes to drinking troughs elsewhere, in adjoining fields. Suitably fenced round, and a few trees planted, removed an eyesore in my mind, but retained a potential water supply. Even in twenty-first-century Britain, water supply is becoming increasingly critical for efficient food production – we waste a lot and unlike the Dutch and Rhineland Germans, we baulk at the cost of recycling. Visiting some Dutch friends in Dordrecht many years ago, I commented that their tap water tasted quite good. Yes, said Jean (our hostess) – 'it's not bad considering half a dozen Germans have bathed in it before we get it!'

When I think of my own village of Caldbeck, and compare it with similar villages and valleys in Norway and Sweden, I'm sorry but somehow somewhere between water mills and the industrial revolution, Britain missed a trick. In the Howk, Caldbeck had a very powerful beck which has never dried up, and the follow up to the huge wheel that turned the Bobbin Mill should have been fed to a Pelton wheel/turbine which could have supplied the village – but perhaps not the outlying farms and houses – long before the electricity main came to us in 1937. And we had the manufacturers within Cumbria at the time – Messrs Gilkes of Kendal would have been happy to oblige. A valley in Värmland, Sweden, I know, had its own turbine for many years and was eventually connected into the National Grid.

Energy poverty/demand may yet cause us to utilise/feed into the grid every watt of power such a gorge as the Howk can produce without any destructive effects. That great water wheel – the second largest in England – was supplied by a simple intake dam and a tunnel which came out above the wheel; as lads we crawled up it in the 1930s.

At Midtown farm where my father was a student, the waters of the Caldew collected in a holding dam (now a lawn) to be released when the Ivinson mill worked and in 1912,

Our Dutch friend, Corrie Kerkwijk, weaving at her loom in Dordrecht, Netherlands. Every time we visited her we took her a fleece from which she spun all manner of cloths. When I went to Fagerås farm in Sweden (1948), daughter Margit worked a similar loom.

on threshing days, the 'lad' had to run up to the dam – a couple of hundred yards – to open the sluice into the mill race. The stored water gave about half an hour's threshing or grinding at Midtown farm before the gate had to be closed, so water would build up again.

The last remaining mill which I remember working, was the one near the church (called Priestmill in 2000) but the water was fed to it by a very large weir which channelled the beck into the mill race. It has now gone completely – only the foundations are to be seen, deep in the water of the beck bottom.

You don't realise the cost and value of water until you have to carry it by the bucketful to the sink – for washing and drinking, or to flush the loo, in a period of frost. Reading through a report to the Cumberland County Council from consultants in 1945, I am amazed at how many of our villages (not the farms) were supplied from good reliable springs, feeding a header tank and distributed to village properties. Treatment was minimal, but from 1950 to 1975 it was a remarkable achievement by the Water Authorities to supply most of our villages and the farms with reliable mains water – despite recurring financial crises after the war. Sewage disposal did not come before the '60s and to this day, as you would expect, many of our farms have their own septic tanks.

As a child I well remember noting a particular method of disposal … walking up from the church after evensong, along the beckside short cut, towards the 'Smithy'. It was dusk of course, and I noted several ladies walking about wearing their overcoats and carrying a bucket near the picturesque little footbridge much admired by visitors today. Nothing suspicious! Until you glanced behind you over your shoulder to see the contents of the buckets chucked into the beck! Well, it is said that a river cleanses itself after a few miles …

Life on remote farms miles from a village involved a good deal of memory for your fortnightly order, and not to forget the little things we all take for granted today. Most farms in Caldbeck had a garden. Ours – the size of two tennis courts – had been an old garth. My mother tended it every day and it kept us with virtually everything 'in season': gooseberries, red currants, black currants, raspberries and marrows. Enough early potatoes to feed us until the few rows from the turnip field were picked in Autumn. We had lettuce, chives, onions, leeks, radishes, two rows of garden peas and half a row of sweet peas. Early in 1940 my father aquired some old window frames from a property demolished in Wigton which were erected (cobbled together) on a wooden frame so we could grow our own tomatoes.

As soon as farmers were issued with ploughing orders in 1940, an area which was traditionally devoted to livestock raising saw every farm with a 'turnip field' which became ever more important. My father cut out turnips as we did not 'feed' sheep but instead we grew mangolds for the cows and thousand head and marrowstem kale. The cows pulled thier own but for feed later in the winter we grew some rows of drumhead cabbages and the cows got two each after milking – they used to go mad for them. As field vegetables always taste better than garden we put in every year about four stitches (rows) comprising carrots, beetroot, cauliflowers and perhaps turnips.

I recall a very amusing incident one evening in early May – double summer time then – we were drilling the last two rows of carrots and wanted to finish the job while the weather was dry so we were actually striking matches to check the seed was running. 'Doesn't look like carrot seed,' Dad commented, but anyway it said so on the packet and we pressed on. We kept looking at the rows as the days passed and the other crops came up fine; we pulled up stems of what appeared, tasted the roots ... no way were they carrots and eventually two very fine lines of Italian ryegrass presented themselves! For which Harrison Ivinson, the seed merchant, had his leg pulled mercilessly.

Many of my school friends remark that for them bananas, grapes and grapefruit were unknown until the nineteen-fifties. Up to the war oranges were 'Jaffas' from British mandated Palestine; dates were in packs like chocolate and from Iraq, or you could buy them in very large pressed blocks weighing about ten kilos. Canary Island tomatoes disappeared becasuse of the U-boat blockade ... Every now and then there might be a few bunches of bananas if you were in the know. Luckily for us, thanks to my father's young days in Newcastle, he'd often gone down to the Green Market on a Saturday late evening where you could buy tubs of apples, grapes, large bunches of bananas etc., sold off because they would not keep. Thus he'd become friendly with a Mr Little who had a shop very close to Tullie House. So when he had to go to Carlisle once per month for the Agricultural Machinery Executive Meetings he would call to see what the old chap had managed to lay his hands on. Captains of ships returning to the UK in ballast would take a chance and fetch a few bunches of bananas or grapes packed in sawdust in barrels and deck cargo. If the convoy was slow they'd end up overboard – or safely in dock – they'd go on to what was in effect the 'Black Market'. As my mother was vegetarian, if we were lucky there would be some fruit to share with friends and the next month Mr Little's generosity would be rewarded with a couple of dozen eggs!

One other thing, photographic films. 'Verichrome' or 'Selochrome' just disappeared but we managed sometimes to get hold of some old stock from Mr Tassell who had a studio in Carlisle where many wartime brides went for their one and only wedding picture. Again they were paid for/exchanged for a couple of dozen fresh farm eggs. Otherwise townsfolk had to do with USA dried egg powder!

The 2-volt wet acid battery had a metal cradle with a handle so you could carry it with you on a bicycle.

Twenty One

Can I Do You Now Sir?

As viewed by a friend who called British West Cumbria 'the little Kingdom beyond the hills'.

Did we have many books in our houses, those of us who were school children going to the 'Secondary' in the '30s and '40s? No. I was lucky, for my father had about 12 shelves of assorted books from his First World War service. As a machine gunner and later tank instructor, he had spent his nights under canvas at Bovington Camp in Dorset reading by hurricane lantern. He had read most of the volumes on our shelves.

Some time in the '30s, he had acquired a set of Encyclopaedia Britannica – too heavy for me to get down off the shelves but consulted by him often when junior asked searching questions.

I am amazed at how well most of my contemporaries turned out when you consider the very restricted sources of information available to them. (Yes, there were 'Library Boxes'! from County delivered to the school but its contents had to cater for the whole parish!) A book as a Christmas present was a very prized gift right up to 1950. Although the Penguin book at 1s. 0d. had appeared in the '30s we could rarely get our hands on one.

For news, we relied on the simplest of radios – such as a radio from a 'kit' for enthusiasts circa 1925, built by my father. Indeed folks came from miles around to Upton House to don the earphones and listen to a programme from the British Broadcasting Company from Alexandra Palace. However right up to 1955/56 the radio on a farm involved a 2-volt wet acid battery and a High Tension one. The latter lasted about six weeks to two months but once a week I had to carry the wet acid battery with me on the bike – and onto the bus to Wigton, and Ellwood's electric shop in High Street. I collected the other charged one to bring back. Health and Safety would

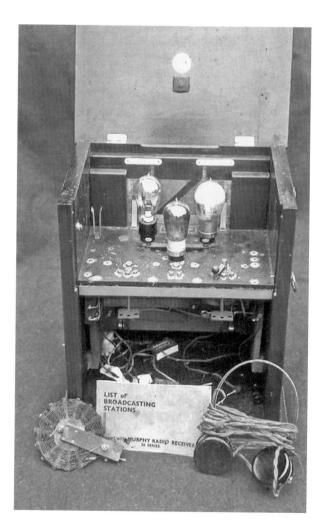

A radio built from a 'kit' complete with earphones – similar to the one my father built around 1926.

suffer severe palpitations these days! Take such a thing on a bus – oops. No way ... that gave us the news and the weather forecast (but not in the war) and a Sunday night treat – music from the 'Palm Court of Grand Hotel'. Of course, families had their favourites from the very limited broadcasts available; the laughter programme for us was I. T. M. A. (it's that man again – the Tommy Handley Show), shafts of wit about life in wartime Britain.

Although our lighting problems were unsolved until 1941, many of the outlying farms in Caldbeck Parish and the Lake District generally after the war were able to have 240 volts electric power by the use of diesel engines driving a generator; equipment perfected during the war for emergency power in hospitals and the supply of military installations in remote locations (the Scottish Islands for example). It was called the Start-o-Matic system and it became a great success. Only one battery – to start the diesel engine which cut in the moment any switch was turned on. So our farmsteads reverberated to the low thump-thump-thump of the diesel engine running somewhere at the back of the buildings (and today wealthy incomers and relatives get uptight about the so-called swish/intrusion of wind turbines).

Come 1950 and 'portable' radios (as big as small suitcases) were running on the 'Mains' – you could receive Radio Luxemburg. However picking up real broadcasts from the continent was just not available – but maybe from Radio Hilversum if atmospherics were good.

Television? We didn't have it until very much later when the Sandale Mast (transmitter) was built for the coronation of Queen Elizabeth in 1952. Mrs Hird at Park Head invited many of our neighbours to watch the programme. Their farm perched on the top of Warnell Fell, faced south-east and could pick up a signal from the Lancashire transmitter.

So I'm sorry to say that our exposure to French was provided by text books featuring Monsieur Duhamel and his family – declining irregular verbs but more vocabulary lists of useful words in both Latin and French. Amazingly, today, although I'm a numbskull about Roman numerals, I can still make sense of Roman tablets which I see in museums across Europe … which may tell me that a cohort of Dacians were on duty at Vindolanda (poor shivering sods) during the occupation of Julius Caesar.

An uncle – a former World War friend of my father who lived in the US for 25 years – used to pass on his *National Geographic* magazines from 1938 and all through the war. They were a treat, read from cover to cover, and I still have some of the old back-copies from 1938 in my loft. With the first colour pictures in a semi-educational magazine, they provided a vision into the future. The editorial staff of the *Geographic* had an uncanny sense of the trouble-spots of the looming conflict in Europe which 'Isolationist' America was determined to avoid. Articles would appear by a writer 'Pedalling through Poland' in 1938, or 'Danzig – Hanseatic City', the Norwegian fjords etc., a feature on Finland – to be venue of the 1940 Olympic Games, etc.

When it appeared in 1938 – the idea of an émigré European from Czechoslovakia being dismembered by the Nazis – my father subscribed to *Picture Post* and continued all through the war. A pity I didn't keep them, as today they are valuable collectors' pieces. Otherwise we never had a daily paper, for my father only had time to spare at weekends reading the *Guardian Weekly* – which we still take to this day, subscribers for over 80 years. Of course in the early years, it came in the post!

Such was the limited exposure of my generation to affairs European and alas, even now, 'foreign' begins at Dover.

1945: the Caldbeck YFC public speaking team were county winners. Left to right: Mabel Brough, Seconder of vote of thanks; Speaker GHC, Emily Ashbridge, Proposer of VoT; Chairman Laura Ridley.

TWENTY TWO

TEENAGERS IN A REMOTE VILLAGE

For us children there were lots to do and nobody became concerned if we ranged far and wide or took off for the afternoon with a friend. Joe Brownrigg, from Matthew Ridding way across the valley from me, would walk up to my home at 'High Brownrigg' for the afternoon to 'play'. One day we had heard of a very good hedge of hazelnut bushes in a hedge near Ryelands. We made our way across the fell and the 'Height' land to the hedge three miles away, climbed the branches and stuffed our pockets to bulging with green nuts and home for tea. No one missed us after an escapade of some six miles.

Later, on moving to the 'Secondary', I made friends with the Ashbridge lads from Wheyrigg farm, now a hotel, half-way between Wigton and Abbeytown. So for a day's recreation on a Saturday, I biked down to Wigton (six miles) and on to Wheyrigg – a further four miles. It was uphill all the way back – tough going really – taking the bike for a walk!

One of the sights of Caldbeck on Saturday or Sunday afternoons in the summer was to see eight or ten buses (Cumberland or Ribble) come over the tops from Warnell – down Ratten Row for a 'Comfort stop' in the village. These were factory outings for workers at Carrs, Hudson Scotts, Cowans Sheldon – Carlisle's industrial factories.

If we were piking hay in our meadows looking down on the village, I used to count them in and then count them out along to Whelpo and out to Ellerbeck on their way to Keswick.

For us kids the treats of the season were a bus trip to Allonby or Silloth or sometimes as far afield as Dumfries arranged by the W. I., the Chapel, or GFS, or Sunday School.

Post 1980, catering on our railways became unfairly a music hall joke … yet in 1938 the education department of Cumbria County Council organised a railway excursion for a special charter trainload of Cumberland school children to Glasgow and a sail down the Clyde and Kyles of Bute to Largs, where we

An annual 'treat' for country children! A day at the seaside in 1934 – the Sunday School trip – all the way from Calbeck to Silloth. Our neighbours (L to R) Isobel Watson, Jeanne Smith, Margaret Watson and myself. No 'dookers' – swimming costumes – but rolled up dresses tucked into knickers.

entrained for home. We trooped down to the pier two by two from the station to the landing stage. I remember watching a new destroyer 'test firing' her guns in the Firth of Clyde as I gazed out to sea. However, every child on that train was served a 'high tea' at their seat on the way home – what an experience!

Come 1936/37: the air-cooled twin cylinder Rover 8, forerunner of the Volkswagen and post-war 4-cylinder Jowett javelin (a car ahead of its time) – and because we produced cream for Carrick's Dairies, my birthday treat was afternoon tea at Carrick's café in Bank Street Carlisle, and chocolate éclairs filled with real whipped cream.

For the adults there was the ever popular bowling green in summer and for the farm lads and hired hands there was the Men's Club. It was located in the old school room above what I remember as the garage for Ivinson's 3-ton lorry. There was a billiard table and it had a fireplace. (Note description of the second John Peel Day and the washout by a rainstorm.)

Although Caldbeck had up to eight pubs prior to World War I, I only remember the 'Oddfellows' on the village green. Run by a manager, it was one of those many taken over during and after the first World War by the Carlisle State Management Brewery. (The buildings are now part of the University of Cumbria.)

There the farmers gathered on a Friday and Saturday night to play dominoes. In the Parish Hall – opened in 1928 – whist-drives, concerts and socials, as well as more serious meetings, were held. Yes, political meetings – I remember some of the rallies between the Liberals' Wilfred Roberts, and Conservative contenders e.g. Ronald Carr, in the 1945 campaign. Then, the Labour party was virtually unheard of in the countryside. When war came along concert parties and whist-drives kept our parents amused. The local GP, Dr Quinn, organised concerts of home-bred local talent. Aunt Ruth George, who was a trained singer, rendered 'Danny Boy' with her lovely Irish accent. (Although her mother was Caldbeck born she spent her youth in Belfast.) Tommy Pearson was a very amusing 'raconteur' or rather he was good at 'Cumerlan' Tyals' – many of them far-fetched!

A film show was a treat and always had a packed house provided about every three months by the Ministry of Information. Propaganda films about the war effort were shown to give encouragement to farmers young and old to increase food production. Caldbeck Parish Hall had mains power, but these travelling film shows using 10 cwt Ford commercial vans, carried a Petter Engine and a generator bolted to the floor to provide the power for shows in villages where there was no illumination except oil lamps.

Very important 'dates for your diary' came in the autumn and into December – before we more or less all 'hibernated' for the winter in the Lakeland Valleys! These were the 'socials' to which your mothers or fathers invited their partners (wives, sorry!) to a 'knees-up'. The usual form was a whist-drive – yes, Caldbeck Parish hall with all the tables out for the company to play whist. Then the tables were stored under the stage in the pit while we went in turns to the supper room for a real good feed which members of the club had provided – all homemade of course. Meanwhile the band began to play and dancing started. The heat of such a full house in those days for farmers used to cold houses caused most of the men to 'louse out' down to shirt sleeves and braces. I cannot remember, but a typical trio comprised 70+-year-old Mrs Teasdale from Greenhead on the piano, Ernie Blaylock the Hesket Blacksmith, on the drums (or piano accordion), and Walter Stott from Nether Row – complete with his bushy ginger moustache, corduroy breeches and gold-rimmed glasses – on squeeze box accordion. I think us kids had to be 12+ to go with our parents, but the important events were the Women's Institutes, the Young Farmers' Club and the Girls Friendly Society. And these became more important and sophisticated as the end of the war came nearer.

Neighbours and families used to visit back and forth to play whist, dominoes, beetle drives etc. – long before the era of Bingo. Often these happened in the long winter nights or when a member of the family came on leave, or in the case of our neighbours, the Watson's two sons – who had been slightly wounded – arrived home together. A particular night we were all partying and time came – rarely later than 9.30 p.m. – for us to go home, which involved 'setting'. So Molly and John Benn, Isabel Watson and I would walk Isobel Grainger from Park End farm along the top road over the open fell as far as the Fauld's cross roads, where we could see her safely on her way down the hill for the last mile.

Laughing and joking as we walked in the brilliant moonlight – not a light to be seen in the valley – we could hear the steady drone of a single aeroplane. Couldn't see it of course, but one of the girls said 'Ooh, it might drop a bomb …' To which John – always a wag – said 'Niver mind girls, you'll be okay. They haven't come to bomb you but to Tom you!' Another such party was at Hudscales when Alex came home on leave and altogether about ten of us were there. It was four miles by the roads and we all walked – there and back.

But it was thanks to the efforts of men such as Tom Ridley at Wood Hall and Arthur Brownrigg, Bob Grainger, Edwin Hird and many others who gave generously of their time to found and host the Caldbeck YFC which has had an illustrious record.

As well as talks, demonstrations and film shows, there were regular livestock judging and grooming competitions arranged and hosted on farms in the district to prepare our teams for the annual rally at Newton Rigg.

By 1945 I had taken my school Certificate and although I enjoyed the stock judging, goodness knows why but Mr Ridley would have us enter the County Public Speaking Competition in 1944, held in the Courts at Carlisle. Emily Ashbridge and I were presented as two guinea pigs from Caldbeck Club … the result was a disaster but a triumph for the individual speakers, the McGilavry girls of High Hesket Club who swept the board.

Never mind, Bob Hutchinson, the school master at Caldbeck, pushed ahead and the next year – 1945 – the rules had changed. We had to have a team comprising of a speaker, chairman, proposer of a vote of thanks and a seconder – that meant you had to have four speeches prepared for each role depending on the 'draw', e.g. if Laura was drawn as speaker, you had to be ready to be chairman, or proposer or seconder of the vote of thanks.

Mr Hutchinson was a huge support to me – timing me to the exact five minutes, voice training, expression, using your hands etc. I think I went down to the village school for four or more sessions with him (I was at the Grammar School by then). Somehow at the time I had read Sir Walter Citrine's book on Public Speaking.

It was April 1945 and came the day, and our club was drawn next to the end of a long dreary afternoon, when the audience and the old farmers were nodding off, navel gazing, and the judges had about heard enough! The draw was a dream come true – Laura was to be chairman with the super confidence she has had all her life. Emily Ashbridge proposer of the vote of thanks, and Mabel Brough excellent back ups. These dear ladies all noticeably heaved a sigh of relief; Geoff was to be speaker – the short straw!

My subject in those far off days with the end of the war but a month away, and much talk of an election and change of government, Nationalisation of mines, railways etc., was 'The Nationalisation of Agriculture'. Wow! The farmers present – old and middle aged – just about fell off their chairs. The title itself was electrifying. Fortunately the delivery went without a hitch. I had set the room on fire and we swept the board, adding to a very successful year for the club.

That summer, somehow we were sent to a big agricultural show on the Town Moor in Newcastle, where we met the new organiser for the four Northern Counties' YFC's, Mr Philip Lyth. Philip had been an agricultural student in 1939–40 and as I did several years later, went to Norway to work on farms for the year! But it turned out to be five years' internment!

Ringebu Folk High School, Norway.

Fitzwilliam House on Trumpington Street, Cambridge, 1946.

TWENTY THREE

DUMPED

Anyway the momentous events of 1944 gave everyone a hope for a future. The second front had opened and the Normandy landings emptied many parts of the south of England, which we now know had the appearance of a vast military camp. Late June, and those of us in Form V re-sat our school certificates. The headmaster had decided in 1943 to enter any of us with a cat-in-hell's chance of passing to sit for the School Certificate. It was a total disaster – two pupils, Ward and Dixon, passed (just) and not very well. The rest of us failed. No boost for our confidence there! A wholesale reshuffle took place; we were divided into Form V Arts and Form V Science. Goodness knows by what criteria we were 'sorted'. I suppose some of us were rated 'academic' – the others scientific or practical.

The Nelson School took the papers of the NUJMB and in those days you had to pass in English or you automatically failed. I did not matriculate – for that you needed five credits and so many passes. I returned four credits and four passes, so I went into the Sixth Form and in those days the assumption seemed to be you were destined to go in for teaching.

First year 'Sixth' was a bit of a 'swan' – a waste of time for the nine or ten of us in that group. We were supposed to be preparing for our higher School Certificates – in English Language, Literature, French and Geography. However, the 'head' was timetabled to take us for the first two periods on Monday mornings and the last two on Friday afternoons. Bob Sayle rarely appeared, naturally, being entangled with administration at the start and end of the week, so we were wasting our time. Fortunately for me my father – ever fearful of the depression disasters of the 1930s – distrusted what our politicians would do to farmers after the war, despite their siren overtures: 'produce all you can lads – help us win the war and we will see you alright thereafter.'

On a hard-worked hill farm with limited options (see later chapters), a hard countryside and inhospitable climate, my father thought wisely that I should have another string to my

One Hundred Years of Hill Farming   169

The new 'Fitzwilliam' on Madingley Road, 1965. In 1946 some of us 'had a dream'.

bow – in other words, some sort of a training. So in early January 1945, I was sent down to London with my uncle from Coventry for guidance in the big city – to the National Institute of Industrial Psychology – for what in effect were aptitude tests.

The 'Doodlebugs' had ceased but London, to me – an apprehensive teenager – felt as though it was in the calm before the storm. I remember one 'Gorump' during the interview, which had been one of the last V2 rockets.

Returning home the report suggested three options. I, or rather we, chose the agriculture option as my father had done 33 years before. My father with his Geordie roots probably considered King's College Newcastle as the best place to go, after all we were northern farmers and there were not very many Agriculture courses at Universities then. A good number of excellent diploma courses at Agricultural colleges with very hands-on farming courses aimed at farm management etc. With the benefit of hindsight I should have gone to one of these.

Being a farmer's son, I did not have to do a year's practical experience, although in my vacations – thanks to the hard work and self-denial of my parents – I did go abroad to work on farms and I have always believed that farmers' sons should work for another boss and not progress from home to college or farm institute and then back to the family home farm.

Eventually, after much pressure and lobbying by an uncle recently discharged from the army, my father was persuaded to try for Cambridge. But that meant I had to either have the required number of 'credits' in my School Certificate or take the entrance examination.

So with three months to go in 1946, the head shrugged his shoulders: 'Well if you go in for Agriculture, Cole, you'll have to study on your own.' Thus I was ostracised as it were from the rest of the Sixth Form who were working for the Higher School Certificate, and studied on my own the required subjects – which should have included periods of Botany at the Thomlinson School. The head had in effect washed his hands of me. If you were any use at all you were expected to train for teaching and most of my friends did so.

However, one good thing came out of this switch which benefited me for the new world of study at the University – I had to work on my own. I found I had no knowledge of Botany (as it was called) and this involved a hard slog – from nothing to first year undergraduate standard.

When I went up to Cambridge that October, I was one of only 12 of that 'intake' straight from school. I had entered 'Fitzwilliam House' – looked down on then as the poor boys' college!

In the 1970s, along with Churchhill College and some others, the powers that be decided to expand and make it fully residential. When we return for our annual 'Reunion' old 'buzzards' like me are just gobsmacked at the quality of accommodation and facilities available to 'freshers' today.

From the 'poor boys' of Fitzbilly House on Trampington Street, the new college is now amongst the top Cambridge four or five, and carries an atmosphere of importance and self-confidence. However, one of my friends of that time became a famous Commonwealth Prime Minister, to whom the pre-eminence and prosperity of Singapore is his testimony.

It was October term, 1946. I was in a completely new world amongst 'men' who had served in a war for up to six years. Many undergraduates were parked out in approved 'digs' all over the town within cycling distance of the colleges, lecture halls, University departments and the library. We were happy to 'dine in' hall three nights a week, because food was scarce and rationing applied to most necessities. The colleges did a first-class job in very difficult times to provide wholesome meals at reasonable prices. The situation was such that our college, small as it was, started to make available a satisfying lunch half-way through that term; otherwise, at lunchtime one had to find a lunch in town somewhere, as landladies were not noted for their generosity with a mid-day meal – nor did they want the humbug. Thankfully all over the country for a few years wartime government had developed 'British Restaurants' to provide a simple nourishing meal – in 1946 – for one shilling! Meat, potatoes, a vegetable and often spotted dick sponge and custard or rice etc., and you could have a cup of tea for an extra 3d.!

There was one such restaurant around the back of Christ College, not far from the School of Agriculture – it was always well supported. No doubt wealthier students could afford a café and others could sip coffee at the 'Copper Kettle' in King's Parade – but we managed.

January arrived and with it eastern Britain suffered snow and the tightening grip of prolonged frost. Fuel – coal – was scare; transport of coal to the Gasworks and Power Stations were at full stretch. Students in lecture theatre wore their overcoats, ex-sailors their duffle coats. Gee! It was cold.

In the afternoons my colleague and I would sit and read in our sitting room, wearing our overcoats with our feet resting on a small stool inches away from the single flame of a Victorian-age gas fire, to keep our feet warm.

For sport and exercise, I was determined to sample rowing with practices two or three times a week, or when the river Cam didn't freeze. As the Lent races neared, to toughen us up our three eights would row down the Cam and through the lock into the Fens and on to Ely – 15 miles – returning several days later to row back. Sweets were rationed to three-quarters of a pound per ration book. I used to buy Mars Bars with mine to boost me up in those gruelling trips.

To travel home was an all day effort. A 6.00 a.m. walk to the Station across Cambridge, two miles from my digs. As I crossed bridges on the way to the Station, the Cam was rising fast with melting snow upstream, and soon the Fens were flooded. Term had ended just in time for me. I had taken my case on the bus the previous night, and paid the infant British Railways 3s. 6d. on production of my travel ticket (in those days the 'return' half of a three-month return) to collect, carry and deliver my trunk. From Cambridge it was a two hour cross country journey via remote rural stations like Sandy (Beds!), Gamlingay (long since gone), etc., to Bletchley to catch a Glasgow bound train for a further six hours to Carlisle.

In that memorable year I had phoned my father – could he pick me up in Carlisle? Answer: 'We've just had the worst blizzard and everywhere is snowed up. Put on your thick underwear, heaviest sweater, heavy overcoat and your farm boots. Dump your bag in the station left-luggage and we'll get it sometime. Take the bus as far as it can travel and walk!' The bus stopped at Goose Green, at the foot of Warnell Fell whence a single track disappeared uphill probably made by a farm tractor. Two miles on my way on the road to Keswick, the track turned left down to Caldbeck. My last mile, guided by the telephone poles to our farm, was through snow nine to twelve inches deep and level all over. A white desert. That Easter holiday, as winter lost its grip, we buried a third of our ewe flock – exhausted. That last storm had caused many of the ewes to just give up, lie down and die. Fed up with digging out the farm lane, my father had left our Ford 8 van upon the fell where it became a concentrate cake store for these last two weeks, and a meagre delivery of concentrate cake issued by the Ministry, and strictly rationed, saved them. It was a lesson that I never forgot with pregnant ewes despite all the jibes that 'Thoo's spoilin' them' – we always steamed up our ewes at tupping time, served them hay ad lib, provided beet pulp then cobs right up to the start of lambing. Big lambs? Difficult births? Too many twins etc. etc.? But despite lambing outside and shuttling them in day and night in the 'Pope Mobile' we regularly achieved a percentage of 180–185 on our hill farm.

On my return from college in March 1947 we were faced with the burial of almost half our ewes.

To crown it all, when my mother presented my ration book to Ivinson's Grocery traveller, the points coupons had all been removed by the old faggot – my 'traditional' Cambridge landlady! The next year I said goodbye to 63 Milton Road and was moved to a new family farther out in the suburbs, who treated me generously as one of their own, and remained our friends for many years afterwards.

As the snow receded we had to contend with the collection and burial of dead bodies as well as the problems associated with lambing storm-weakened ewes.

The very large and comfortable farm house at Fagerås Gård in the province of Värmland, central Sweden, 1948. It had 'centralupvarmning' as well as very large log burning stoves, which consumed silver birch 'splits' a metre in length.

TWENTY FOUR

THE FIRST YFC POST-WAR TOUR

Sweden 1946

In spring 1940 the Germans invaded Norway to acquire the fjords as bases for their attacks on Allied convoys during the battle of the Atlantic. They also wished to secure their supplies of iron ore by sea from Narvik (Sweden being in a delicate position as a neutral country).

Philip escaped by walking over the mountains into Sweden where he was interned but allowed to continue working on farms until he could take a blockade running ship in 1944 carrying Swedish ball bearings for our armaments industry. Thus he learned fluent Swedish. Like me afterwards, he'd been impressed with the advanced state of their agriculture and decided to use his contacts in the Swedish Farmers' Co-operative Movement, SLF, and their young farmers' organisation, to arrange a tour of Sweden. I was lucky, with Mary McGilvery, to be selected.

It was August 1946 when we sailed from Tilbury Docks, ten lads and five lasses now, on the Swedish Lloyd MV Saga. On the tour we were treated with a generosity which was almost embarrassing – visiting farms, stock breeders, world famous plant breeding stations, Svalof, and Uddeholm iron works, dairies and numerous slaughter houses. I developed a taste for hot dogs and senap (mustard) and also 'Sild' – pickled herrings. We travelled by train mainly, as well as by bus and lake steamer.

We experienced the very large arable farms across the rolling plains of Skåne (very similar to Denmark), to visiting the remote 'Seters' (clearings in the interminable forests) on the Sweden–Norway borders. To this day I still have friends made during that visit. We stayed on farms, in hotels and in the 'dormitories' of the Folk High Schools whose work interests me to this day and are a model for rural communities.

Twenty-first anniversary re-union of the northern Young Farmers' Tour of Sweden, 1966. Left to right: George Shipley, Driffield YFC; George Lewis, Cartmel YFC; Jane Horton-Faarkes; John Dixon, Driffield YFC; James Parr, Eccleston YFC; Jean Galley, Durham YFC; Elizabeth Lumley, Addingham YFC; Philip Lyth, Northern Counties' organiser; myself (G. H. Cole), Caldbeck YFC.

After about 5 days progressing south into Skåne, we had visited three slaughter houses (which were light years ahead of anything I was to discover in England up to 1958), we arrived at the pretty little town of Hörby. Just after our coach arrived a middle-aged lady pedalled up on her cycle to take me out of the party to visit her home.

She was Signa Westergren, with whom my father had played as a child in Blyth, Northumberland, in 1909. Her father and my grandfather had been sea captains and their family lived in Blyth for three years. My father had sent a note to Signa saying that some English young farmers might turn up at the Hörby Andels Slakterei and to keep a look out for me. My father and Signa had corresponded through all those years of my father's army service in World War One and her rise from 'Kaffe girl' in the Slaughterhouse Office to eventually in the 1970s, Managing Director.

Subsequently we visited her several times on our tours of Sweden – a remarkable lady who spoke perfect English, learned in Northumberland, listened to the 'Archers' every day and then 'Emmerdale' on TV. Living where she did she could watch Danish programmes, East German programmes and Polish programmes. It was on a visit to her that my wife and I first saw colour TV.

Everyone in Hörby knew her because of her magnificent work in the Farmers'

The Larsson family of Fagerås Gård. Left to right: Margit; Karl-Olaf; mother Maria; Lars; Mr Gunnar Larsson (father); Nils-Johan; Klara; Erik-Gustav. All worked on the farm except Lars who was a blacksmith.

Co-op. She'd been honoured by the government with a gold medal the size of a teaplate.

She had 'carried' the company through three crises: deputising for men who became alcoholics (common in Sweden in those years), and improved the business to retire as General Manager – remarkable. The farmers loved her.

During our travels on that first visit to Sweden I became friendly with our guide Mr Yngve Kämpe. So impressed was I, that with his help to find a farming family I set off to Sweden again in June 1948 to work for the Larssons at Fagerås Gård in Värmland, central Sweden.

The fare from Newcastle to Oslo then was £12 return – steerage – on the 3,000-ton vessel 'Bretagne' taking about 20 cabin passengers. There were 12 of us travelling cheap – benches and a communal table for meals, hammocks etc. in the for'ard hold! Taking the train from Oslo central to Fagerås I was met at the village station by Nils-Johan, the only one of the five brothers and two sisters who spoke a very little English. My one Woolworth's suitcase of pre-war vintage was carried on his bicycle to the farm three kilometres away.

Don't know why but the Larssons were a very friendly family and Mama Maria took me under her wing and treated me as one of her own from the start!

It is Spring, 1941 and our neighbour Tommy Watson is ploughing the stubble on the hillside at Paddigill Farm in preparation for a crop of oats. The Caldbeck Valley stretches out below and there are snow drifts still on High Pike and Raughton Ghyll. The ploughing out orders had been issued in Autumn 1939 following the declaration of war.

TWENTY FIVE

OVER THE MARE'S BACKSIDE

BRRRT!

It was fortunate that just before we purchased our orange painted Fordson tractor in 1938 I'd acquired some experience of working with our horses, Lady and Tib, in 1936 and 1937 – I was then 8 or 9 years old. Unable to handle the heavy braffins over a Clydesdale's head or the rather clumsy saddle which took the weight of the cartshafts through a chain over the saddle, I could nevertheless drive, lead and back a horse bogey etc. (see illustrations).

My first morning at Fagerås and Mr Karl-Olav yoked up 'Maira' to a 4-wheel haywagon standing beside the slipway in the big barn, slapped her over the backside, made a sound like a wine cork popping and she set off at a cracking pace round the corner and off up the farm track to the hay field. We were carting home the cured hay off the racks (the 'hayhorses' as they were called), so you had to draw up the wagon alongside the rack. First pass – okay and 'whoa!' – the horse just went on so we did another 'circuit' and came up alongside again; 'whoa!', but Maira carried on so we turned around again with Papa Larsson convulsed with laughter. Alongside the hayrack he made a high pitched Br-r-r-t – the horse stopped dead with me splattered over her backside. Never mind, before the day was over I had control and yoking up was dead simple and easy to do. The farm had a Munktell tractor similar to our Fordson which ran on TVO for ploughing and cultivation with the heavy harrows. It had just been converted back to TVO after the war when it ran on producer gas from a charcoal burner fixed to the side of the tractor – a large clumsy piece of tackle like a 50 gallon oil drum! I never drove it but worked more with the horses on the arable jobs.

My most enduring memory was one day I was rolling a field which had been cropped in June, ploughed and then sown with

The harness used in Scandinavia was simple and easy to yoke up to a wagon, implement, roller, harrows or mower. This is a strong, sturdy, sure-footed 'Fjord' horse.

the grass mixture common at that time of Italian Ryegrass and Broad Red clover – a 2 year mixture primarily for hay (cured on racks) as feed for the 20 or so dairy cows.

Hard frosts in winter in Värmland meant that 'seeds' mixtures would not last and became infested with dandelions.

It was during a pleasant job on a sunny August afternoon – the horses pulling away steadily and quietly with me riding on the roller – when to my great delight a large female Elk came ambling out of the forest up to the horses, sniffed, snorted, and must have been assured its 'cousins' were busy so it returned to the wood

Erik pumping paraffin into the Oliver tractor.

unaware that a human was about. It was better than seeing them in a zoo, but a few years after that time when the elk population was low – clear felling of relatively large areas of forest became the favoured method – the population exploded to such an extent that these days there are road signs in Scandinavia advising motorists of elk crossings. Herds tend to stick to chosen tracks and often move in groups. They are large beasts and modern cars crumple if you carelessly hit one (an offence!)

I had arrived with my pre-war Woolworth case enclosing a basic change of clothes, boiler suit and

Part of the large farm building at Fagerås. Tractors with loaded wagons could ply the loft above the livestock boxes and cow byre.

wellies, two work shirts and a better one. On fine dry days I wore tre-skor – wooden clogs.

Three – nay almost four – weeks passed and no sign of a wash day. Margit baked 'Knackerbrod' (Ryvita or knäckebröd, to give it its correct term) once a fortnight in the cabin or old house. The coffee kettle was emptied once a week and topped up with a large spoonful of ground coffee each morning. So by the end of the week the coffee you drank – thank goodness in small cups well laced with lump sugar – tasted like engine oil. (Coffee was a much prized gift in Europe in those days.)

Then one damp morning I was told 'hamta hast' – go and catch Maira, yoke her up and take her to the back door with the hay wagon. Whereupon Margit and Klara piled on heaps and heaps of bedsheets and clothes – wash tubs, scrubbing boards, the lot. We set off down a track into the forest where we came to a small wooden cabin beside a stream with a fire hearth and a set pot … the girls washed clothes for about three days! This was common in rural forested Sweden right up to 1952 and most villages and hamlets had a communal washer hut by a stream (and by the way to this day Caldbeck still has such a C19 hut as you turn down Friar Row towards the church).

There were about 25 Swedish red and white dairy cows on the farm (animals like our dual purpose shorthorns). If we were on milking we started at 5.30 a.m. and came in for breakfast at 8.00 a.m. We then had half an hour off. There was a magnificent pear tree in the garden and I used to stuff my pockets with them to munch while I attended to the units – to much speculation as to their effect on my digestion!

They'd had the telephone on that farm since 1912 – we had ours at home as a priority phone because of the ROC in 1940. Dairy cows, calves, and all the young stock were housed in the ground level of the huge barn – the dung went out by a scraper

Nils-Johan Larsson puts a block of ice from the sawdust heap in with the evening's milk for overnight cooling.

system over a heap below the building (but on the smaller farms dung was shovelled through trap doors in the floor to a 'midden' below).

The milk was cooled but then the drums were stood in a very large vat of cold water over night and after each milking we went to the large sawdust heap and dug out a block of ice weighing about 25 kilos and put it in the tub. It had been sawn out from the lake or river in winter and stored in sawdust for use as a cooler in summer. In those days Sweden was at the dawn of an electricity powered industrial revolution. We didn't have a 'fridge' even though it was a large farm with a large family, but the water supply was pumped automatically from a deep well 200 metres away down the field to a 200 gallon tank in the loft.

From time to time we had parties when neighbours came across for the Sunday evening for coffee and cakes and a sing song. Erik Gustav (18 years old) had very bad asthma but was a beautiful pianist. At these parties we often had real ice cream – it was out of this world to a youngster from a country recovering from the war.

Such ice cream as there was in Britain in 1946–1963 was very 'ersatz' and I believe had a high content of cornflour in it, to such an extent that in the 1960s the new Professor of Agriculture at King's College, Newcastle, upset Mr Wall, and many others in the dairy industry, on a TV interview describing the British offering as, 'this muck that parades under the name of ice cream'. A not unusual remark from an outspoken New Zealander on a mission to shake the Ministry of Agriculture tree quite a lot.

But to our Sunday evening parties – on my birthday for example – a note would be given to the driver of the milk lorry to bring back a kilo or more of ice cream from the Mjeri on his return run.

Another activity we indulged in on Sundays was to catch and eat fresh lake crabs.

Over another weekend Nils-Johan, with the hay all in the barn, his friend and I would do a tour of Värmland on bicycles, cycling up the west side of the Fryken lakes and back down the other side – about 178 miles in all. We endured quite a lot of rain which didn't matter – the principal concern was not to get a puncture as the roads in those days were all gravel, sealed in summer by being sprayed with diluted wood tar to bind the surface and keep down dust. Accommodation? We stayed in the Youth Hostel in Torsby but otherwise we slept in outlying hay barns – with permission of course. Complementing my experience from the YFC tour a couple of years earlier, I began to realise the vastness of the forest in central and northern Sweden – I have liked trees, timber and woodlands ever since and have been convinced that much of our poorer land should primarily be growing timber as an increasingly valuable crop in the foreseeable future in the northern part of a country with an excellent climate for growth but a miserable 12% of our land area under trees. From experience here, trees and sheep are compatible on upland farms to the benefit of both.

In all my stay at Fagerås and subsequent visits I only once remember Mr Larsson attending a farm stock sale – never an auction. Each morning he listened to the farming news on radio – broadcasts were 7.00–9.30 a.m., then 12.00–13.00 p.m., and in the evening 6.00–9.00 p.m. – for the prices quoted per kilo for veal, pork etc., as well as reading 'Lantmannen', the farm weekly of the SL (Svenges Lantbruksforbund). If the price was right and/or the stock was the required weights, he lifted the phone to the Slakteri to collect 'x' number of calves or pigs – the lorry came, loaded and off on their last journey. To this day farmers in Denmark and Sweden (and Hungary) can boast that no animal spends more than two hours in transit. No trucking unfortunate but valuable livestock around the country for hours on end.

Swedish-style Ryvita, or knäckebröd, with a central hole for rack storage as sold by a shop in Twickenham, London.

The beautiful Gudbrandsdalen Valley in 1952 and the river Lagen. Over the years the village commune of Hunder and Øyer have developed and hosted the Winter Olympics. Apart from a hydro dam just out of the picture the valley is quite unspoilt.

Twenty Six

'Tivoli Jaunt'

My ten weeks at Fagerås came to an end so I went to visit a Young Farmers' contact at Kungsbacka in Halland province on the west coast where Norvin was the Farmers' Bank manager in the town, aged 26. Staying with his family on their 22-acre farm for a week, I would accompany his father, Mr Ottosson, up into a forest clearing where his three dairy cows in milk were tethered and grazing. Walking up the track one evening, Mr Ottosson kicked over something about a foot long and said, 'Se hit en huggorm – i morgen jag trampa under fötterna!' He had come across an adder on the track and stamped on it. Yelp! I'd been plunging about in the forest oblivious of the danger, for in that part there were boulders everywhere on which the reptiles were in the habit of sunbathing.

Along with Norvin's two friends, we sallied forth on a Friday for a 120-mile drive to Copenhagan and a couple of nights on the town – notably the world famous 'Tivoli Gardens'. Our trip in a 1938 Vauxhall was not without incidents – a puncture, a broken fan belt, and an overheating radiator – all of which Erik (a milk lorry driver) coped with as a matter of course. In those days it was a ferry crossing from Copenhagen to Malmo. Now, the train whizzes across in 20 minutes with wonderful views over the sound and the wind turbines.

I had decided, while I was over there, to sample Norway as well for a month or so, until the leaves turned and autumn had begun. From my Geography studies at school I knew about the fjords but that eastern Norway was mainly farming and forestry. To this day I still regard fjordland as all tourists and foreign waiters!

To Norway and the Gudbrandsdal

My onward journey from Kungsbacka was accompanied by Norvin to Göteborg where we met his friend, the head of the Customs Office at the harbour, and enjoyed a motorlaunch tour on the 'Paddan' around the harbour with him. He persuaded me to take a 'sleeper' from Göteborg to Oslo, as it was an all night journey in 1948. So my 'Woolworth' bag was sent off that afternoon 'luggage-in-advance' to Lillehammer. Change trains at Oslo central – the only station at that time – and a 9.00 a.m. departure on the Trondheim train. All steam, this enchanting journey took all of seven hours, following the shores of Lake Mjösa, Norway's largest lake. I was impressed by the beautiful large farms reaching down to the lake shore.

Onwards into the impressive Gudbrandsdal where, with several 'guests' we were met at Hunder station, now very popular with the winter sports enthusiasts; from Oslo it is but one hour away by fast electric Inter Regio express today.

The Nermos had a very large Ford V8 station wagon specially imported under the Marshall plan to help revive the tourist industry. I should remind you that this was 1948 – three years after the end of the war – and Norway and her economy had been ruined.

For example, the world's largest income-generating merchant fleet had been destroyed or sunk. The northern-most province, Finnmark, had been destroyed – the population driven out, thanks to the scorched earth tactics of the retreating Germans in front of the advancing Red Army. Recovery was gradual, as we noted from our visits in 1952–1954, 1966 and 1969. It gives me huge satisfaction to have witnessed a country well-nigh destitute in 1948 become perhaps the seventh richest economy in the world with a quality of life and an environment which is the envy of the Western world. A country which has spent its oil revenues so wisely and whose politicians accept that country dwellers in the remotest parts of that 2,000-mile long country are entitled to the same facilities and living standards as the urban dwellers.

Nermo was a huge tall 'Viking' man who spoke no English, but with a brain as sharp as a needle, and like the rest of the family, a paragon of kindness. For a start his driving used to terrify me as he laid back at the wheel of this monster and we rolled around hairpin bends up and down as we climbed into the mountain on narrow roads. When my wife first went there thirty years later, her ears popped!

Johannes was every inch the farmer and a very shrewd businessman too, whose family had a water powered corn mill and a family hotel – popular with Norwegians who came from the cities to 'get away from it all' and wander off over the mountains. Just then, in 1948, they had an international clientele, a Brussels banker and a lovely old man, Mr Svenson, who was a shipping owner. With considerable risk but shrewd foresight, Johannes anticipated the changing pattern of Norwegian visitors who, before the war, came to a hotel served by a station, ferry landing etc., to stay for a couple of weeks and go walking in the mountains. Eight years after my first visit the family built a smaller 'mountain' hotel three kilometres further up in the mountain on the treeline to cater for these walkers. Later on he was a leading member of the local committee which secured some of the venues in Hunder parish for the 1994 Winter Olympics – the ladies downhill ski run and the 'luge' track. Gudrun, his wife, was a real asset to the business – an excellent hostess who spoke English, French and German, hence the international contingent of guests. End of season and I was given a large room at the

The barn at Nermo in 1948. The cow byre is at the far end; the light over the door had no switch so stayed on day and night! Today the barn loft is a conference and function centre. On the left ground floor is a ski preparation workshop. The cow byres are now comfortable holiday rooms.

back of the hotel on the third floor, and was expected to dine with the guests for the evening meal.

The farm had a large Norwegian barn with the cattle at ground level and the barn proper was very long, and had a small thresher in it, as well as the usual hay winch. Grain crop (barley) could be stored on part of the same floor as the hay, which was forked down to the cattle through trapdoors. It is now holiday apartments and a fully equipped workshop for the various ski and 'luge' teams who come each year to train at the track across the other side of the valley.

The main job that week was to harvest the potato crop, about two hectares. We also threshed some barley, all powered by electric motors. The field is now a golf driving range alongside the lower fields, which are one of Gudbrandsdal's most popular golf courses. Remember at that time, 1946–48, we in Britain were being sold clean 'Atomic Power' – the answer to all our prayers, from Calder Hall, which would be so plentiful

John Nermo on a Ferguson T 20 carting barley to the farm barn on a bale carrier in 1952. The low profile of these tractors enabled the crop to be taken up the ramp and right into the loft; they were also remarkable on steep hillsides. The 'Stabbur' is to the left. Today these fields are now one of Gudbrandsdalen's best golf courses.

Johannes Nermo, a very tall man at 6 foot 6, and his elkhound hunting dog, Rack.

and cheap you'd leave the lights on all day! I used to toddle along to the bathroom before bed and go to the veranda to look out over that beautiful valley (I still do) for the view and the twinkling lights. However, one Friday night I happened to get up at 2.00 a.m., visited the loo and made my customary glance over the view.

To my surprise the lights were still on, so I thought these folks must indulge in late parties! The next night I followed the same routine – and the lights were still on! Also, there was a light over the door to the cow byre, which was on next day, so I looked for

The workmen's house or Stabbur and the family home beyond.

the switch – there wasn't one! We have a joke on each visit because I say to Ann-Gunn 'that bloomin' light over the back of the Nermo house has been on these past 63 years!' It surely needs a new bulb!

Later, in my first week, Johannes disappeared for three days with his pals to reappear at a celebratory party on the Saturday evening, when I was asked to come out onto the entrance to the hotel – to find 18 very large dead Elk awaiting collection next day. That

Looking down on the River Lågen over a very typical farm in 1954.

The Saturday milk lorry with its dual cab was always crowded with the young folks returning to the huts in the mountains – bicycles, clean washing and an afternoon at home in the valley.

year, the 'hunters' in the parish were licensed to cull 18 – they all went to be served up in 'posh' restaurants and hotels in Oslo and on the west coast. For the Elk season the hunters take themselves off into the fjell and sleep rough in seter huts or barns. Many are converted to 'holly cots' these days – as in the English Lakeland. Very odd isn't it, that our 'bank farms' in Lakeland with Scandinavian origins have adapted to the same change of use.

Two days into my stay at Nermo and my 'luggage in advance' case had not arrived. I had only my boiler suit and clothes I travelled in, plus my pyjamas. My predicament was becoming desperate when Gudrun phoned the station to enquire of its whereabouts. Norwegian customs had sent a message – would the owner please send the case *key* to Oslo so that they could open and examine its contents! Remarkably some guard or conductor took the key to Oslo central; Customs examined and released the case, and back it came. No 'tracking' of parcels etc. then!

Autumn was coming very fast, and each day the golden glow of the Silver Birch trees on the mountains crept further and further down the hillsides and into the valley forests. The seter farm cabins were being shut up for the winter, and the dairy and cheese making utensils brought back down to the valley steadings. The cows had already come down into the barn but the horses and sheep remained up there. So one day in early October, Hans the driver/general maintenance man, collected up a group of four or five neighbours to drive us high up into the mountain, and as far as the 'track' went in 1948, and dropped us off with our sandwiches and halters – or rather, bridles. We then set off to walk through the scrub bushes (Rowan and Alder), and broken Silver Birch trees for several miles, to a rendezvous or, I suppose, a 'corral' in the wastes, where a herdsman awaited us along with about eight horses, loosely penned. I had been used to walking three or four miles around

Fauld's Brow Common, driving Swaledales, but this was an 'expedition'. We ate our lunch – black bread, black puddings and coffee – the men 'cracked' with the herdsman who had lived on his own for weeks on end and we then set off for home. The horses were going home from their seter summer. I guess we walked about ten miles and just made it back by dusk without getting wet. I slept soundly that night! We had no sheep at Nermo so we were spared that trek, but as the days passed the tinkle of bells became more common as more and more were brought down.

Sunday mornings were more or less 'free' but I was collared by Mr Svenson – a sprightly 75-year-old regular guest at Nermo – to go for a 'walk' (2 or 3 miles) with him, up into the forest. I had a basket and he had his walking stick to point out what were to me toadstools and colourful fungi. 'That's a good one, get it – climb up among the rocks or fallen tree trunks to collect those specimens.'

Returning to the hotel we presented the basket at the kitchen to the delight of Gudrun. I would not have known one fungus from another and to me everything but our own humble mushroom was poisonous, but old Svenson knew what he was up to and luckily I was not down late for the meal that evening to witness a crowd of delighted guests queuing up for 'svamp' – a rare delicacy indeed. Imagine, today these 'toadstools' are protected, as are the 'Cloudberries' which only locals are allowed to pick in season.

In my childhood, I'd had a father who would not allow me to pick and choose where food was concerned, and this meant I'd try anything from farm made 'surmjelk' (sour milk) to raw herrings or 'sild'. To this day I adore them as well as home-made knäckebröd – or Ryvita, as presented in our stores.

Even today, Scandinavian countries impose a heavy tax on alcohol and drink sold through a 'Vinmonopoli' costs you! At that time alcoholism was a problem. In the 1970s the Bergen Line ships on the Oslo or Bergen Newcastle run were bursting with 'Vikings' coming for the weekend to Newcastle to shop at Fenwicks, Marks & Sparks, and the other big stores. Clothes and all manner of goods were much cheaper here, but booze was a great attraction, so the Sunday night return ferries witnessed good natured but 'loaded' shoppers until the ships docked in Stavanger or Bergen.

In my impecunious ignorance it is doubtful I had ever tasted anything more destructive than a glass of cider. But one night, reading in my room about 9.00 p.m., the office girl came rushing in with an urgent message: 'Will the English boy go and help Hans start up the central heating boiler'. We messed about with it for half an hour in the cellar and got it going. Next day I was surprised that I seemed to be the only one at work around the farm buildings. For some reason about lunchtime I had to go to the Stuga to find Hans – he was having his mid-day break. Opening the doors to the various rooms it was plain to see why there were no staff about! They were all on the bottle, drunk, blotto, or 'foo' as they say, on branvin, or schnapps to you – neat!

My departure date was closing fast – it was mid-October and the snowline was but a few hundred feet above the farm, and moving downwards. I can never forget the kindness I enjoyed during my first 'solo' visit to Norway. To catch the ship from Oslo meant I had to board the overnight train from Trondheim in Lillehammer station at 2.00–3.00 a.m. A very kind guest at the hotel arranged for me to go and stay with her and her husband, so I could walk to the station and I could sleep in their spare room until 1.30 a.m., make myself a coffee and walk along Storgatan to the station. In 1948 Lillehammer was really one long main street. Over the years it has grown steadily without losing its atmosphere of a provincial town, even allowing for the impact of the Winter Olympics in 1994.

My voyage home promised to be comfortable as we nosed our way down Oslo fjord. However, turning westwards into the Skagerak and the open North Sea by 7.00 p.m., things started to turn nasty and I didn't fancy below decks steerage class in the hold! I put on my warmest clothes and found a reclining deck-chair in the protected area behind the bridge, and stretched myself under a couple of rugs (usually handed out to those who like to sit out in the fresh air of a North Sea crossing). I did go to sleep – or rather dozed – as the storm raged, with the rain and squalls driving over the deck. I was sheltered by the bridge as we were sailing south-west, head on into the teeth of the gale.

Not exactly a comfortable crossing but I stuck it out and wasn't sick. Only next day, on my homeward railway journey to Carlisle, did I feel tired from 24 hours of sea air, but apart from a drunken gait as I walked along to Carlisle bus station, I was none the worse.

Subsequent Visits

Four years were to pass at college and in the army before I treated myself to a long leave on demobilisation in 1952, with a holiday back in Norway, before I returned to the job I'd had in industry.

On this visit I set out for Sweden in our 5 cwt Ford van (new in 1946 it was basically a model 'T'). I could kip down in it if necessary and it provided mobility to visit friends across Scandinavia. With a friend from my earlier visit to Värmland in 1948, we set off to visit North Central Sweden and cross into Norway, making our way down the western fjords and over to the farm at Hunder – that was the plan. But it was early May and in the springtime as the frost comes out of the ground, the road surfaces can break up leaving dangerous – often deep – ruts (tjälskada) for which our Ford with its single transverse springs, was unsuitable. Until the 1970s on many of the main roads across Scandinavia, you would encounter large mechanical graders working along the highways, scraping and smoothing the gravel from the roadsides back onto the roads. The corners were rough with corrugations – nasty if taken fast.

We had progressed steadily northwards from Värmland up into Jamtland (almost to the Arctic Circle) and as the daylight lasted until 10.00 or 11.00 p.m. we were pressing on towards the frontier crossing. In 1952 the road divided where you changed sides – Norway drove on the right, Sweden on the left. We were aiming to get to Hell – every English tourist likes to send a postcard from Hell! We hit a series of ruts about 18" deep – that did it! We had cracked the rear spring and broken the spring mounting arm on the front. As sheer luck had it, I found a bent piece of pine 4" diameter and 2 ft long, which exactly fitted between the rear spring of the chassis and the van body. A bit of heaving up the body and the wood kept the body off the tyre. The front was a more serious problem, so it was like driving on solid wheels from Hell to Trondheim, 50 miles away, so we just limped along to the Ford dealers, which we reached about 6.00 a.m. – dead beat. A tough welding job for the garage, who said it would take all day and they fixed us up with a B & B where we slept most of the day, we were so tired.

The repair cost us 150 Kr – took a chunk out of our spare cash. You could only take £50 with you in those days, so we had to severely curtail our tour. The garage said if the welds lasted 150 miles it would go 50,000 and they had made a first-class job. The welds lasted until the van was sold many years later, with the repairs still in place.

Over the years and after many tours in Scandinavia, the roads have improved beyond recognition. On a trip to the North Cape in 1986 my calculations of distance, time and speed allowed for routes where 25 mph would be safe. In 2,500 miles to the Nordkap, we encountered only six miles of rough road involving a speed reduction.

Motoring down the Norwegian coast from Narvik to Lillehammer we commented to Ann on the magnificent bridges connecting the outer islands to the mainland and the E6. 'Yes,' she commented, 'the tourists and incomers drive in and the locals drive out.' Echoes of the Lake District National Park!

Reflections/Observations

Our visits to the far north of Scandinavia impressed us greatly, with the excellent quality of farming north of the Arctic Circle. Small farms, herds of 15–20 cows, but a countryside well farmed, well mechanised, and well maintained. If you – or indeed planners – want to see a thriving productive socially cohesive countryside, go to Norway, where they seem to have got it right.

Yes, seter farms have been made into summer holiday homes; forest cabins rented out to urban dwellers, and all with electricity, telephones, and modern comforts.

You realise that a careful country has spent its oil income on infrastructure, resource sustainability, quality of living and investment for the nation's future.

October 2008, we planned to return to 'Nermo' the farm which I had discovered in 1948, to celebrate a 60 year friendship, and so many visits over those years we have lost count. Alas, a month before our planned departure, the ferry service from Newcastle to Bergen was withdrawn. Apart from inconvenience and loss to the Norwegian tourist industry, there is a great cultural loss – particularly with the north of England. We have so much to learn from the Scandinavians – in education, quality of life, and environment. Above all, for the British in a changing world, to learn to mind our own business. To help developing countries with aid and expertise, instead of wasting our national wealth trying to act as an overstretched world policeman, foisting off our so-called 'values' across the world.

Officer cadets out on a map-reading exercise in 1951, with G. H. Cole in the centre.

TWENTY SEVEN

ARMY AND INDUSTRIAL EXPERIENCE

A day in May 1952 ended my army service and a return to my old job later in the year after an extended 'holiday' back in Scandinavia working on farms, which I had come to look upon as my second homes.

During my service I had not been posted abroad due to an early knee injury during my first six weeks of training, when I pulled (damaged) a cartilage in my knee. I was faced with an operation and possibly a stiff leg for the rest of my life or a prolonged 'convalescence' over 6–8 months. Treatment: I was expected to go on the cross-country running team three times a week – it was agony to start with but gradually my knee mended so it was W. O. S. B. (War Office Selection Board) and off to OCTU at Aldershot for two months (drilled by RSM Britten whose commands with 1000 men on parade could be heard from one side of the town to the other!)

During my rehabilitation period I'd been 'trained' as an AVM (Armoured Vehicle Mechanic) – yes, I can drive a tank! – and climbed to the high rank of Lance Corporal. I had been stuck in such 'dumps' as Ashford and Solihull, postings from which we northern lads could never get home on a 48 hour pass. I had also learned how to 'bull' my boots, blanco my webbing and paint grass green! (beside the path outside the hut!)

Cadet training school was a complete change; it was very tough – I kid you not – but it had a funny side. We were greatly amused when a careless move on parade would be admonished – 'Mr Cole you are a clumsy bastard' – to which one rejoined if the instructor was in a good mood; and all of them were human ... 'Pardon Sarge, but I do have a birth certificate.'

On commissioning I went to Sedgefield as a platoon officer and was seconded to Newcastle in charge of the command supply depot for Northumberland and Durham, then to York in charge of a logistics exercise moving a Supply Depot from Catterick to a camp on which Drax Power Station now stands. When I became an officer I weighed ten-and-a-half stones. In eight months I rose to eleven-and-a-half – good food, good exercise and a healthy life. I reverted to ten-and-a-half stones after the army and I'm fortunate to still have a trim figure after 60 years.

Although it is sometimes said that conscription taught a few young people bad ways, no doubt these few would have gone bad anyway. In the '50s the West was obsessed with the Russian 'threat' (which never was as the history of the period 1950–2000 reveals). I am convinced of the tremendous value of conscription to the younger generation. As I noted in the countries behind the Iron Curtain during our travels with our motor caravan in 1970–90, their armies were no real threat, for we found them not brandishing guns and weaponry but engaged in groups doing good and useful public works – living in camps as a community, learning to get on with each other – but subject to discipline.

Abolition of military, alias 'community' service, has been a great loss to the nation in my opinion. The Germans still have military or community 'service' and it shows. I am not in favour of armies or military solutions to international problems.

We and the Americans have squandered our wealth, expertise and production, on trying to police a world which came to an end in 1945.

So in mid-August 1952, after the summer shut down, I was back in the Training School at Ford of Dagenham. An eight week course on Ford products and servicing preparatory to going into the factory where staff trainees were given time from two weeks to a month in every department. This included work on the Blast Furnace, the pig-cast and the 'knock out'. Newly cast engine blocks came along the line still almost red hot belching acrid smoke and fumes, where they were given a shake or a knock with a hammer to free all the moulding sand which dropped under the floor to be reclaimed. It was a 'hell-hole', hot and stinking of sulphur dioxide. Rather than just watching, the line foremen liked it and gave you more of their time if you would have a go. I became quite adept at balancing the fan belt pulleys for Vee-8 engines.

November came along and the dreary routine of travelling from Romford to Dagenham in a stuffy bus was unpleasant. Fine days – believe it or not I cycled – for exercise; I took the bus when it was wet or foggy.

The editor of the agricultural journal of the company was up for promotion; the company training officer sent me along to 'Walnut Tree Walk' to be scrutinised by the late Colonel Maurice Buckmaster, head of Public Relations. A great chap who trusted all his staff and shielded his department from the criticism of other hard-nut managers who had come up from the line and remembered Ford pre-1939. As an old friend discussing MJB said, 'he was in a different class to the other divisional managers – he knew which knife to eat the fish with'.

That December there was the Smithfield show in the Great Smog. We had a very special exhibit to transport to the stand at Earl's Court – a full scale 'see-through' plastic tractor; all the pistons, gears etc., worked. Imagine transporting that from a factory in North London through the 'smog' with visibility down to about 4 metres. That year the fog and the sulphurous sooty stench killed off several of the animals. They just couldn't stand it

In the 1950s the Smithfield Agricultural Show was held at Earl's Court – originally a shop window for the (livestock) meat producers. The World Wars and the mechanisation of agriculture caused those industries which supplied farmers to use the winter show as a shop window for their wares. After all, farmers had a little time on their hands at the end of a tiresome year, and a little money in their pockets following sales of grain or livestock for the Christmas trade.

Earl's Court was a far cry from the Smithfield meat market. When empty of exhibitions, shows etc., it was an inhospitable place. The allocated company 'stands' would be delineated in chalk across the hall.

I have mentioned that the post-war divisional managers at Fords were time served men who had worked their way up through the rough and tumble of a very competitive motor industry pre-1939.

Sir Patrick Hennessey – the MD when I joined the company – began his working life in the foundry of Henry Ford's factory at Cork in Eire before Dagenham was built. Few people realise that in his drive for survival and eventually to dominate the motor industry, Henry Ford the first was a ruthless operator. The model 'T' almost crucified that generation of car makers in the US because of its low, affordable price and mass appeal to aspiring motorists. The competition tried every means they could to 'screw' Ford – ganging up with railway companies to refuse or deny the transport of iron ore to Ford's factories or refusing to supply tyres, for example. So, Ford bought the railway; and tyres – he bought the Firestone Tyre Company, and young Henry Ford the second married the daughter, a Miss Firestone. So for years most of our new cars were initially supplied with Firestone tyres. In the meantime he acquired the Kelsey-Hayes wheel company, and Briggs Motor Bodies at Dagenham. It always used to make us laugh in those days – little did they know it but the 'toffs' who rode around in Bentleys and RRs actually travelled on Ford wheels! The manufacturer of the world's cheapest cars for the masses supplied the world's most expensive cars!

During the war Beaverbrook (the Minister for Aircraft Production) had a factory built at Trafford Park, Manchester, and commissioned Ford to build Rolls-Royce 'Merlin' engines for the Spitfire and the Lancaster bombers.

The manager there (a Mr H. A. Denne) was a real 'driver' if ever there was one. With the end of the war, Trafford Park closed down and he moved to Dagenham as Export Manager. Just remember the nation's financial crises in the 1950s and such a man was vital to the company's export drive. To return to Earl's Court … the export manager was quite a card – not only was there a production battle on but Ford and Ferguson were at each other's throats for the fast-growing home, as well as export, tractor markets.

There was about a week to get all the exhibits in place – to turn a barren hall into an attractive arena.

The first unfortunate soul to arrive at Earl's Court that Monday morning around 8.00 a.m. was greeted by a despondent H. A. D. seated head in hands on an upturned bucket, the only seating he could find, in the middle of our stand the size of a tennis court, with what was to become a legendary outburst: 'Not a piss-pot washed, not a whore in bed, and a troopship moored in the middle of the river – get moving!'

So much for life behind the scenes in the Tractor and Export Divisions. I was always amused because having to go out on farms to demonstrations and agricultural shows, I usually turned up in 'country dress' – sports jacket and flannels etc. But the staff in the offices were sitting at their desks in rows, always with dark suits and white shirts.

A firm called 'Collars of Wembly' would post you a box of white starched collars twice a week so they always looked clean in those pre-great London Smog days. The office girls used to complain they could only wear an underskirt for two days before it looked grubby. I'd just been in the army and to see office workers so regimented in lines of desks struck me as hilarious. In the army they would have been grousing all day long.

For the following three years I was responsible for the Company's agricultural sales magazine with a circulation of 30,000, eventually running to 50,000 copies. The work was interesting and full of variety – I was lucky going all over the country to attend Agricultural shows, write stories on farms unconstrained, and not desk-bound to the regimented offices at Dagenham. From time to time I would be sent out with staff photographers on photo-shoots for the Company's advertisements. There were amusing tussles with the rising stars in Tractor Division who were pushing the New Fordson Major diesel (the first 'cheap' mass produced diesel engined tractor by comparison with the traditional engine makers, e.g. Perkins of Peterborough). Henry Ford and Harry Ferguson had fallen out over patents on the Ferguson System. Harry S. had gone to bed with Sir John Black of Standard Motors, Coventry. An expensive lawsuit ensued and was settled eventually because both Companies were indulging their lawyers' lifestyles in suites at the Waldorf Hotel in New York!

On a visit to Dagenham Henry Ford II told the Tractor Division with the 'new' Major, the only cloud in the sky was a grey one with Ferguson written on it! Go for it.

One day I had to go out with the cameraman to check the correctness of the agricultural details for the pictures. It had been damp weather and the farmstead was rather muddy where the tractor was loading muck onto a spreader. Good pictures were taken and a bit of mud on the tyres of the tractor seemed quite unimportant to a farmer's son. But I got into trouble – there was mud on the cleats of the tyres and readers would imply that the 'Majors' might get stuck in the mud! The retouchers were brought in at the photo-blockmakers and told to remove/paint out/get rid of the muck! To my mind the result looked very clinical and it inclined me to think that farmers would automatically conclude, 'that's a retouch job'.

Through my journalist public relations work, I travelled far and wide across the country and soon after my appointment I was sent to the Paris Agricultural Exhibition. Other staff went over by plane – business travel in 1953 was quite a novelty. It was quick of course, but I chose to forego an evening at home and travelled on the 'Night Ferry' via Newhaven and Dieppe – a train discontinued long ago. My return trip on the Saturday (in my own time of course) was a first-class seat on the 'Golden Arrow' Pullman. Very posh! The ultimate in luxury: lunch on the train; afternoon tea between Dover and Victoria!

In May 1955 I organised a farm tour of southern Sweden for 15 farmers and dealers with their wives. The party was made up mainly from large arable farms from south-eastern England and Berwickshire, except for two gentlemen who were friends and had town milk rounds. Their first night in Lund and we all went out for a stroll round the centre, but returned to find two very 'glum' dairymen commiserating over the price of alcohol – they hadn't realised that drink in Sweden was taxed at deterrent levels by the Vinmonopoli. Thereafter they stuck to lager, lemonade or 'Pomac'.

My work in Industry and the army had enabled me to see many parts of the country and different types of farming at first hand. I had made many friends and I should have taken my friend Donald's advice and gone out to New Zealand for a year – but it was a 4-week voyage in 1952. Trouble was, being an only child, had I gone out I would have stayed for a lifetime. No one then could envisage Auckland to London in 24 hours and our Golden Wedding expedition with son, New Zealand daughter-in-law and two grandchildren made us realise what we had missed. As with France, I resisted visiting the country until retirement because I knew we would fall in love with it.

Unloading 'seconds' or poorer grain from a threshing day we put through a contractor's 'hammer mill' for pig feed.

Twenty Eight

'Survival in a Hardening Economic Climate'

My life and work in the Public Relations Department at Ford Motor Company was varied by the nature of the job but hectic, especially when deadline dates to print came up for the magazine. I was lucky – very lucky in those days of the 1950s – not to be desk and factory bound. I used my time well for my work and travelled about the country as much as possible. It may seem glamorous moving about staying in hotels, but you are living out of a suitcase as it were. My supervisors never queried my expenses, as they took the view that if you'd been out and about all day you were entitled to a comfortable bed, room and decent meals, as opposed to one company I worked for later in life who were penny pinching to their staff. I guess because we were well treated and given a bit of licence was the reason why I would go into the office on a Saturday morning to work on the magazine, because I'd been 'out' all over the place for the magazine the previous week. Unrewarded overtime was not frowned upon until long after I'd left the company.

However, like my father years before, neither of us have ever been enamoured with towns and cities – preferring a quality of life and satisfying experiences to the glamour of a large salary, the hectic rush and bustle, and eventually the chance of a duodenal ulcer!

To me – a northerner of very temperate habits – London life was, as it is today, all very artificial. A different world apart from the north where working men would go to the pub, drink their ale at a shilling a pint, play dominoes or darts and go quietly (usually) home. London was all 'shorts' and gin & tonic – a night 'up' town may be once a month to see a theatre show – a quick supper at John Lyons and don't miss the last tube or bus!

So in 1955 I'd had about enough and yearned to go back to farming. I married that August and began farming on my own account at High Snape near Harrogate.

I suppose I was innocently bold to go from 'office' work to the 'graft' of a run-down ranch of 160 acres. Most of my contemporaries had progressed from school, then back home to work for Dad – possibly doing a short course at Newton Rigg (Agricultural College). Then they followed father, easing into the business as he gradually withdrew, but was at hand to help, advise, take stock to auction in a busy season when everything is happening; to stand in at times of illness or sickness, or when you take a day out at the local show. Many farmers' sons are 'let in' gently to a business which is running. Most of my friends going from school back home to work avoided National Service and the three years I spent at University. In effect they were well established in farming before I had even begun.

Yes, there can be other problems in families, for example 'paying out' the sisters – who often used to get a raw deal in the days when the eldest son was assumed to take over the farm. We are sure today that my Grandma's death-bed wish was that 'my mother would look after the boys' and to my father's detriment and inconvenience, the family pride severely restricted his farming operations for 40 years. Not to worry, but right from the start I was paddling my own canoe – I had to suffer for my mistakes – with no one else to blame.

Six miles from Leeds and three from Harrogate, the land was heavy clay just up on the downslope of the Pennines to the Vale of York. I had a mortgage on two thirds of the purchase price – £700 in savings of my own – enough to live and pay the first half-year's rent (i.e. mortgage).

The farm was badly fenced with dilapidated 'gee-gee' fences (post and rails, a hangover from the Harewood estate, and hunting in the Bramham Moor hunting country).Useless for hill sheep, no electricity in the buildings and it was typical of farms in the district which had been part of 'Figaro's Estate'. The loose boxes and barn had reasonable doors painted a sickly standard estate green, but nothing else! The house doors were the standard colour to every ex-estate farm being painted regulation issue 'faeces brown'! Ugh!

The bank manager had never come across a young farmer who was not going to produce milk in those years, but rear stores

Drilling wheat – High Snape Farm, Kirkby Overblow, Yorkshire.

and plough – so no regular monthly milk cheque! Never mind, he was prepared to wait for the income as it came at harvest/threshing because cashflow accountants were then only starting to influence farmers and farming in the purely arable areas of Britain. Farmers were still in the era of maximising production and saving on imports for government.

My father generously started me off with a selection of livestock he could spare from Brownrigg. They came down in three 'runs' just after October – a cow in milk (good old 'Cherry'), a heifer in calf and sixty ewes. Next came half a dozen six-month-old stirks and the standard Fordson tractor, purchased in 1938 and which had worked all through the war, and the Lister two-furrow plough. Finally, a set of seed harrows, chain harrows, a small 'hill farm' tractor trailer and an Edwardian (very delicate) dining suite. Each return trip took a load of baled hay back to Cumbria because the pastures on the farm needed to be cut, and baled, in the change over earlier that summer.

There was a subsidy to farmers rearing suitable calves for beef production. That winter, in buildings which were inconvenient and made for hard work, I reared twelve calves. A ploughing out grant was in operation of £12 an acre, so I took advantage of this to turn over about 60 acres. With buildings unsuitable for livestock it was logical to go in for grain production. Clearly I would not plough those acres with the old Fordson, good as she was, so I sought a quotation from a local contractor for the job, which introduced me to the pernicious grant/production bribery system operating in farming in those years, by government. The quote was, 'If there's subsidy at it it'll be £12 (twelve pun) a yaker (an acre) – if nut than £7 pun a yaker!' (Everyone had to have his bit of the subsidy.)

I've mentioned that the farm was on the east-facing downslope of the Yorkshire Dales, and that winter I was to have a sharp lesson from the Almighty of the exposed nature of many farms in that zone, when the equinoxial winds sweep down from the Pennines. That March night was a 'howler' – the slates on the house roof rattled all night with mercifully few taking flight! However, dawn revealed considerable damage in the buildings. Opening two loose box doors revealed my half dozen stirks none the worse but staring up at the sky – most of the roof had gone!

With so much wheat crop to drill, it is remarkable that my ewes performed so well. We had crossed them with a Clun Ram as this seemed to be in vogue at that time, but the excellent mothering qualities of the Swaledale meant we had very few losses for the amount of attention I could give them. You considered you had done well to rear a lamb per ewe but much later – 30 years later – we were working at 1.8 plus lambs per mother. Then a set of triplets was a 'photo opportunity' with hill ewes. In the 1980s twins were almost the norm here, and one year in particular – thanks to my wife and mother in law – we had in a special paddock 6 mothers and 18 lambs; all lived and did well – 24 sheep and lambs altogether. A satisfying sight in that little croft, segregated to ensure all were fed.

Just starting out in farming one had to work very hard, count your pennies and do as much as possible yourself. The Agricultural minimum wage was not high but would have strained such finances as I had available. Like my father in the 1930s, my hobbies just ceased – no time for such pleasures. I decided to take students who lived 'as family' and were pleasant company in your house, were keen to learn, and their wages living as family were manageable. They were only allowed to stay six months. Through my contacts in Scandinavia I had a source of excellent lads who became my lifetime friends. Ulf Horsne (Sweden), Harald Hennings, and later his cousin from Schleswig-Holstein Germany, Jerry Bergstrom (Sweden), Anton Bjerke (Norway) and Per from Sweden.

Because of my experiences in Scandinavia I spoke sufficient of the language to be able to get by, but you had to be patient and be prepared to show them English practices. But one year we put four acres of red clover ryegrass hay onto tripods – so they had to teach me. The resulting fodder was out of the ordinary in quality but the process too labour intensive.

Other potentially disastrous things could happen. One spring it was very cold but dry, and there was a lot of ground to make up and harrow, prior to drilling, so to attend to the ewes I set Anton off with the Fordson to do some discing – quite heavy work for the indomitable old bus. Half an hour passed and he came back into the yard to say the tractor was getting 'varm' – would I go 'teta'. Luckily he stopped the job so by the time I went back with him she was cooling down! My fault of course! Because it was cold and frosty those nights she had been drained off – no cooling water! Given half an hour to cool down and filled up with water (the radiator capacity was around three and a half gallons) the old bus survived with no damage but it was a close run incident. No wonder the standard Fordson originally designed as the M. O. M. tractor of 1918 by Henry Ford was simple, hard as nails, and the village blacksmith could fix 'em. No cabs, comfort seats as today – no electric starter and as many know at the cost of a broken wrist; if you didn't hold the handle correctly they could 'kick'!

Years before back in Cumberland 'Bertha' had an ignition problem and a local lad, John Brown, who was an agricultural contractor as well as an excellent mechanic, came to fix it. In the splutter to keep going we had gone to the dealers in Carlisle for a reconditioned magneto. It gave up the ghost so John repaired the Bosch Magneto 'in the field' and upon completing the change-over said sarcastically, 'Hum, Lucas – best if they stayed makin' oil lamps for bicycles!'

Other salutary lessons were appreciated quickly – for example when you go to auction it is a good idea to take a spare pair of shoes with you if you have jobs to do in town afterwards. I had taken about eleven nine-month-old stirks to York Auction *(illustration in 1958)*, where I found a ready demand for well-reared calves off a hill farm. This day the confounded Ministry Inspector wanted to know every ear mark of the bunch: 'this one – no that yan – in't corner – an that 'un anaw.' So yours truly, buffeted by nervous beasts, had to reach over one to read the one by the pen side. Meanwhile I was soon aware of a welly full of warm skittery s**t deposited by another as I read the number – yuk! No change of footwear so I had to paddle about for the rest of the sale with a welly full of liquid s**t.

After a year or so the fences had been repaired to a large extent – at least 'hill jocks', as my neighbour called my Swaledales, could not get off the farm. A 4-acre block in the middle of the land was enclosed by these post and rail fences favoured in hunting country with 12" spacings between the rails – so it was made into a 'naughty prison' in case my sheep attempted to stray. 'You'll never hod them' was the prediction I was given. So a couple of barbs in between the rail spacings were put in and my neighbours were never troubled by my stock.

My father met me at Kirkby Stephen as I'd decided to buy a hundred tip lambs to run through the winter; it was 4.30 p.m. and how to get them home – a lorry? We decided to go to British Railways who would load and transport them at a very reasonable cost to arrive at Pannal goods siding next morning at 10.00 a.m. My worries began when considering taking 100 Swaledale tip lambs away from the station and across the main Leeds–Harrogate road and up the hill towards home. Ask the Police for assistance to hold the traffic for a moment while one sheepdog and I drove them across? One solitary 'Bobby' turned up and indifferently looked on while leaning on his bicycle. Even in 1956 that road was 'busy'. Never mind, I succeeded and the lambs headed up the hill on the road home … Alas, the houses of the well-to-do 'naise peepel' who had their expensive residences on the road, had gardeners, and were all too lazy to get out of their automobiles and close their gates. Of course the hungry lambs turned into the first gate which presented, and across the front lawn – 'Shew! Shew! Get your sheep out of here,' cursed the old gardener, 'Shew! Shew!' As luck had it, that residence of quality had a second gate – no doubt so that the owner could sweep in and out with his limousine. So my lambs just came out of the other one. with me admonishing the alarmed gardener to 'Shut your 'b' gates onto the public road in future!'.

Never mind, my sheep did well. But to give an idea of change in the countryside – my father happened to be visiting a couple of months later. On viewing the ewes he exclaimed 'Heavens, what dirty sheep!' They had left Lakeland with clean rain-washed fleeces to live under the smoke-polluted factory drift from the West Riding mills and factories – they'd become black and grey. Since then the atmosphere has been cleaned up dramatically.

Events progressed steadily – I had gradually acquired the machinery necessary for basic operations without seriously overstretching my earnings. I'd purchased a new tractor and the old Fordson went in part-exchange for £20. I wish I'd kept it.

For good reason, I resisted buying a baler or a combine for example, for it was more economic to use contractors, thus avoiding heavy depreciation costs and scarce storage. It had become clear that my wife had no interest in farming, so as I'd cleared my loans I sold that farm and returned to Cumbria with my machinery and some livestock, aiming to buy another farm to work with the family business.

As always, or in most cases, when you sell land or a farm, it is essential not to dally too long before you reinvest to start again, as the price of land across these past 60 years has been inexorably upwards.

I looked at places over a wide area, near Thirsk, Stockton, Dalston, etc., but finally settled for a homestead I could afford with no 'monkeys in rigging' as the old sailors used to say – no mortgage, no loans.

Bramley was habitable by standards in the district – just – but it has required a life of steady unspectacular progress to turn it around from a farm 'let' to a tenant who paid a very low rent (which his gimmer lamb sales covered), and provided him an easy living on an improved hill sheep farm. An improved farmhouse – modest but not lavish buildings. It had the advantage of lying within a ring fence but the disadvantage of being just within the National Park.

The Fordson Major discing, taken from the driver's seat of a Ford Dexta, High Snape, Yorkshire.

A range of Cumberland Farm buildings from the 1800s to the present day: a sandstone barn, a painted 'Dutch' barn of the 1930s and a later cement and asbestos cattle shed.

TWENTY NINE

CHANGING DIRECTION

Diversification To Survive

In order to finance the long-term improvements needed on a rundown former tenanted farm without heavy borrowing, I needed an additional source of income to survive. To this day there are still countrymen persuaded to 'pledge' their holdings and borrow way beyond the ability of their land to produce. So often you note – and feel envious – of those who purchase, amalgamate or do up derelict country properties to create dream homes with all the 'mod-cons' they enjoyed in the city. Farmers' sons fresh from Institute courses, fired up and keen to show Dad how to do it (for profit of course!), spend his money and then glow in the spotlight of a write-up in the farming press which promotes the goods and services of the companies whose advertising keeps these papers in business.

For a while I worked at Calder Hall but was not impressed with the long-term potential risks. Shift work gave me four days off in a month which was useful on the farm. But it was a popular headmaster in Workington who encouraged me to take on a temporary teaching post in a Secondary Technical School. From there I went back to University to complete a diploma course and then went into Further Education. In effect I was one of those people who 'retrained' and altered their careers in the '70s. In the General Studies department I was teaching English and Communication, but my work gradually expanded to Environmental Studies and Local History.

The farm was very valuable to my work, especially with young people from town backgrounds. By then colleges had acquired mini-bases so we were able to use the farm as a teaching aid in many and varied ways with on-farm visits using mini-buses to transport students.

It is unfortunate these days that we have become so obsessed with safety – hygiene, infection risks, over regulation etc. – that teachers are often reluctant to consider outside visits or excursions.

The Nursery Nurse classes we would bring out here at lambing time, hoping that a ewe would give birth – blood, gore, fainting at the sight of after-birth, bleating, etc. Ideal to show prospective nurses that babies are not all cuddles and gurgles!

Evening classes involved many happy hours helping students of all ages to progress in Local History Studies, for example. A deal of our work in the General Studies department involved helping them to advance their careers by studying and passing various GCE courses to enter a profession. (One lady in particular sends me a card every Christmas as my work helped her to three GCE passes and onwards to Teacher Training College). Often study visits with local history students took us across the northern counties to places quite new to them, but almost on their doorsteps, exploring the wealth of our heritage.

Many of the students in those years did not have much of a chance to gain the respect of a certificate or some achievement, and had a 'chip' on their shoulders against education. Also, some were obliged to attend college as part of an apprenticeship course, but they had hoped to be free of 'school' for good.

Typical of a minority – a student noisily barging his way into a class for which he was very late, would be asked by a mate, 'Hey! Where was thoo at nine o'clock this mornin? He was askin' for tha.' Answer: 'Huh – if 'e thinks aas cumin for nine o'clock, aas nut – it's me day off!'

Amongst the craft students there were funny incidents very often. A class of engineering craft students I had to take at 4.00–5.00 in the afternoon on the fifth floor would have been 'in class' sitting on their backsides and paying attention to their craft lecturers – you hoped – most of the day. At that time all would be itching to get away home.

Not keen to write, the classes often included a tape recording and then a section of discussion. Sitting on the front row tables was a big heavy athletic chap always in his overcoat looking rather menacing. Behind him sat a little 'mousey' pointed nose fellow with glasses, who I discovered was determined to be a nuisance and take a 'rise' out of teacher by constantly interrupting. This went on for the first two weeks. The third week, to my delight and utter surprise, the 'chitter' began as usual but the big chap was having none of it. He turned round – banged the table so hard the little fellow's glasses fell off, and his bag bounced – and he roared 'for f***'s sake shut up – ah want t'ear what t'fellas got to say!'

Many teachers indulge in all manner of exercises and pastimes to expunge the rigours of the day's work from their minds. My relaxation was the farm – I could drive home over the hill and immerse myself in a different world, welcomed by my sheepdogs and to care for my animals, who gave me a different type of appreciation.

Hard work it was, but two weeks at Easter (lambing time), five weeks at haytime, half term in October to prepare for winter, and then the Christmas break, all enabled us to have a satisfying life.

THIRTY

'An Everyday Country of Storied Folk'

Or Demolishing the Myths about Country Living

When I moved to Bramley in 1960 there would appear to be some sort of a farm at the end of a kilometre-long track – leading to nowhere! Despite lying only 10 kms from the nearest industrial or mining villages, there was little to worry about from theft. We didn't have much – a radio, possibly with a tape recorder, a second-hand TV with one channel (BBC!), a car in the cartshed along with hand tools, fencing tackle, drainage rods and perhaps a diesel oil tank.

I could go way across the fields to fence for a whole morning, perhaps returning at lunchtime for a snack … but the house wouldn't be locked and I'd leave my tools on the trailer where I was working even though I might be alongside a country road. However, as full employment waned and the mining and steel industry declined, arose a generation whose families had enjoyed rising wages and a good life from 1940–1960 and now increasingly found themselves short of money, and little work for idle hands. Miners particularly enjoyed their hound trails, ferreting, rabbiting, to name but a few 'recreational pursuits'. There had always been a degree of poaching ever since 'Adam was a lad' but gradually poaching intensified. The woodlands planted just before and after the war were growing up, providing excellent cover for deer, foxes, pheasants, partridge, so the temptation was too great. The increase in small time poaching intensified so that these 'night workers' discovered opportunities. Theft was not confined to poaching game and furry animals, but 'support' for the local hunts provided opportunities for the undesirable light fingered workers to 'recce' our farms/buildings/sheds/hogg shelters, in daylight – so that roofs of valuable Buttermere slate, for example, up to

14 kms away from the National Park boundary, would be plundered and removed. The thieving was exacerbated by the National Park's insistence on Buttermere slate. A crime which should have been countered by a Planning Authority encouraging the construction industry to develop lookalike substitutes and so knock the bottom out of the market. Also our deer society noted poachers from West Cumbria travelling to the Highlands for their quarry. A 'gentleman' from West Cumbria was caught when he got lost and his van stuck on a dirt track, because he knocked up the resident of a remote 'bothy' for help! He had called on the estate game keeper! The growth of the Kielder and Border forests hugely increased the scope of the poachers for venison.

But these raiders or their scouts who were ostensibly 'hunt supporters' on foot, used legitimate hunting to spy the countryside not only for small game but for suitable supplies of Christmas trees, holly, hand tools, gardening gear and machines – indeed anything which could be 'lifted', shoved in the back of a van, boot of a car and taken for a ride; why of course, initially, to the nearest car boot sale!

There used to be holly hedges along the old 'iron road' from Mosser to Lorton forty years ago, but the bushes and trees have mainly gone – to thieves and an ignorant public which likes to pretend or assume that anything growing in the countryside just 'happens' and is there for the taking. (A notable TV presenter was on record advising her interviewer (when asked where people should get their holly for Christmas decorations), 'oh, just go out in the car at the weekend and go cut some!') Villagers in Dean planted daffodils on their village green, to find weekend visitors taking them by the bunch! There were several holly trees in my wild wood bordering the country back road. My neighbour noticed a one-and-a-half tonne pick-up truck parked beside the wood one Sunday afternoon in late November. As it was there for a considerable time he went to investigate and was told by two 'Geordies' that they were just 'gettin' a larl lock o'holly'. 'Too true, Marra!' replied my neighbour, 'thoos chopped doon the whole bloody tree.' And what was happening? These cagers were travelling across from the North East marking the sites of suitable holly trees in the summer then returning near Christmas to ravage the trees or bushes. Along my drive there used to be some six small trees on which I found branches broken off every year – slowly killing them.

I was so maddened at such destructive plunder that in November 1969 I had some part-time helpers park the tractor trailer under each bush and carefully snip off the ends of the branches suitable for decoration into the trailer, where we stored them for three weeks, watering each day up to one Saturday a week or so before Christmas.

My wife and I bagged up all the holly which completely filled our Ford Van at the time, and set out for Newcastle at 6.00 a.m. As we drove down Westgate Road we stopped at a greengrocers on the shopping parade, explained who we were, showed the shop owner our passports and driving licence etc. and said 'how much?' He took the lot for £25, no problems. So we had a day out shopping, a good meal on the way home, made a fair profit and spared our trees from plunder.

I returned home one night in December 1968 to find a car parked at the farm gate

– no lights and the 'watchman', a youth of about 16, sound asleep; but I could see the bush saws and choppers on the back seat. I should have been naughty and let the tyres down. Eventually a lady and her daughter appeared from the wood – very embarrassed. What was their business at one o'clock in the morning? 'Oh, my daughter had been to a boozy party at Embleton and felt a bit sick, so I took her for a walk down the farm road.' Their home was just four miles away and they were country folk at that. I wasn't mad until next day, when I found the large sacking wrap laid out beneath the bush ready for the plunder! But of course, I had not caught the culprits with their plunder in their hands, so as so often happens in these situations, without a witness the landowner is helpless – a creature of ridicule.

In the 1960s we were at a farmers' ball about ten days before Christmas at the Royal Oak Hotel in a local town – Keswick! After the dinner and with the festivities well under way it became clear that the waiters and staff had become noticeably thin on the ground! Sure enough going out to the 'easy room' about 11.45 prior to the drive home, I was met in the corridor by the waiters now well togged up for a winter's evening carrying in large branches of holly!

No doubt the innocent unsuspecting suppliers of the hotel's Christmas decorations were away from their farms and gardens having an enjoyable evening – having paid the management in cash and kind!

But you couldn't spare time to take holly to Newcastle like that every year … How to guard the trees from the marauders without causing damage? We tried spraying them with silver paint on the accessible parts; but this made the holly more decorative. My neighbours all thought I was crazy – 'Hey, that fella at Bramley decorates his holly bushes', remarked children on the school bus. The answer was a creamy mixture of Limbux (whitewash) tossed up over the trees. After a few weeks this washed off but it was a particularly good deterrent for it wasn't very nice to get an irritating eyeful of whitewash on a dark moonlit night!

Our badgers were from time to time being attacked and dug out, no doubt to supply that cruel and disgraceful sport of badger baiting, still indulged by the riff-raff in certain parts of the country. Such activities are a smear on the face of the country and the supporters are of the same low mental calibre as the S. S. scum who could perpetrate or ignore the treatment endured by the inmates of the Second World War concentration camps. The digging had to be made more difficult by mats of weldmesh stapled down and now grown in, but the general public needs to be constantly reminded of these mediaeval 'sports' – badger baiting, dog fighting, cock fighting – which still take place with the perpetrators travelling hundreds of miles for their cruel entertainment.

In many respects, as a society we have not moved very far. A few pretend to care about the environment – others make a sport of running down hedgehogs, for example, on our roads. We have become so far divorced from our rural roots that politicians and – I have noted – eminent professors in agricultural academia, start from an assumption that the countryside, its soil, water, and limited resources, will always be there.

Planting trees at Brownrigg in 1948.

Shorthorn beauties: four curious heifers; below, 'Three Shorthorn Cows' painted by B. C. Norton in 1876.

Above, a small corn stack, and below: one of the pleasanter spring jobs on a Cumbrian grassland farm – a vintage restored Ferguson 35 at work not far from Carlisle, chain harrowing pasture.

Left: A blue Forson Major mowing. Below: 'Harvest home': a picture postcard shot of a 'block cart' with extension frame or harvest ladders, and a school boy leading the mare back to the stack.

Gallon galvanised cream churns, with a box of Swan Vesta matches for scale. They are stamped 'Carrick's Low Row – capacity 3.9 gallons or 5lbs & 3oz'.

Mounsey's shop in Main Street, Cockermouth.

An oak settle, now in a museum in Scotland, used for storing bread: the wood was so solid the rats couldn't get past it to the bread.

The 'Light you to bed' Kelly lamp, again with Swan Vestas for scale.

Mrs Brew's shop in Caldbeck.

A solid oak herb pudding bowl and pestle.

Start of the hound trail at Loweswater Show in 1966.

Hesket Show in 1960.

A combine harvester cutting barley, with Skiddaw behind and a magnificent cloud pattern in the sky. This combine, operated by just one person, and the two on the facing page, represent the change in Cumbrian farming from 1936 to 1990.

The binder at Waterend farm, Loweswater, operated by two ladies, daughter driving and her mother operating the binder, in 1959. Note the menacing skies!

A small 'bagger' combine harvester in the late 1960s, one man driving and the other bagging, photographed at Welton, looking south to the Caldbeck fells.

A steam powered cultivator. Two operatives sitting on the cultivator, with the traction engine on the headland, as demonstrated by Lawson at Mechi in the 1890s.

The standard Fordson, designed in 1918 (the M.O.M. tractor) and still in production until 1945, ploughing. The tractor which won the war!

The grey 'Fergie' tractor ploughing.

Above: A Zetor tractor off to do some logging. Below: Anton with 'Battling Bertha, in red and blue paint, shortly before sale. Her reconditioned cost in 1938 was £60, which included six months' guarantee.

Mardale village under Ullswater
reservoir, visible in times of drought.

Back to the fell heaf: on the mountain slope (left) above the Dash falls – Mr Johnson and his son Mike. A black and white print coloured by the famous artist Edwin Thompson, taken in 1960.

This photograph of our home, Bramley, shows the alterations to
the back (now the front) of our house; compare with the picture
on page 255.

The best painting of our home, Brownrigg, Caldbeck,
by Jack Wilkinson, my father's uncle., c. 1935.

A double-decker Cumberland bus at Egremont toll house.

Snow at Mosser.

Trouble in the play pen!

A line up against a gorgeous blue sky of about twenty Friesian heifers, taken in for summer grazing to keep the pastures short and sweet!

Hoggets at Bramley, in Autumn. View to Loweswater and the 'jaws' of
Honister in the far distance; Melbreak to the right.

Sheep shearing at
Bramley.

'Jessie', who always warned us three days before she was about to lamb, showing the TLC towards her newborns that is such a feature of the breed. Additionally as this picture shows she has lambed in one of the woods which were planted for shelter.

Ella 'topping-up' triplets in the old cow byre, used a a nursery.

Troutbeck market, scene of many sheep sales, as it was in the 1970s.

Cockermouth auction mart, before redevelopment by Sainsbury's. See before and after pictures of the old market later in this colour section.

Small dairy farm at
West Newton.

Bramley Farm from Bramley Seat, 795 feet above sea level, showing the new woodlands.

A black hay barn with a curved roof alongside a Nissen hut. The hay barn was built between the 1930s and the 1950s, by Main of Glasgow, and was usually painted red. The Nissen hut marked the start of post-war intensive poultry-keeping, Beckstones Caldbeck.

Midtown Cottages, Caldbeck, showing the picturesque little footbridge much admired by visitors today and the beck, into which the dubious contents of many a bucket was thrown.

The golf course at Nermo farm, Øyer Gudbrandsdalen, in 2012.

The river Lågen in Gudbrandsdalen, in 1954.

The little narrow-gauge
train to Kalvaryta,
Greece.

The Kalvaryta Gorge: the
train track doubles as a
footpath…

The view from the cab
of the Flam line train,
approaching a tunnel, with
safety rock guards over
the window, Norway.

The three Nermo girls in National Costume. We are on our way to Midsummer Night's Celebrations at Maihaugen museum in Lillehammer, June 21 1952. Left to right: Aase, Kari and Anna Lisa.

Identical Siamese twin calves, at the Swedish Animal Research Institute Viad, seen on the Young Farmers' tour.

Our motor caravan swinging on a crane, being loaded on to the Hurtigruten ferry, the coastal express, at Harstad docksde.

Our caravan at Kåfjord by Altenfjord, across the water where the German super battlship Tirpitz was berthed. We are having lunch.

The Stave Church at Ringebu, slightly off the main tourist track. We always attend a service here when we go to Norway.

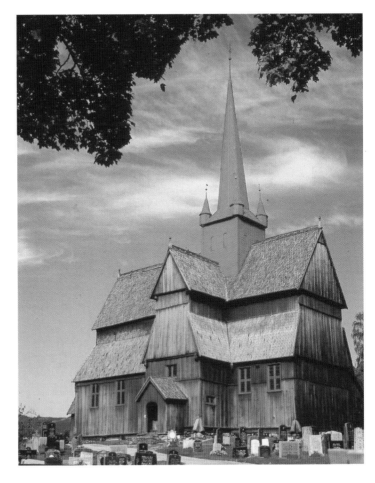

Touring Iceland with our 4x4 farm vehicle we travelled across the centre of the country, experiencing a virtual 'Lunar' landscape. The road guide advised that after several kilometres we would pass a farm … 'in a grassy place' where there'd be a large diesel or petrol tank by the roadside with a hand pump, and that the farmer's wife would walk across to fill us up if we needed. On the way we came across a family droving their flock to fresh pasture close to Mount Blafjell over what is termed a stony desert. The party consisted of their 4x4, carrying the 'tuck-shop', two saddled, and six other Icelandic ponies; as we approached they were having a meal. The flock fell upon the fresh grass greedily … it extended to the size of two football pitches! In Iceland the sheep are housed from September to the end of March and it makes me think of the position on our fells and commons today, following our experiences of the winters 1947, 1963, and 2013. The decline of hill farmers and their families, the younger generation unwilling to 'go to the fell' … we too may be forced to winter our sheep indoors with severe implications for Lakeland, the Welsh mountains, and Dartmoor.

The 'filling station' on our Icelandic trip (see long caption above).

Progress: Cockermouth market before and after the development of Sainsbury's.

Winter snow with strong sky and contrasts
over Longlands and Skiddaw.

THIRTY ONE

'PLANT A TREE FOR SEVENTY-THREE ...'

As my father notes in his reminiscences, he began to plant a few trees – what he could afford – in the grim years of the 1930s.

And so the jingle came out of the Thatcher years. 'Plant some more for seventy-four – see them die in seventy-five – see them sticks in seventy-six.' But that was a politician's trick. When I bought this farm there were several areas of ground – wet, peaty, difficult to drain or death traps for livestock. The fences were very poor, a mean landlord unwilling to spend any money and the boundary was only turnable if the tenant was prepared to 'shepherd' every day – kick out visiting neighbours' stock and cobble up the holes. Compared to Caldbeck where neighbours did maintain their boundaries and were apologetic if their stock troubled you, here I encountered a culture of indifference. 'Some o' thine and a few o' mine.' But for someone trying to improve the holding by working at a job to augment the cash, I could not afford to waste my time rounding up neighbours' stock. To get the message across tactfully to lazy ignorant people, I had to round up, pen them in the backyard, and send a message to collect. I was always treated to a barrage of impudence and would be reported to the Police, to which I countered, 'Hold on a minute – I'll phone the Police now.' Fortunately the local 'Bobby' was on hand, came at once, and, as opposed to the current set-up in the countryside, to the torrent of accusation he quietly said 'Best thing, X, just take them home and keep them at home'.

Nevertheless, I endured this sort of abuse for 20 years as I proceeded right round the farm, erecting good and turnable fences where the ownership responsibility was mine. There are still farmers about who imagine they are the inheritors of the countryside, a gift to society, and have a divine right to graze/crop their own land plus their neighbours' land. Fencing law is bedevilled by preconceptions but is relatively simple and logical … you keep your own stock on your own land. If I keep deer or pythons, my neighbour is not expected to fence them out. Likewise there is a myth – conveniently believed by lazy farmers – 'that a wood fences itself'. This idea has grown up because if – as in my case – a wood is planted on the boundary, the owner erects a stockproof fence to protect his trees as they grow up … logical. It may well be that my plantation fence runs on my own land within the boundary marked on the map and delineated as 'away'. Thus it comes about that after 20 years or so, that protective fence falls into disrepair, the trees are up and neighbours' stock get in, do damage or get tangled up in the undergrowth. Tough! The owner of the trees has a claim against the strays.

Having endured the trespass for 20 years I then 'impounded' about 25 sheep, notified the police and instructed the owner to collect on payment of 5s. 0d. a head. When he came fuming offensive epithets to the policeman and my wife, he had to pay up and go quietly. As it happened it was a dry spell and as one of my graziers had died the aggressive shepherd neighbour came begging a few days later, anxious for 'keep'. So I said 'X, I'll let you put your sheep in for six weeks to get you out of a jam for free and return the 'fine' *if you repair/renew the fence.*' Oh yes, yes, yes etc. etc. and promised he would do it. But he never got the message so to this day I still have the £12.50!

But my fencing work was rewarded for another reason. In 1960 farmers with TB free status livestock had to be double fenced to stop the infection with Bovine TB. Thus my land was classed as suitable for agisted livestock for summer grazing.

By 1963 I had commenced planting up the difficult corners of my fields which were inaccessible to tractors and machinery. Small bits of land which fulfilled the jingo-ists wishes and made improvements to these odd corners, but from AD2000 have proved an administrative curse.

In 1972 we planted up the two largest areas of wet or peaty ground – about 18 acres in all. Main gutters were dug out – a boundary beck cleared with a crawler digger and drainage/planting furrows put in with a Cuthbertson plough. But problems arose because a small beck was slow flowing and inhibited the flow of the open drains. The River Board wouldn't play; it was nothing to do with them, and all the time my very expensive drainage was silting up. I contacted MP Fred Peart for assistance, who reluctantly sent up his area drainage expert from Lancaster to look at the problem. He decreed that the beck was a River Board responsibility as this tiny 'Dub' beck was a 'named river'. But by the time the River Board got round to dredging it out well nigh two years had passed and the trees were swamped. This allowed Willow to take over the area further restricting the drainage flow. Oh, of course to the environmental/ landscape conservationists that's marvellous, but that land is still a swamp. And all that was needed was for the Ministry of Agriculture to serve an order on two farmers further downstream (who of course would not agree) to lower the stream bed by around three feet at a point where there was a natural rock obstruction. Subsequently the wet ground across the beck from my land – about ten acres of it – was fenced off and allowed to revert (to what I don't know), but had I just left mine as a swamp (so called 'habitat') I would probably be very, very much richer today.

The good cropable fields were divided by overgrown hedges which had been given no attention since World War One. As my father was getting older and we were taking his draft ewes to lamb and run on, we double-fenced where the hedges had been and planted two or three rows of trees for shade and shelter against the westerly storms at lambing time. Today they look good, but are in urgent need of the chainsaw and thinning out to leave the Ash, Sycamore, Scots Pine and Poplar. Not that such species find favour with the National Park, but they do make the countryside look warmer, more comfortable as it were, so that today's barren windswept land on a hill farm has an 'overcoat'. If you have ever been to Iceland you will understand what I mean. Because trees like company, when the Vikings went to Iceland they found a wooded landscape which looked like home. But clearing land for farms and using timber for fuel let the wind in and denuded the landscape. Today when my Larch trees take ten years to reach, say, twelve feet, in Iceland they struggle to make it in forty years.

A wood on a steep hillside was felled in the 1914–18 war and never replaced until I decided to reinstate it around 1988. It now boasts a fine crop – *alas* all desperately awaiting thinning. This brings me to another problem of trees on the family farm, which politicians are incapable of understanding and aiding investment in co-operatives of machinery for the harvesting – the skilled labour and machinery.

Yes, timber operations are exceedingly expensive, but in Scandinavia these costs are frequently dissipated by producer-owned forestry co-operatives. Putting it quite simply, the nation and politicians must heed the message – the simple truth about the man who is far-sighted enough to plant. 'As the owner grows old, the trees grow bigger, stronger, heavier, and need expensive tackle to harvest.' The contract machines you see on TV working in Kielder Forest cost upwards of £400,000 a go. To my mind this is where we need to foster forest/small woodland owners co-operatives for efficiency and maximum utilisation of such an investment as happens in Scandinavia. During the Thatcher years it was the 'toffs' who saved the Forestry Commission from sell off and destruction to be altered to a neutered toothless set-up called Forest Enterprise. (You disagree with me? When I began planting here in the late 1960s the Chief Forester at Peill Wyke would come out here, look at my proposal and advise – for nothing.) The powers that be were desperate for farmers prepared to consider a few woods. Today those Foresters have disappeared into the 'woodlands of bureaucracy' and I'm told to employ a consultant! Everyone in Britain must be able to have a sip at state funds or the grants paid out – touché? I need a Landscape and Environmental Inspector assessment (a 'yield' forecast) to consult with the Water Authorities, planning permissions etc., and I am expected to pay (or borrow funds) for all these 'experts' before I even apply for the grant – even to extract firewood. All these 'hoops' to negotiate because government is too stingy to reward the small farmer or woodland owner. Somehow society has got

Two pictures twenty years apart. Bramley Farm and the valley before and after planting.

into its head that ownership of woodland equates to wealth. Never mind! Such schemes as pass all the criteria make for wonderful television programmes.

Years ago as a member of the then Timber Growers' Association, I urged government sponsorship of machinery pools for hire to small farmers and growers. All very well for the agents of the large country estates to tell me 'to hire a contractor, old boy' when in their capacity Lordie can afford and use a few estate workers for brashing, thinning etc. I have used contractors who want to get in and out as quick as possible and from experience leave me a big mess to clear up after their departure.

I am always suspicious of government schemes to persuade farmers to plant up a few acres here and there. It is a 'given' that for maximising your wood you should not need to haul timber for more than 200 mts from a hard public road; and not many years ago there was a terrific 'hoo-ha' across the Borders when councils were going to charge woodland owners for timber lorry traffic along country roads. On this farm, extraction of logs to a convenient pick-up point on the farm lane can involve a haul of anything from 200 mts to 750 mts – totally uneconomic – and for this reason alone much of my timber will end up as firewood. In the Borders we could organise a fleet of tipper lorries trailing a 'chipper' from farm to farm dealing with stacks of thinnings or chip wood to places like Workington, Lockerbie etc. Therefore, when I hear government ministers and advisors bumming up farmers and small landowners to plant, I smell a rat – all sounds very noble, very plausible, but we have been left in the lurch too often. Several years ago some of us were invited to the launch of the 'new' English woodlands scheme – Mark one, two, three or four; I cannot remember which version we are on now! But at that meeting those of us who had planted woodlands, and in my case given an annual maintenance grant payment of £420 per annum, were told it would end!

Thank you – but get on your bikes. Along with others, we were not amused and left on our own. Just take pencil and paper – no calculator necessary – and work out how much woodland maintenance you will get for £400. And at that time came a young student from Newton Rigg seeking employment. He had lots of certificates but little experience and expected £120 a day. No farm woodland scheme can bear such costs. So now our pile of blown timber firewood grows.

To all farmers considering trees, woodland and timber – only plant (i) if you love trees (ii) you need shelter (iii) to hide a piece of bad land or an eyesore. Or your son and heir will curse you – 'silly old goat planted those trees and they're going to be a brick around my neck', as they are worth little or nothing by comparison with costs of extraction.

When I first considered draining or guttering wet areas or bad ground on this farm, my father said, 'Be careful, 'cause you can drown yourself financially in a bog.' Today those woodlands enhance the landscape and the appearance of the farm immensely, but the best answer to my problems would be to fell the lot and start again ... but life is too short.

***

The little bits of woodland – many no bigger than a tennis court – are all on the SFP map and over the years we get no money for them or our trouble. My wife and I have spent whole days locating these tiny areas picked up by the 'Spy in the Sky'. The general public have no idea of double-fenced hedge rows, septic tanks etc. etc. deleted from your SFP. They just think farmers are mad to put up with it, and so they are, because as this sort of nonsense is inflicted on the industry supposedly by EU regulations, many farmers' sons say to hell with it and clear out to stack supermarket shelves. In the end the public will pay a huge price to maintain the landscape as the public imagines it, and current generations of farmers' sons have gone like the miners, never to return.

In the Lake District National Park we suffer from a vast army of interested vociferous parties who muddy the waters or to mix metaphors proffer their policies as a cure-all regardless of others and especially the few farmers who remain.

We have the FOLD, the LDNP, and Forestry Commission in cahoots to fell out the large conifers in Borrowdale, Buttermere etc. because 'they' class such species as alien (to their interests) and then we are concerned about the decline in the red squirrel population? Because my woods are about 60% mixed conifers we have a large and thriving population of our native reds.

For years we have suffered from an assemblage of young 'experts' on landscape design, ecologists, planners etc. to name but a few, with certificates galore around their necks but very little practical experience of farming or the economies of farm forestry. Regularly farmers are bombarded with 'features' in the local and national farming press. 'Money grows on trees' read one headline last year. *Farmers' Weekly* and the CBLA Journal regularly publish attractively illustrated articles of pretty new woodlands to soften the hearts of those persuaded to contemplate such praiseworthy work. Never any pictures of tractors stuck in boggy ground, of rutted farm roads and tracks or the humdrum fence maintenance work involved over a 30-year period. No! You just have to collect an initial attractive government grant.

Time served foresters now assure me that changes are coming about and not before time. A few years ago these experts decreed the Beech a non-native species! Really? I guess they have been around for about 400 years … But notwithstanding the National Park gave the go-ahead to fell some fine stands of Beech in South Lakeland to the anger of locals. Sycamore is classed by these people as non-native. To which I retort, 'So what?'

Look around many hill and lowland farms on the Solway Plain where you will see Ash and Sycamore everywhere and doing well. Thank goodness around the steadings of many of our remote upland farms these are the only trees which will grow without much attention.

The 'interested bodies' (some 22 of them on a count I did in 1960) cannot have it both ways – shouting about 'blocks' of conifers or raving on about 'wild Ennerdale', unless they are prepared to invest money and a lot of TLC to create the landscapes they crave over a period of a century.

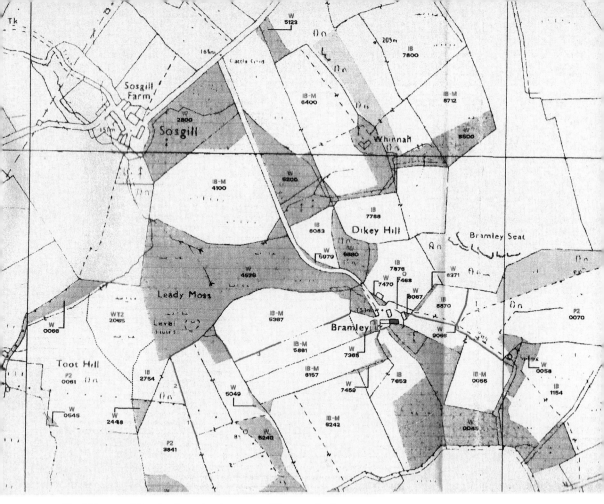

The ESA map of Bramley Farm showing some of the woodland.

Twelve years ago we planted our last three or four acres of steep hillside. Yes, there was a crop on it – useless gorse! Good for a few dickie birds – a menace for livestock – a haven for rabbits and vermin and ever so 'purdey' when in flower. But we have plenty of cover for these already. The Landscape Architect came along to have a look-see as there might have been a cat-in-hell's chance of grant aid – for Mountain Ash, Rowan, Thorn, Oak (sponsored by me!) etc. But my position was simple. I had battled to keep the gorse in check for years and at 60+ I had decided to plant trees to smother the gorse. I refused the grant on the presumption that I wanted something to look at in my lifetime. The public have to remember that the species they would like take up to 200 years to grow – by which time the supporters of these interested bodies will be long dead and all furniture will be made of IKEA style woodchip. However, you may yet have a problem in the supply of Pinewood computer paper!

About 1985 when the trees down the farm drive were becoming a feature of the farm, a young lady from the LDSPB walking along with my wife said – 'Very nice, but

I wish Geoffrey wouldn't plant all these conifers.' My wife was very quick off the mark saying, 'Just be thankful that some of us are planting trees.'

The 'jungle' woodlands amounting to some ten acres of our total sixty acres of woods are still there – Willows, Ash, Sycamore, Tsuga, Rhododendrons, Honeysuckle, Norway, Sitka, Scots Pines, Silver Birch are thriving despite regular 'attacks' for firewood. The landscape of Britain needs friends. In an overcrowded island the uplands can and must produce a crop. Look at the sketch books of Cumbria in 1735 and you will see our Lakeland valleys clothed with woods almost to their summits. Let us be thankful that some of us care.

How I developed an interest in trees and woodland is a mystery. Old snapshots of 'Brownrigg' show a high-lying fell farm – its house and buildings in a slight depression shielded against the westerly winds by a half-acre screen of large Elm trees. Over the fields there were about four large Sycamores, seven or eight Ash and a dozen or so storm blasted thorns. The lonning/drive, or garth, leading down to the steading in Brownrigg in 1930 was bare and unimpressive.

My father describes earlier how he made his first plantation and the costs involved. Understandably shelter becomes very important on an exposed livestock farm. As one grows up trees and woodlands grow up with you, virtually unnoticed until you suddenly realise they are there.

When the war was imminent all our spare cash was put into (I suppose) something of the order of a thousand yards of new square mesh fencing. Believe it or not, with oak posts, these lasted well into the 1970s.

With the war over and less pressure on our land at Brownrigg, we began to plant up about three small wet areas or parts on which there were problems at haytime. Most of these small woods grace the landscape today providing valuable shelter but yielding nothing more than blown timber to use as firewood.

It was my Scandinavian experiences which stimulated my love of forest and persuaded me to put the bad parts of my farm to some use. The only purpose in the early times post-1960 was to hide the bogs and gain shelter.

At last it would seem that there is likely to be growing demand for firewood. At the time of writing, it would appear that we will clear`fell about 20 acres and thin out another 20 acres. To do this we will suffer a lot of mess and disturbance. At my age the replanting will of necessity be a contract job. And when the contractors move in and work starts, I'm pretty sure we will hear complaints from various people and organisations about that vandal landowner destroying those woodlands! Ironic and funny really, coming from the very people who didn't like those conifers 45 years ago.

Leady Moss, an area of boggy land furrowed ready for planting and below, the same wood a decade later. In places there are up to four metres of peat and a transect revealed that this area had been a pre-historic lake or 'mere' surrounded by silver birch woods. The skeleton of a rabbit was dated to be 5000 years old.

My father and his dogs set off to drive up our sheep back onto the fell after straying down the roads to Wigton and Carlisle for a sweeter bite of grass.

THIRTY TWO

HILL FARMING MATTERS

A Common Asset

'The fells and the Common lands are not just open space for walking. They are the vital part of the hill farm economy.'

Back in the 1960s my father was one of the first farmers to turn to the motorbike as an aid to shepherding on the open common. This was a logical follow on to saving effort and work during milk production. My N.Z. friends had used 'scramble' bikes in the high country for years, training – in many cases – their sheepdogs to ride pillion over many miles of rough terrain.

Our problem at Brownrigg was that our flock whose 'heaf' was just outside the fell gate, but on the highest part of the Common, were always tempted to head downhill to the wet parts of the common, near the Blue gate (no doubt the location of such a fell gate before the assault of the motor car) in search of a drink, especially in a dry spring while suckling their lambs.

They were then tempted to stray down the roadsides towards Wigton, Rosley, Goose Green and also to the Caldbeck village green in search of a good fresh bite.

Indeed, before the two cattle grids were installed at the Blue gate crossroads in the 1960s, we had a time-consuming problem. My father would get up at 5.00 a.m. in summer, run along to the top of Warnell – about three miles – and drive the 'ratchers' back onto their fell, and then down the Wigton and Rosley roads. Tired, the sheep would stay quiet until around 2.00 p.m., when another drive up was needed – same drill, same mileage. So my father adapted the old M/C and sidecar combination for this purpose (see illustration). This saved a lot of walking for himself and the dogs. The combination had served us well in the war years as a milk churn transporter.

From time to time with our neighbour, Tommy Watson at Paddigill, they drove up in turns. Trouble was in fetching your own sheep back to the fell, you brought up the neighbours' sheep as well.

When the cattle grids were installed in the '60s (they were planned in 1938 for £700 each! The 2011 cost of a cattle grid at Branthwaite near Fellside is £18,000) – the problem eased but the sheep from the Ratten Row heafs continued to graze the Common on the village green and still do today, much to the annoyance of the new residential 'incomers' who continually protest about these naughty sheep who eat their roses at the crack of dawn. Alas, the sheep have an ancient right to graze the Common and the rule in the hill areas of the Lake District is, you fence 'against the fell or Common'. In another situation the sheep have priority when they wander across the unfenced roads of the Caldbeck and Fauld's Brow fells – if you are fast enough, stupid enough, careless enough, to kill one and get caught, then tough! You are liable. What's more, sheep are so used to honking motors that they take little notice … why should they, having been heafed on those fells for hundreds of years before your prize bit of scrap metal was ever invented?

These days fewer farmers are prepared to risk putting cows and suckler calves onto the Commons because of the heavy cost of insurance for animals in collisions – even though the species composition of our grazings is deteriorating because the cattle aren't there.

Since the 1980s the invention of the 'Quad' bike has eased the work of shepherding on hill farms tremendously. With its many applications and intelligent use on steep slopes, the declining workforce (for 'workforce' read single handed owner occupier farmer, trying to 'cope' with an increasing workload) on our hill farms have managed to continue earning a meagre living from poor hill land. Alas, it has brought problems. They are not toys and there have been many fatalities and serious injuries amongst farmers. Riding across a 45 degree slope the last thing you need to hit is an overgrown

The lambing cubicles at Bramley and in the background the quad bike with trailer, irreverently called the 'Pope Mobile' – invaluable for bringing in mothers and new-born lambs at all times of day and night.

molehill, to find yourself tipped upside down – or in my case stuck wondering which way to turn to avoid capsize! Also there is the temptation to let the kids use the bike or ride with you – both practices now totally illegal, but catastrophes are still too common.

Worse, from the farm management point of view, is that all farms are now targets for organised gangs who steal these costly machines. Insurance for them is heavy; 'informers' seem to let the crooks know when a new machine has come to a farm and a familiar pattern emerges – a stormy, windy or wet night, double glazing of the farmhouse, heavy bolt clippers to cut anchor chains to tractors. Very large tractors – used to block in the quad – manhandled out of the way and 'hey presto' perhaps two or three quads loaded from various locations into a Transit van and off down the M6 to some shady deal way down south, or for riding on the sands at a seaside resort.

Sophisticated 'gear' can be designed for wars in Iraq etc., but we seem to be incapable of producing a 'quad' bike with satellite security built in at minimal cost. Worse still, in my opinion, every machine should be registered with its road registration number stamped on the chassis, even if never being used off the land means no need for 'plates'. But according to the Radio and TV programmes the countryside is a haven of honesty, neighbourliness, safety, and apparently low crime. The statistics reveal a very different story.

Before my father adapted the M/C and sidecar for shepherding, he had attempted to 'pen' the flock for the few hours he would be away, to spare the daily shepherding humbug. Advising both our neighbours, who agreed and had no objections, an area of about three acres was fenced off in an angle in the fell wall close by our gate. Plain wire was used – no barb and nothing which could be considered permanent. It worked for a couple of weeks and then a large gap of several yards appeared – mysteriously of course – rendering the pound useless.

This would be done by someone who imagined that we were attempting to 'enclose' a piece of common land. It shows how fiercely guarded are the rights of common access and pasturage even in these days. And quite rightly so because 'authority' and the 'state' are constantly having a go to nibble away at the commons throughout the land – be it for a car park, store, playing field, water storage, filtration plant etc. etc.

Books galore and histories of hill sheep have been written yet visitors wonder at how we 'know' our sheep, those who imagine sheep to be brainless, but our flocks in hundreds know us too.

My grandfather, helping my father load some sheep onto Willie Tyson's lorry, went ballistic when father said 'put them in a pen Willie, and I'll be along shortly'. 'You'll lose them! They'll be stolen – how will you know yours?' Most of us know the sheep we have bred – certain features, faces, fleeces etc., even if they are not rudd-marked.

I reproduce here a page from the *Lakeland Shepherds' Guide* which is updated every so many years and we all buy a copy. It shows you the 'lug-mark' and the 'smit-mark'. The book is divided into areas/districts and 'commons'.

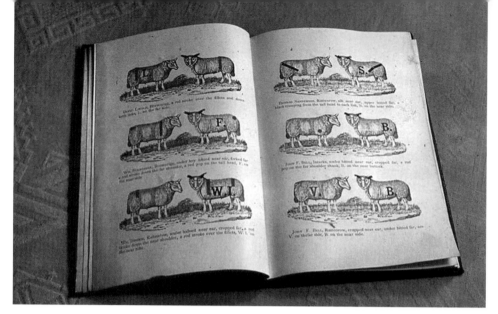

The Lakeland 'Shepherd's Guide' showing smit and lug marks for the flocks on the Lakeland fells.

The early volumes are now quite valuable and collectors' pieces. They are also interesting sociologically and to students of agricultural history. Study reveals change – farms have been bought up with their 'hefted sheep'. Sometimes an owner who has acquired a farm with rights on the common may keep the flock's marks to run them on a part of the common where the grazing rights exist, away from his own. Or he may absorb them and the holding disappears (ceases to exist).

Many years ago, a certain gentleman purchased a farm in Hesket Newmarket which had grazing rights on Carrock Fell. But he promptly turned out 600–700 sheep on Ratten Row and Fauld's Brow Common, much nearer his home farm. Well of course – unhefted sheep on a new fell, and the sheep didn't know where they were. Residents in Caldbeck just about went mad – sheep were all over the place, being chased by traffic and angry villagers along the roads to Hesket, to Uldale and to Fellside (in the 1980s the grids kept them from straying down to Wigton, Welton, Seberham etc.).

One day I was over at my father's farm to do some jobs. 'Wils' turned up an hour or so after we had expected him to start. He was fuming! 'So I borrowed X's Land Rover and trailer and took them b******s back where they belang – and kicked them oot onto't fell.' (Carrock Fell.)

Such tricks – turning sheep, horses, goats and cattle onto the common, willy nilly – causes chaos and bad feeling. My father mentions attempts to 'stint' the commons (fell grazing rights in the 1930s before the war) which fizzled out in the drive for maximum production during the conflict and subsequently the 'headage' payments afterwards with no restrictions. Even to this day we are groping towards workable controls over common grazings but there are still heated arguments in commoners meetings, bad feelings and stupid tricks – not helped by the National Park, English Nature, and all the interested 'bodies' piddling in the pot.

Two final comments. When my father decided to change over from Herdwicks to Swaledales, he bought 25 hoggetts at the autumn sales at Troutbeck and brought them home. After a week or so inside with the main ewe flock, they went 'to the fell' – in our case, just outside the fell gate 400 yards from the farm. After a day or two they had gone … some were recovered at Westward, others in the village or on Ellerbeck. The last half dozen outside Carlisle, where the crematorium is today – 13 miles away. The only way to make them 'bide quiet' was keep them in that winter and turn them out in the spring with their lambs, when they couldn't travel so fast!

Here in Mosser, one of my neighbours bought a small bunch of ewes with lambs at foot. It was an enclosed farm but one old lady was missing after the first week. Never seen again for many weeks, when she turned up in September with her (by now) fine lamb, at her 'home' farm about 12 miles away (cross country) back in Eskdale!

Those of us who love hill sheep always marvel at the hefting instinct of our sheep. The ravages of a foolish Ministry of Agriculture in the foot and mouth disaster caused havoc, because officialdom imagined you could buy hoggetts or replacements down at the supermarket in packages of 25 off the shelves! (A Booker, Morrisons or Sainsbury 'loss leader line'.)

A Pavlovian Trick!

Eventually at Brownrigg, we cured the problem with an act of Bribery! The flock was turned out onto the fell from the inside fields very early each day, free to range about as usual. However, come five o'clock all would collect back on the fell outside the fell gate awaiting the 'off'.

As ewes will go mad for tasty sheep rolls, a few buckets scattered in the overnight pasture and there would be a stampede to gobble a few. Expensive? No not really. No time wasted driving up, and better suckled lambs for the autumn sales.

A hefted flock of sheep on our large areas of fells and common have considerable income value and are in effect the 'raison d'être' for many hill farms. The sheep have been born on their heafs for centuries. Areas unfenced, unidentifiable to the uninitiated, the flock's home area is the place to which they return naturally. Of course odd ewes stray from time to time in adverse weather conditions, storm, drought, over grazing etc., but the 'heaf' is their patch. And when our sheep dogs are driving, any 'strangers' coming along with your sheep will gradually shed themselves off, and a well trained dog almost knows to let them drift off or stay behind.

A couple of French farmers' wives on an exchange visit to Cockermouth from the Massif Central, observed that in autumn and up to spring our sheep had red backsides. The farmer's wife explained that at tupping time the rams had their chests marked with a 'raddle' (in the old days powdered red haematite iron ore was mixed with a gummy oil), to indicate to the shepherd the ewes which had taken the ram and when most lambs could be expected. Hoots of laughter from the French ladies – 'So that's the origin of that English expression, "I'm tickled pink!"'

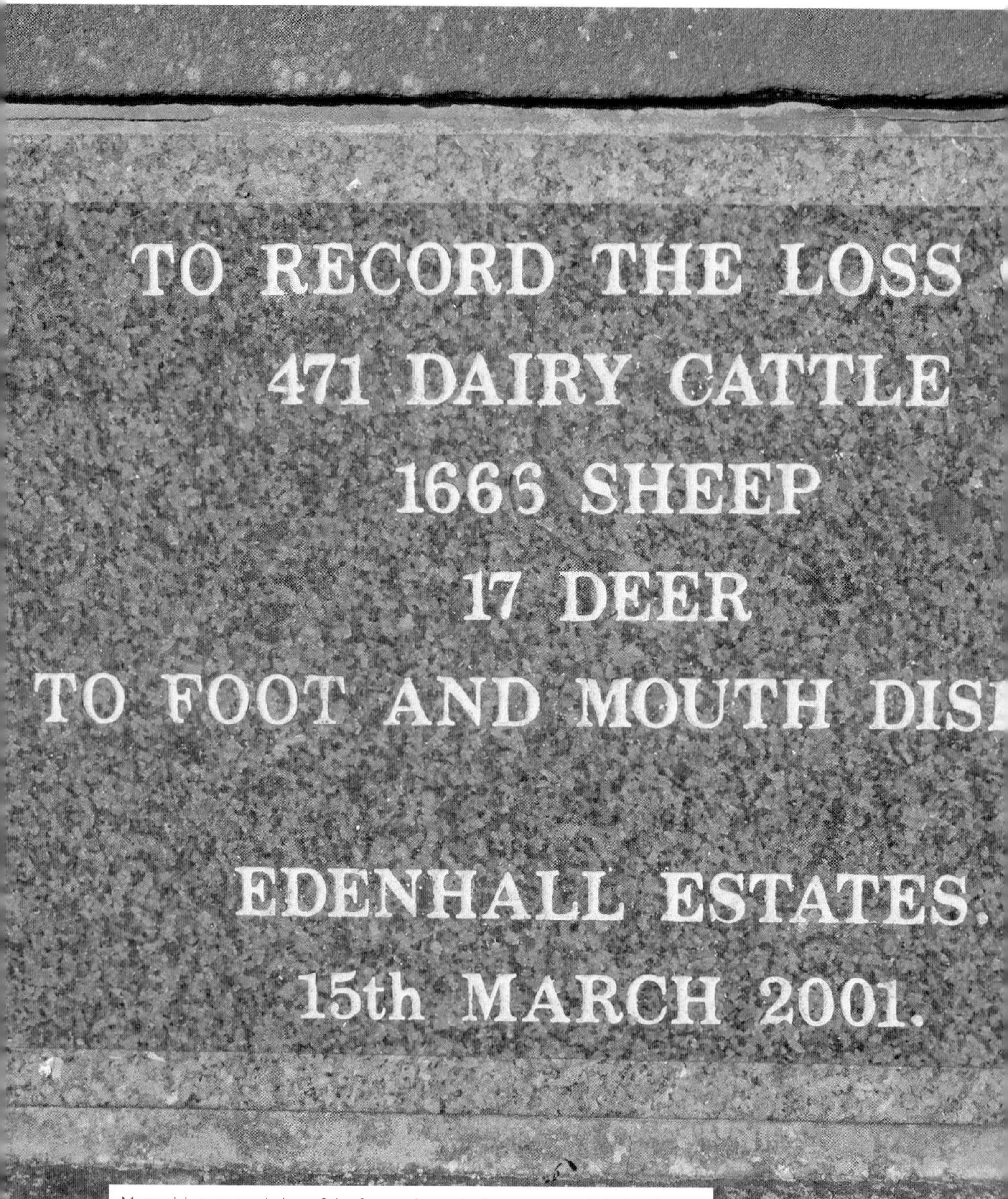

TO RECORD THE LOSS

471 DAIRY CATTLE

1666 SHEEP

17 DEER

TO FOOT AND MOUTH DIS

EDENHALL ESTATES.

15th MARCH 2001.

Memorial stone to victims of the foot and mouth disaster on the Edenhall Estate.

THIRTY THREE

Observations Of A Farmer Who Survived A Bungled Disaster And The Resulting Trauma And Deprivation

Or the Slaughter of the Innocents.

'The following notes and observations were written during the crisis and in the following six or eight months while we recovered from the trauma of the crisis.'

- I make no apologies and pull no punches. If my criticisms are harsh to organisations, ministries or people – tough luck. About 5 million innocent healthy animals, as subsequent research has shown, were *murdered and almost as many destroyed quite needlessly* because of clumsy petty movement restrictions. Officials and ministers claim it was the world's worst outbreak. It wasn't but British incompetence and arrogance made it so. We have only ourselves to blame. At this farm we see European TV news programmes daily by satellite as well as news from France and Holland regularly.
- To be brutally sarcastic right at the start – to the politicians seeking to get an embarrassing crisis out of the way of the general election; to the NFU (representing only 35% of farmers and less than 1% of the rural population), whose greed and selfish inflexibility in the pursuit of a £500m export trade were prepared to destroy all other country-based enterprises while pretending to be countryside guardians, protecting the family farmer.

    When the ministry field officer came to this farm to supervise a 'movement' he was given the M/R of a place six miles away at the top of Whinlatter pass. A neighbour received two letters warning that his stock were to be taken (just a little mistake) and the holding number related to a farm near Hexham.

- In reading these notes you should remember the geography of the county and the disease. If you draw a line from Ulverston – Windermere – Ambleside – Keswick – Cockermouth – Maryport on the map then you will see that most farmers to the west kept their livestock, but were harassed tirelessly and needlessly by officials and vets whose brief was quite obviously to teach the awkward brigade who resisted the contiguous cull, *or demanded their own vet*, a lesson and to try to frighten farmers to believe that MAFF were all powerful. These farmers received no financial compensation, were unable to trade and were forgotten by an NFU always greedy to grab as much compensation money for the bigger farmers who pay the biggest subscriptions. The thing which annoys some farmers the most is the sanctimonious piety with which the Union's leaders have attempted to justify their actions.

- Many of my friends and neighbours in these areas are in dire straits. This is a result of the crisis which only now is coming to light. Too many of us in these parts of Cumbria were sickened by the shots on the TV screens of 'blubbering' big farmers who received massive compensation but heard the delightful rustle of new, crisp £100 notes.

- In the first week of April 2002 we sold the last five of the previous year's lambs. (They should have gone in March 2001!) So we had sold nothing for 12 months … our neighbours across the valley sold eight heifers a year later than they should have done – overloaded with too much stock, they could not make hay at a hill farm they owned 20 miles away and had to purchase large quantities of straw and silage as a result.

- What have they lived on you may well ask? Other friends drew down their retirement savings for months literally to keep themselves in groceries – their small farm B & B ceased to exist. Because I had had a second job my small pension eased our problems and we in turn helped our cousins by offering them work to thin our woodland so that they could sell logs for firewood; they have lived from hand to mouth. Like many others we lost around £3000 in grazing rents, but little noise and no pressure on MAFF from Ben Gill and company at NFU HQ until one of his 'yes men' had a rough ride at a rare foray into these Western lands from a bunch of angry farmers' wives, whose B & B had collapsed with the rest of their farm business – but it was too late then. MAFF had already overspent on its 'bribery' exercise so it saw no reason to help us. Other farmers I know took the hint and made haste to grab any job they could before there were hundreds in the queue. One lad I know in his forties, encouraged by a wife already earning half the family's keep as a nurse, and an eye to the future, now cuts public lawns for the local authority. A survey into the social consequences of F & M carried out by Newcastle University was seriously flawed and out of date.

Their team appears to have been asking the wrong questions and ignored a whole section of farmers who kept their livestock, are still suffering, were ignored by the government and forgotten by the public and the Union. Ask them about confidence in their future or that of agriculture, or how they see their prospects and a very different picture would result. I am to be forgiven for my sarcasm but very few in this part of the county had been able to put up the shutters, close the farm gate and take themselves off on the grand tour of relations in Canada, Australia and New Zealand.

Those of us who fought and struggled to keep our livestock are being made to suffer for the bungles, the failure to embrace vaccination, and all the infighting between DEFRA, the politicians and the Union; in just the same way as the service industries and the tourist trade has suffered.

Too often Ministers were heard assuring the public that this is a dangerous disease. It is nothing of the sort. In the 1922 outbreak the Duke of Westminster – determined to protect his valuable pedigree herd – isolated them and his workers for the duration and kept everyone away. Also, up to 1960 old Dutch farmers on the Friesian Islands knew that to control an outbreak in a herd you ensured that all your animals got the virus and then it was simply treated with TLC and bathing with salt and water, often walking them along the seashore.

There was a distinctive mood around in Cumbria in May, expressed in subtle terms by leading members of the NFU which could be summarised thus: 'let's get all you lot shot out (culled out) so that in the shortest possible time we – "the big boys" – can restock while the price of our replacements is low'. I must be brutally frank – what they wanted was to 'trouser' as much of their over generous compensation as they could, and they didn't care who else suffered. Fortunately this changed as the outbreak dragged on from June into August.

If you have ever seen a flock with a bad case of 'Orf' complete with maggoted pustules in hot weather, you have seen a potentially fatal disease. But no way is F & M any danger to humans as is the case with BSE nor is it life threatening to the animal unless it is already in weak condition.

+ Now we have a situation in Cumbria where the big dairy farmers who populate the councils of the NFU are so keen and in such a hurry to get back into milk production that they have imported/introduced cattle into the county from the south and south-west Midlands with tuberculosis ... Who will farmers blame for the spread of a disease *much* more dangerous than F & M? Why, the innocent badger of course. And too late we witnessed the chief vet for Cumbria announcing 'that steps were being taken'; but of course the cow had bolted. The south country farmers, anxious to quit dairying, saw them coming with their pockets bursting with money!

+ Does anyone wonder why ordinary farmers despair of the blatant incompetence of DEFRA?

- It is not general knowledge that on the day before Margaret Beckett's carefully choreographed visit to Cumbria, a TB infected newly purchased cow on a farm in her itinerary near Carlisle had to be shot. No doubt neither Beckett nor the general public were made aware of that. The farmer concerned was one of a group which some of us term the 'Cumbria Quintuplets', those farmers wheeled out in front of the TV cameras by the NFU who can be trusted to speak the Union line. As a friend of mine dryly observed, Beckett visited those farmers who wear a collar and tie and don't smell of silage when they come into the studio! It also illustrates the government's misguided faith in trusting its experts rather than embracing local people on the ground who may not have a string of qualifications behind their names, may express alien viewpoints based on vast experience gained over the years, combined with good common sense. I warned Labour MPs in March 2001 what their 3-km cull policies would do to the hill flocks … for way back in the 1930s my father had had experience of the difficulties involved in re-hefting strange sheep to a new fell and he shuddered about an outbreak of F & M long before World War Two.

- When the virus threatened to run out of control amongst the pig farms around the Fiefdom of Ben Gill, we had the man running about seeking a ban on helicopter flights over the area lest air turbulence increased the spread. The NFU and MAFF didn't have a clue on these matters. As Prof. Browne and Drs Sutmoller and Bartelling told those willing to listen, 'the disease could not walk, fly, jump or swim, but it could hitch a lift on vehicles and clothes'.

- We absolutely failed (*because we did not use the local knowledge of local vets*) to listen to the Dutch or the Germans and French, who told us that a narrow country road 2.5m wide, a railway line, a drainage ditch (in Holland about 2m wide), a wood, a stream, a river etc. etc. were all effective barriers. Who were the persons who decided on the quite arbitrary 3-km cull zone? This was done without any scientific evidence whatsoever. As a result we made fools of ourselves; cost the domestic and European taxpayer billions. Little wonder the Argentine Minister of Agriculture commented that Britain must be a very rich country to afford such colossal waste … my farmer neighbours are furious that many of the sheep, for example, could have gone for meat but as usual a prodigal Britain does not have the cold storage capacity.

- This stupid policy did nothing to control or contain the disease but (a) it tore the heart out of Cumbria (b) it sickened the public here and beamed it by TV into every European home to such a degree Europeans have vowed that they will not tolerate such reckless stupidity again. So that regardless of what ministers may say or the NFU protest, Britain will be forced to vaccinate in future – why on earth should the European taxpayer foot the bill for our arrogant fecklessness.

- At one stage at the height of the crisis, the rumour was going around that it was EU Bureaucracy which had prevented our ministry from taking the prompt action necessary to stop the disease in its early stages. However, if this was the case how did it come about that France, Netherlands and Ireland succeeded and we failed? A nice story and in the best British tradition of laying the blame on someone else. Those of us who remember the 1952 and 1967 outbreaks are well aware that even where farms were next door to each other one got the disease and the other did not. And I gather that it has emerged that of the 109 farmers who resisted the contiguous cull only ONE eventually went down. Whether the storm was raging unabated or not, there was *not that degree of urgency to shoot out the farm without blood tests first.*

+ What happened was absolutely criminal as you can only take/destroy livestock if they are diseased.

+ It is to their great credit that the House of Lords threw out Tony Blair's new animal health act *which would have effectively legitimised everything which MAFF got away with and every illegal act they perpetrated on the farming community during the outbreak.*

+ At the time the reason was hushed up, for we now know that 98% of sheep were disease free, and a mere 2% had antibodies, and these were not showing any signs of infectivity. Farmers were kept in the dark by a massive campaign of deceit, media manipulation and threats, that if they resisted they would face solicitors' costs of £25,000 or that they would receive either no compensation, reduced compensation or would have to pay the costs of carcase disposal themselves. In fact, when the solicitors Burgess Salmon realised the full horror of what was happening they were prepared to take on the Ministry for £2,500.

+ I have a dreadful sinking feeling that those who took us into the F & M disaster were the very same people who were in post over the BSE affair. Those staff and scientists prepared to do the wicked bidding of their political masters and worse still to 'rubbish' those who were prepared to put their jobs on the line to save the British farmer, his beef industry and the victims of CJD. In fact a complete re-run of the Prof. Lacey/Dr S. Dealler confrontation between arrogant civil servant scientists who were prepared to sell their reputations for a bag of shekels and produce the mollifying reports or the conclusions that ministers wanted to hear ... *and now we know that that little exercise in political chicanery cost the British and European taxpayer about £4 billion plus, plus, plus.*

+ Soon after the army was called in the Brigadier told MAFF and the politicians 'that you could plot where the next outbreak was going to be, from the routes of the milk tankers'. We had two nasty scares here when a tanker came from St Bees (where there was an outbreak) to a neighbouring farm. Fortunately the farmer's wife would not allow any vehicle on the premises without carrying out her own cleansing. Another vital cause of the spread was the contract milkers passing from farm to farm.

The NFU wanted to keep the big dairy farmers happy (cash flow and all that jazz), in a crisis situation, and Tony Blair who wanted to give the impression that

Plastic mats soaked with disinfectant appeared on various roads in the area.

the countryside was open for business when it clearly was not – a classic example of a disaster caused by what military tacticians call divergent objectives. From friends in France I know that when the outbreak occurred in Mayenne they could not believe their eyes – everything stopped; gendarmerie and road blocks were everywhere for three weeks – no movement – and when it was over they disappeared as quickly as they had come.

As Prof. Browne and his international experts criticised, there was too much reliance on personnel untrained in basic hygiene method and practice (workers often allowed to go home to a clean area after a day's shift on infected premises). Having worked at Calder Hall many years ago I would have expected the same sort of strict and often irksome procedures to have been applied as one went through when emerging from or going into a radioactive or contaminated area – *at the very least*, a complete bath, shower and a change into freshly laundered clothes.

When I heard that some army personnel were being billeted at hotels in the Borrowdale Valley, I telephoned my MP to complain and I think the policy was changed. Just fancy anyone being so ignorant as to actually allow men working on the most infective sites to commute each day to the heart of the Herdwick country!

However, it was well-known amongst local people in the crisis areas that the slaughtermen and the vets were frequenting local pubs, sandwich bars, fish and chip shops etc. for their meals or were sending out one of their number to 'shop' for the gang.

These two examples underline the opinion of many that those directing the MAFF response in Carlisle and London – as well as the MAFF veterinary division – had a very poor appreciation of elementary hygiene and bio-security.

On the one and only visit I made to the 'Shepherds' Inn' at Carlisle during the crisis in late August, I noted to my horror the whole place very well populated with off-duty vets from their nearby hotels, all drinking and socialising … sorry, but this sort of conduct should not have been allowed while the battle was raging at its greatest intensity unless these 'troops' had been totally decontaminated and withdrawn to an isolated rest area. (I was obliged to attend this venue to meet a Canadian cousin who had made the reservation oblivious to the fact that the place might be full of vets. Needless to say our disinfection that evening was total …)

We know of one farmer friend who – advised of a routine inspection visit – met the Ministry vet at the farm gate. Asked where he had been, the farmer went into 'orbit' to learn that the vet had come from a premises where an outbreak had just been confirmed on the radio.

MAFF made a *supremely stupid and insensitive mistake by ignoring local vets with local knowledge* in favour of a host of foreign vets. Although I am reluctant to question their professional competence (there were language difficulties and some were unfamiliar with common British diseases like fouls or animals slavering when casting a tooth), because they were recruited by, paid by, and imported by MAFF, in an encounter with a truculent farmer they could be relied upon to toe the official line – *To save your backside, and avoid arguments, when in doubt, confirm it as an outbreak … Destroy.*

+ In a blind panic when some foolish scientists blamed sheep as dangerous contacts, walking time-bombs, disease shedders and other semi-sophisticated, pseudo-scientific but equally emotive nonsense, the NFU actually jumped on the bandwagon especially the dairy farmers. Subsequent research has blown these foolish remarks by very senior ministry veterinary 'experts' clean out of the water. These men were so anxious to please Tony Blair who, following his visit to Cumbria in the early spring, took 'personal control' and told his 'flunkies' to get this thing out of my way before the election. They forgot their science, and obliged.

+ It was a department of state which literally ran out of control.

+ It has been very noticeable since then that Cabinet Ministers only came to Cumbria on carefully managed and controlled visits.

+ There was not nor has there been any subsequent scientific proof that sheep were infected or a cause of the spread. Anyone can make a mistake or misread the advice offered but Blair and his officials were blinkered, thought that only the 'Brits' knew how best to proceed, could not/would not listen to the Europeans, the Americans, and experts with international experience.

+ For someone in his seventies with a memory, it is a familiar and humiliating pattern. It would not be so bad if Blair had the sense to say, 'sorry we were wrong – we made a mistake'. But that is not in the ambit of British politicians since Lord Carrington (of Falkland fame) and Sir Tom Dugdale (of the Crichel Down blunder). It was not until mid-August that Prof. Browne and Drs Bartelling and Sutmoller were asked to call at Page Street on their way back home through London. After the lecture in Penrith I quizzed Dr Bartelling whether 'it was just a social call for coffee?' His look told me everything – DEFRA could not/would not be moved. The British answer, then as now, is to kill everything in sight.

* Following Tony Blair's 'DIKTAT', MAFF proceeded to bribe farmers on a colossal scale; (a scale I would only have associated with a banana republic) to yield up their animals under the unscientific contiguous cull. Even the European Commission became alarmed at the scale of the bribery. Yet the NFU pleads that 'farmers only got the value of the stock they had lost'. It is no secret amongst farmers who remember, *that those who got it in 1967 never looked behind them.* It would have been a very good idea if the compensation to those who lost their stock by disease had been halved and the money given to those of us who struggled through great hardship to keep our animals.

* A young friend who worked for me part-time spent £1000 on draft ewes in the September before the crisis. His sheep were taken on the contiguous cull and none of the flocks removed under the same 'shoot out' in the valley were subsequently shown to be infected. He received £18,000 in compensation. I wish I could invest money that way.

* The upshot of all this bribery was that we have virtually destroyed 50% of the Herdwick breed and people are only now realising that almost 75% of Swaledale flock has gone. So now there is mayhem and hostility in the countryside with commoner arguing with commoner, farmer against farmer and English Nature (stooge and servant of DEFRA) along with the NFU trying to get back into farmers' good books by attempting to assist with the re-hefting of the hill flocks and paying out yet more money to repair the damage of a thoughtless policy inflicted by London. What is worse, Dr Richard North advised 'ignore the hill sheep, push 'em back onto the hills and concentrate on the cattle'. This was also confirmed by the world experts mentioned above (with experience from countries where F & M is endemic – South Africa, Mexico, Argentina, Brazil etc.), but DEFRA was too arrogant, would not listen, and determined to shoot its way out of the crisis with a policy originating in the nineteenth century.

* We know that early on, Britain was caught and did not have sufficient stocks of vaccine. However we did have enough to have treated all the cows in Cumbria before they were turned out to grass. But then to make matters worse, we were offered the new American vaccine to use in an actual outbreak but the British turned it down.

* A telephone fax poll by local MP David MacLean at the time revealed over 80% of respondents in favour of vaccination yet NFU officials locally and in London were shouting their heads off that farmers were against it. Why couldn't NFU and MAFF have conducted a proper poll at the time, putting before farmers a summary of all the data for and against? It could have been done in a week with a bit of push and what is more MAFF had the addresses of every farmer on their computer.

* No attempt was made to experiment – by treating some farms, by vaccinating others, by letting the disease take its course on some isolated farms … Prof.

Browne offered a farm gate test which he had developed and reckoned in a year's time the test instrument would be no bigger than a mobile phone – but once again was refused. Blind panic prevailed with certain members of the NFU jazzing on the ministry to get everything shot out. There is sworn evidence that a certain gentleman at NFU headquarters said in a council meeting 'that he couldn't give a monkeys if half the sheep in the country were taken out'.

- Who was the scientist/official who authorised the cleansing and disinfection of farm premises? Who could be stupid enough, who could be so impractical to imagine that farm buildings could be decontaminated and cleansed as if they were a hospital operating theatre. This never happened in 1967; premises were mucked out and hosed down and the farm gates locked for as long as it took for the infection to die. Little wonder Tony Blair threw a 'wobbly' at the cost. DEFRA was writing to farmers asking them to concoct a diary to cover their cleansing operations so that Britain could claim its cash back from the Commission!

- It was put about mischievously that the public would not eat meat or milk from vaccinated animals, stories which were later strongly refuted, but to the satisfaction of the NFU the die was cast, the damage was done. However it was a classic example of the Prime Minister's love affair with multi-national big business. Must not do anything which would affect the interests of the multi-nationals. So 4 million plus sheep went into the pits, that were recorded. The government and the NFU should be ashamed of their actions – they stink. For years the public have consumed imported meat from Argentina without a peep of protest. *As the Dutch neatly put it at the Haag veterinary conference in December, the public were not being asked to consume vaccinated meat, but meat from vaccinated animals.*

- There was altogether too much secrecy indulged by the ministry. Farmers needed to know at once exactly where each outbreak took place on the news, so they could plan any business forays or shopping trips to avoid possible contact with infection. A friend of ours used to go to the supermarket at 2200 hrs so that she didn't meet many people. When we went to Carlisle on business in June we went by train to avoid the roads around about. And the media management was on a scale which would have delighted the late Josef Goebbels!

- Whenever a farmer showed signs that he would contest the contiguous cull, MAFF proceeded to subject him and his family to harassment, threats, repeated telephone calls at all times of day and night, by vets/officials of all ranks of superiority. They would threaten to come next day to take his animals without any tests as to whether they were healthy or otherwise. If he insisted on having his own vet he was told he would have to bear all the costs; he could not get compensation; that he would be subjected to veterinary surveillance, visits of a most irksome nature every day for weeks; that they'd 'get his animals by stopping all his movements' so that the stock would have to be taken on welfare grounds. It was a deliberate, vicious, insensitive policy designed to wear down resistance to the point where the farmer and his family were so shattered that they just collapsed under the strain, and were treated as anti-social criminals in the farming community.

+ They would also say they would come at 10.00 a.m. the next day but the whole wretched threatening circus would arrive at 6.00 a.m. – police, army, vets, slaughter men, lorries etc. etc. – in the hope they would catch the farmer off his guard so he could not mobilise his solicitor, or the media, neighbours, photographers, to give him some support. *When a farmer stood his ground and took MAFF to the brink they yielded and went away.*

+ There was an excellent tape from the BBC 'On Your Farm' programme in which a young couple on the Shropshire border and their neighbours resisted a contiguous cull because, as one of the young wives said, 'She was a WHY girl' and it was quite clear that the man urging on the local MAFF to cull them was none other than the NFU County Chairman who lived over the hill!

+ It must not be forgotten that FMD (Foot and Mouth Disaster) helped the banks and money lenders tremendously. Having allowed farmers to borrow way beyond their means or the equity tied up in their farms over fifteen years of declining farm prices, the prospect of a reformed CAP with emphasis on modulation and environment was terrifying. But FMD saved them; government compensation let them and their clients off the hook. Such a suggestion is hotly denied by the banks, who are such virtuous organisations.

+ From contacts I have developed with a high official at the Netherlands Ministry of Agriculture, the Dutch people and Europeans will never again tolerate such barbarity in the C21 – the voters thankfully will not stand for it.

+ Consequently from September we endured the wholesale testing of sheep across the north of England. It is the most fantastic exercise in Codology I have ever witnessed. Last autumn I went for my influenza jab. Why should I do that? To develop antibodies of course. It took 2.5 days and 4 staff to test the sheep on a neighbour's farm (in the process three or four 'escaped'). On this farm they tested about 50 out of 70 – they all passed. Hurrah, you say. But suppose, as my neighbour's wife pointed out, those with antibodies were amongst the untested sheep? Then what? DEFRA has succeeded in turning science on its head.

+ It is the animals with antibodies which you should be protecting never mind all these nebulous arguments.

+ Europe is a wonderful scapegoat, for in a crisis situation the British are well known for blaming everyone but themselves. In all this disaster it is the womenfolk of Devon, Wales, Cumbria and Scotland who deserve the highest praise. It was they who took on MAFF officials and the Police, who challenged Ministers and asked questions. Especially vet Wendy Vere, Elli Logan, Suzanne Greenhill, Lizbeth Gwyther and many others. I noticed the farmers at meetings sat there on their hands and said nothing, too nervous that if they cut up rough at some future date politicians would take revenge on them, because in the past MAFF had fed them with subsidies and they still imagined that the 'status quo ante' would return – very doubtful and an impossible expectation.

+ At a conference at Rheged in the November attended by Ben Gill, organised by the banks – it was laughable to hear their representatives assuring all of us that they were going to be ever such good and virtuous boys they would never let farmers get into such an indebted 'pickle' again. Well? One wonders.

Perhaps the most frightening consequence of the FMD is that it has changed whole villages and the population structure, as I noted while working on a project along the Eden Valley in 2007. Coupled with National Park and district Planning Departments failure to come up with affordable and/or rentable homes for locals, we are witnessing villages filled with wealthy retirees or salaried commuters along the M6 corridor etc., resulting eventually in an ageing population of whom the Senior Lecturer at Lancaster University warned in 1964, 'if we are not careful, Cumbria and Lakeland will become one huge Geriatric Ward'.

For farmers, perhaps the most frightening result of the disaster in 2002 is that we have failed to learn as the PIRBRIGHT incident revealed. A Ministry. which at the height of the F & M disaster issued farmers a DVD lecture on Hygiene and Bio-security could be so careless and cost cutting as to neglect its own drains and release the disease into the surrounding area. The NFU made noises – one local NFU council member, to his credit, remains sceptical and refuses to accept that 'proper controls, precautions etc. are in place'.

We all hope and pray that such a plague never happens again. Britain will be forced to vaccinate. Farmers and their Union should not delude themselves that massive compensation will be doled out by the Treasury and Europe will not pay either. Farmers will be expected to take out or be covered by their own insurance. After all, at the height of the BSE crisis one famous interviewer on the BBC 'Newsnight' programme taunted a member of the NFU saying, 'What's the problem – surely this is normal commercial risk, for which you should insure!'

We now witness a delayed response to the 2002 crisis following the 2007 Foot and Mouth outbreak on the doorsteps of the Pirbright Laboratory – a £200m redevelopment of the whole complex. From the practical farmer's viewpoint we are entitled to ask if that outbreak had not happened would we have just muddled on hoping the wheels of the Defra chariot didn't fall off?

+ Yet government plans to close the Animal Health and Veterinary Laboratories Agency (AHVLA) as part of their austerity cuts have come under severe criticism from the cross-party Environment, Food and Rural Affairs Committee. True to form, Britain will spend on wars instead of health, food, and matters environmental – no comment.

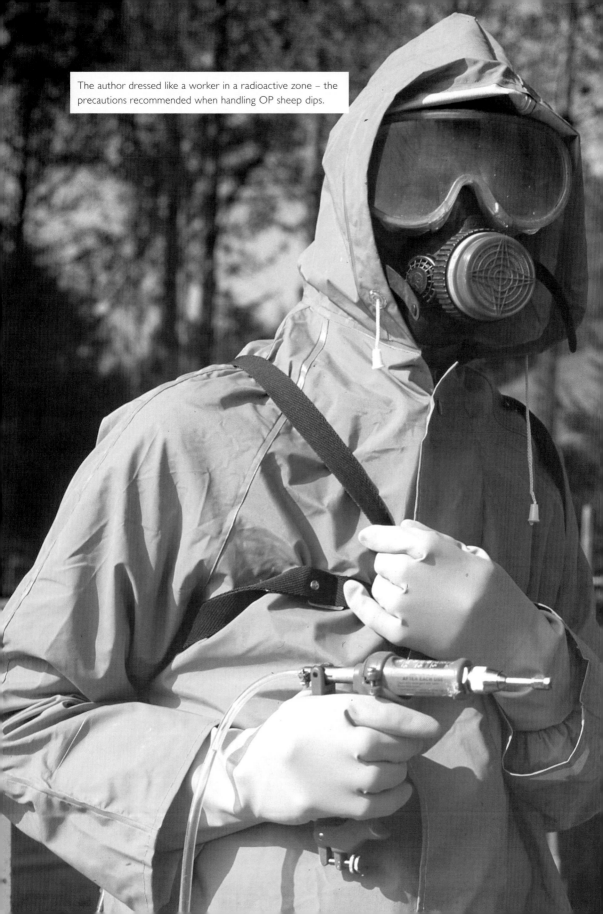

The author dressed like a worker in a radioactive zone – the precautions recommended when handling OP sheep dips.

Thirty Four

Scientific Advances

*Improved management maintains output with costly
side effects but … in an uncertain future*

Advances in veterinary science

For sheep treatment we had to rely on the old-fashioned
sheep dips based on carbolic or arsenic. Shearing days and the
children were used to tramp the fleeces into the wool bales –
like hammocks suspended on ropes from the barn beams. It
was inevitable that bare legs invited a transfer of the sheeplice
and keds onto your body and onto the bedclothes – annoying
little 'critters' whose bite when they had progressed through
shirt and underwear to your skin caused you to scratch. The
short period of DDT dips prior to the ban on its use means
we have not seen one in years.

A nasty job in the winter months was to dust the cattle,
stirks, bullocks, with Derris powder for lice. In warm close
packed buildings the hosts could sweat and you'd find these
lice all along the animals' back feasting away on the hosts'
blood. Derris powder came in large shaker canisters so
rubbing the animal's back, which they liked, and sprinkling
the powder, meant clouds of dust. Whether it was dangerous
or not, none of us seem to be any the worse.

If you bought one of the expensive cars in the '50s, a
Rover, Armstrong Siddley, Humber, Jaguar or Bentley, with
leather seats, then the hides would probably have originated
abroad. The curse of British tanneries came from Britain for
the skins were usually damaged with Warble fly holes along
the back. The fly lays its eggs on the backs and flanks of cattle
just about driving them mad in summer. The beast licks its
coat and injests the eggs which enter the gut and over three
or four months the larvae bore their way to the top of the
animal's back looking like a series of boils. Untreated, the
emerging larvae drop to the ground, pupate, and the cycle
begins again. Very painful for the beast, the treatment was a
Derris solution applied to each 'boil' with a shaving brush as

you located them by running your hand along the beast's back. With the advent of pour-on treatment skins have much improved to the benefit of the leather trade and relieved the suffering of cattle.

Beasts housed for long spells in old-fashioned pens with wooden feeding troughs often developed ringworm (which disappears with good grass in the spring). It is a nasty skin complaint and easily noticed. Unfortunately it is infectious to humans. I cannot recall the official veterinary treatment in those days (probably iodine) but at that time the Parke-Davis Company marketed a quite expensive disinfectant tablet of blue coloured soap 'Neko' at 2s. 6d. A lot of money in those days. We used to wet the tablet and rub it onto the beast's sore – which soon cleared up. The soap contained mercurial iodide. We used it on ourselves too, as a preventative and cure, as well as a shampoo! I guess for safety reasons it will have been withdrawn these days.

As the 1970s merged into the 1980s, as well as the over-wintering Swaledale Hoggets which came from Gilsland, more and more of our 'draft' ewes moved over from Caldbeck. Our altitude being lower – the winters less harsh and stormy – the old ladies thrived and did us proud. In those days to offer hay 'ad lib' in a rack with some sugar beet nuts for supplementary energy in hard weather, you were accused 'thoos spoilin them'.

Thanks to the excellent quality sheep rolls manufactured by Stobart's family mill at Hesket Newmarket, we indulged in 'steaming up' these ewes about a month or so before lambing. It was this practice which increased our crop of lambs from around 115% to an average of 175–180%. Indeed, because of the prolificacy of the Swaledale ewe we never wasted any money with 'scanning' when it was becoming accepted practice. We just assumed 'twins' and the flock rewarded us hugely enabling us a good 'crop' from a manageable flock of 150 – and we still wintered the 200 Gilsland hoggets each year. Pushing about 40 lambs through the auction one late August day, my cousin exclaimed: 'hoo many bl—dy sheep hesta got at yam?' 'Well, nothing out of the ordinary but if we have a death we have a public enquiry!'

The BSE crisis, sickening as it was, only affected us insofar as we purchased our sheep rolls from a well-known local provender miller whose ingredients had nothing to do with one of the 'market forces' causes of the scandal – ground up animal wastes incorporated into animal feed, i.e. feeding herbivores with carnivore offal. It was amusing to watch – sometimes I'd be down to the last bag of 'cobs' from Hesket and needed to dash to a local merchant for a bag or two to tide me over until I could fit in collection of another load. Not so daft – the old ewes would sort out the good wholesome 'cobs' from the others in the mix!

After the ban on DDT sheep dips, careless shepherding and other factors resulted in the development of a variety of sheep dips for blow fly, ticks etc. – none really 100% safe. Up to DDT post-war, we relied on 'concoctions' of carbolic or Jeyes fluid with a very strong disinfectant smell. Then along came the OP-based sheep dips, which killed the maggots, the ticks, and a goodly number of sheep farmers with what was in effect Gulf War syndrome. British governments, as opposed to the Americans, still refuse to recognise the dreadful consequences of such a toxic chemical. I was lucky ... after a day's compulsory dipping for sheep scab (there was a serious outbreak at the time), I went to bed to wake up feeling I had a mild dose of influenza. A neighbour was laid up for several days. Realising something was the matter I made some enquiries and stopped the practice at once. But then as now the auctions began to insist as a condition of the autumn sales that all stock presented must be dipped (solution unspecified). Farmers to this day – against all advice and pleas from the wool trade – persist in dollying up their offerings in 'bloom' dips, which stain the fleece yellow or deep red-brown etc., costing the weavers about a 25% loss on each fleece, for which of course they dock you.

How to avoid OP dips? I realised that my sheep smelled very attractive if they had been dipped in a solution of five gallons of Jeyes fluid in 250 gallons of water. It was thanks to the persistence of Brenda Sutcliffe, Elizabeth Sigmund, and the Countess of Mar, and considerable help from the regional *Farmers' Guardian* newspaper, that forced a partial solution to the problems and the withdrawal of compulsory dipping for 'scab'.

Government vacillated for a ban – it was feared it would open the flood gates to compensation; then Gulf War Veterans, as well as farmers would have claims. Many farmers suffered and still do, but like too many problems in Britain where big business is involved, procrastinate long enough and the sufferers would either die, give up, or go away. Recommendations for goggles, masks, total waterproof clothing, gloves etc. were issued but no enforcement. Since the scandal the 'pour-ons' have helped whereby a squirt from a spray gun along the sheep's back does the trick. However as these new dressings are dangerous I always dressed up as in the illustration, just in case.

As Frank Hickson found out when he had collapsed three times, the effects are so serious to some operators that the mere smell or presence of treated sheep can cause a 'turn'. And we used this chemical in shampoos for head lice in children until quite recently!

I have alluded to the BSE disaster and the effects it had on farmers and the meat industry. It was a classic illustration of laissez-faire in a trade and industry where common sense regulation was subjugated, relegated to the paramount importance of profit by government in hock to, and scared stiff of big business. The *Guardian* cartoon, 'the Lady who complained of shit on the meat', reveals all and as described in an earlier chapter – the farmers collected the blame.

In the decade since Foot and Mouth and its huge cost, the spread of Bovine TB is of great concern to farmers. Prior to 2001, Cumbria was free but the serious problems existed in the South West for which the badger is blamed. Now the compensation costs of slaughter have politicians worried. It was Gummer who professed the policy to only fund 'near market' research and this ruled out any development or discovery involving years of patient study. Had we put as much investment into developing a Vaccine over all these years we would have had one available by now.

It is sickening that despite inconclusive tests and trial eradication of badgers, NFU presidents seeking election or approbation whip up their members into a frenzy – 'cull the badger'. In my experience in Scandinavia years ago where the cows, cattle, pigs and calves are often housed warm below the hay lofts, I noted that most of them had airshafts and extractor fans. Thanks to cash-flow economists pedalling the theory that for efficient milk production or fatteners, animals should be warm and your expensive

'Abolition of regulation, cut backs in inspections, blaming Brussels and all set for a full blown crisis.' Cartoon by kind permission of Steve Bell.

feed not used to grow their coats! So in recent years large farm buildings were enclosed with token attempts at adequate ventilation but poor air-flow.

Although one side of our barn/lambing shed is open to the elements, I noted that when the weather was bad and we could not get a through-put of ewes and newborn lambs (24 hours intensive care!), then a 'fugg' built up.

We have forgotten two factors in disease spread; so long as animals are dry and well fed they take little harm from cold; and TB is spread because there is no air change – no forced ventilation. Farmers and their leaders – too reliant on the 'needle' to cure all ills – have forgotten why places like Blencathra Sanatorium were built in the 1920s. What was the treatment for TB before penicillin, terramycin etc.? Fresh air and warm blankets out on the veranda!

There are now several farms in the Eden Valley and elsewhere with new buildings which are basically a roof with a wide overhang and all sides open to fresh air. Amusingly one I viewed and photographed in the Eden Valley has never had a case of bovine TB and to quote the farmer's daughter, 'badgers have created a sett in the mound of earth dug out for the building!

The National Trust and the Gloucester Wildlife Trust are already vaccinating badgers against TB but this involves expensive trapping. An oral vaccine incorporated into some feed which badgers love, e.g. peanuts, is probably the best and most economical way forward. Already New Zealand has developed an oral vaccine to eradicate TB from its detested and destructive possum population. In Britain we are told DEFRA is developing this, but like the Foot and Mouth saga with tests for infection, we won't move or approve ''cause we didn't develop/discover it'. Ultimately, stopping TB in the cattle herd means a vaccine for cows not badgers. But we need a test to distinguish between a vaccinated cow and a cow with TB. But the big breeders in the farming industry go into spasms about their livestock export trade – same story as the F & M test. We would be accused of selling the rest of the world vaccinated cattle, not cattle TB free. Pride seems to drive common sense out the window.

The effectiveness of the proposed cull with night shooting by professional marksmen is probably a recipe for even greater dispersal of badger families. Said one commentator 'it would be impossible to design a better way of causing perturbation than by shooting'. We have forgotten the huge rows and angry demonstrations not so long ago over 'live exports of animals' into Europe. The police will be faced with an impossible situation and someone will be shot – for the livestock industry a tragic own goal.

Already there are disturbing reports across the country of criminal gangs engaging in badger baiting using packs of attack dogs to inflict unspeakable cruel suffering and death on badgers for betting and sport. Apparently this is an increasingly popular pastime indulged by marauding gangs from housing estates. Cock fighting and dog fighting, banned in the nineteenth century, are likely to be joined by a new cruelty. It is to be hoped that no farmer or landowner is ever accused of turning a blind eye to such activities.

Personally I am in fear of public reaction by the thought of a national or regional cull. Such an operation will turn into a P.R. disaster at the very time when farmers need all the financial support and public goodwill. Farmers should be directing their fire and anger against our foot-dragging politicians over thirty years or more. We can waste billions and enrich shareholders in our creaking railway system but investments in the health of people or animals are rarely seen as urgent. Consider alcohol addiction and obesity (the need for dietary control); instead there are 'campaigns', as with smoking for the past fifty years – a modest improvement, but how many of your friends succumbed to the weed (smoking)?

Some politicians are aware of Britain's precarious situation over food security in a rapidly changing world in which Western Europe and the US do not hold all the aces. We chase a mirage created by the chemical industries etc. offering salvation through G.M. technology.

There are those who imagine we can produce all the food we will need thanks to technological progress, so we can discard food from the fells – softwood timber from the hated but highly productive blankets of conifers from upland fells, and abandon such valuable reservoirs of hardy fell breeding stock to the recreational lobbies, etc.

In 1999 an apparent glut of sheep meat and disastrous prices caused government to plan a 'cull' of the hill sheep flock – 120,000 from England, 100,000 from Wales, and 180,000 from Scotland! There's a terrific amount of hoo-ha by the meat trade about whether Joe Public will eat frozen meat, but isn't it strange that he'll enjoy 'New Zealand' after 13,000 miles in a refrigerator ship!

But Britain has never had adequate cold storage. Always pampered, the British consumer is able to source his food from anywhere – or so it was? In any case a short while later and the cull took place with four million healthy sheep going into the pits of the Foot and Mouth disaster. The result was that we almost wiped out the Swaledale breed and the Herdwicks too. Perhaps the consuming public and their opportunist representatives should be reminded that in New Zealand the ewe flock declined from 68 million to 44 million in the last decade. More important still – who are the main buyers for Australian and New Zealand sheep meat? Why, those who can afford to pay – fast growing India and mighty China.

All those good people who like to look upon Agriculture as 'the countryside' which far too many politicians, writers, broadcasters, recreation groups, regard as belonging to everyone, need to be reminded of man's necessities of life, always drummed into us by our Geography teacher Harold Duff back in 1940 – Food, Clothing and Shelter.

Generations have grown up since 1954 when rationing ended, for whom food prices as a proportion of income have gone down. It will be very painful because consumers are going to be left with little 'disposable income' to spend on themselves after the 'business' of just living – weekly hair-do's, trinkets, motor cars, fly-now-pay-later holidays, to mention but a few, will be the stuff of dreams.

To remind younger readers whose grandparents were around in 1945 to 1950 (my generation survived through it), Britain was so desperate for more food (American lend-lease had ended in 1945) that the Attlee Government contemplated 'grading' farmers into classifications as 'A', 'B' or 'C'. If a farmer fell into group 'C' the threat was eviction and take over of the farm. Tom Williams, the far-sighted Minister (with advice from NFU President James Turner – later Lord Netherthorpe), pulled back from a potential Communist-style public relations faux pas which would have made farmers hostile for generations. It was the wrong way to deal with the situation. A reminder of how desperate was the nation for margarine that huge sums of money were invested in the catastrophe which became a humiliating disaster – the East African ground nut scheme. To plough up the bush in Kenya and Tanganyika and grow ground nuts for

Millhouse and the bridge over the River Caldew bone dry – summer 1976.

vegetable oil. It is doubtful whether more cargoes of 'seed' went into East Africa than came out in crop yield! But it was a good example of the lengths to which a desperate nation would go to honour the meagre ration book entitlements of 1946 (2 ozs butter, 2 ozs margarine and 2 ozs lard – enjoy!)

We are not being told by politicians but dangerous food shortages move ever closer. Professor Tim Lang continually reminds of the need for much increased food production in Britain beyond the immediate supply needs of the supermarket chains. Suddenly a staple food will disappear almost without warning – potatoes, vegetables and so on. We know that meat production requires vast amounts of cereals throughout the world so it may well be that sheep meat from the fells could become an expensive 'treat' to future generations.

As I write these lines the 2011–2012 water drought threatens hose-pipe bans and restrictions in southern Britain. My picture is a reminder of the summer of 1976: Millhouse bridge with the River Caldew stone dry. See also a photograph in the colour section of Mardale village reappearing from Haweswater reservoir.

The National Water Grid – the grand scheme proposed in the '70s – was abandoned as too expensive for a country which had neglected any environmental infrastructure investment (except motorways!) since World War Two. Water from Kielder in the Borders via the South Tyne (Tees) and Yorkshire Ouse, to the Trent and Rutland Water, and onwards to Cambridgeshire in the eastern counties – the national bread basket.

Far-sighted Scotland's first minister envisages exporting their surplus to England in the same way as he aims to export Scotland's electricity – hydro, wave and wind-generated to the 'Nimby' English. In the North West Cumbria's preservation lobby had better resign themselves to raising Lake levels by just a few feet and be prepared to start pumping with a huge demand in power consumption.

Remember that when Manchester *took* Thirlmere there was no hint of a 'payback' to Cumbrians, but already voices are being raised that we in the North West will be expected to supply – and worse, farming and agriculture are persistently at the bottom of the priority list for water supplies. I can just go and collect my spring water in a tank!

Our woodlands, timber and afforestation are a very underdeveloped resource – ignored as far back as 1918. A result of grudging minimal investment in a resource which used to, and still can, employ so many 'hands' in our small towns and a countryside currently 'geared' to high tech agriculture in unsuitable areas. Instead we have handed over an industry with such potential for employment creation to highly mechanised and financed companies making good profits with few job creation opportunities for the 'lost' generation.

Having invested my work and effort into 60 acres of woodland, perhaps I may be forgiven for feeling 'smug' as we and our friends don't have to worry about keeping warm.

Nationally our energy supplies can only be described as precarious – be they solid fuel, gas, oil, hydro or wind. We vacillate between short-term prodigal fixes and uncompleted long-term investment in well-nigh everything we do except defence; too keen to preserve the image of a world power. The 'anti' lobby has had a good run of press and TV coverage but it is my view that 'little Britain' will need to use and develop every source available just to survive. The billions we allow to be wasted on defence would install solar panels on every property in the country and I will not be at all distressed to see wind generation on every farm, village, factory or small town in the land.

Despite 'Fukushima' complacency assures us that somehow sometime the disposal of nuclear waste will be solved? Very strange that Cumbria County Council was the only one volunteering a repository. But consultation about a 'safe' nuclear waste repository is a blatant charade – a national and international problem shunted into a political siding. Like many Cumbrians I am in favour of 'nuclear' so long as the next new power station is built just across the Thames on the old Battersea Power Station site. I am rather annoyed when I go to London and the South, to see the new commuter trains everywhere while we in the north and west have to put up with the clapped out rattle traps 'cascaded' down to us provincials. And this 'gripe' can be applied to most other comparisons. This may be a sober reality, but it is not generally appreciated that when Chernobyl exploded it sterilised an area larger than the Lake District, creating a wild 'no-go' area for centuries to come. But the technology has moved on! Well, has it? Who would have expected that a natural disaster – a Tsunami – could destroy Fukushima.

The time has indeed come for a Northern Assembly of Cumbria, Northumbria and Durham north of the Lune–Tees line lest the overpopulated wealthy South just continues to 'take' exacerbating all the problems and accelerating population drift Southwards.

As the Scottish Devolution debate intensifies we see our local government in a mess – reorganisation imposed on reorganisation with copycat local politicians replicating the manoeuvres of Whitehall and the Treasury. Funny thing, the Swiss Cantons can make referenda work but we like to hide behind the myth that ours is the mother-of-parliaments, to which a European journalist quipped – 'the crotchety old grandmother!' The trickery, shady deals, of crony capitalism by the 'genteel' of Whitehall have little to teach the Sicilian Mafia!

Mitchell's auction in Cockermouth – its site, dictated by a railway siding, has been shifted out of town and, you've guessed it, redeveloped as a supermarket.

THIRTY FIVE

FARMERS AND POLITICS

The following chapter is based on a memorandum submitted to the 'Environment, Food and Rural Affairs Committee' of the House of Lords in December 2001.

Long before the ructions surrounding the live Export trade in sheep and calves, the BSE crisis, Salmonella in poultry and eggs, E. Coli 0157, overuse of antibiotics and Organo-phosphates, British farming was in a disastrous condition. As one Cumbrian farmer succinctly put it when he was criticised for investing some of his compensation money for the livestock he had lost into racehorses, 'Ah's honest' … 90% of them wuz bankrupt afoor Foot and Mooth struck and the compensation they received got them and their bankers off the hook … so at my age now ah's gonna enjoy a bit o' pleasure.'

From 1980 to the present day, British farmers have suffered the same exploitation as befell the Danish farmer from 1880 to 1910 and the events which eventually forced change happened in an almost identical sequence.

Much publicity and spin is being attached to the 'Future of Farming'. However, attempts to repair the damage caused by the F & M crisis and prepare the farming industry for the drastic CAP reforms proposed by the EU, have resulted in the formation of numerous agencies – all tripping over each other. As Professor Riordan observed when the Yorkshire Dales ESA scheme was piloted, 'we British are experts at scattering a little money around like confetti and none of it doing much good'.

Ever since 1979 the Tory party has noised on about the need to reform the CAP but they did nothing about it, because basically they were paying out European money so why should they care? Farmers are largely Tory voters, ignorant of the effect that Thatcher's 'handbag' rebate was having on them and ever keen to fall for the well-spun Tory line that it was these wicked Brussels Bureaucrats who were to blame.

My shelves are littered with report after report on the

reform of the CAP from Chris Patten to Gummer, Gillian Shephard to Waldegrave etc., and today one hears gibes from farmers pumped up by the NFU propagandists that government has 'no policy for the countryside'. Well, it has, but it's not one that finds favour with the big farmers who populate the general council of the Union and falls in with their narrow vision of a countryside devoted to ever more production of food.

The continuation of production subsidies throughout the 1990s has been the ruination of the family livestock business.

The New Zealand experience between 1982 and 1995 showed a fall in land prices to 78% of its 1982 level, reflecting the output potential of the property not the capital value of the price support. Lower returns encourage farmers to apply less intensive methods ... the removal of subsidies meant less specialisation – away from monoculture – and less pressure on hill grazing (something we are trying to bring about with more regulation in Upland Britain), so the sheep population fell from 70m to 46m. The farming, landowning and financial lobbies continue to warn of disaster if subsidies go. But this continues the bureaucratic stranglehold of rural Britain.

The very people who industrialised our countryside these past seventy years would go on being rewarded from the public purse just because they occupy it, so closing it off to the new blood and fresh thinking, which is needed. Adapting the old methods of mixed farming and crop rotation based on biological processes with tractor power and computer control to remove farmers from the shackles of overdrafts, and the reliance on oil based chemicals. The N.Z. experience showed very few farmers went bust – most adapted successfully and enjoy more market flexibility in the new world of increased food demand. All *production* subsidies must be discontinued forthwith – exceptions only to preserve unique environments or rural infrastructures.

Despite the screams of 'let down', this change must take place because the accession timetable for the new applicant members of the EU cannot be stretched out for the benefit of those large farmers in arable Britain, who already run off with 80% of the subsidies. My cousin, farming 700 hectares near Newark, the best land in the country, has no need of a subsidy, acreage payment, set-aside etc. etc. If he cannot make a living or adapt on such land then he deserves to go out of business; he has up to twenty options available to him. On this poor hill farm I have about six – suckler beef, sheep, calves, forestry, limited B & B (gratis the Planning Board), or a second job to pay for the groceries!

It is as if the problems created by the misjudgements made over the past sixty years could be fixed with a few short-term schemes, or contracts that tick a few 'green boxes' and persuade the taxpayer not to worry – all is well in the countryside. We see a veritable plethora of 'Funding Agencies', apparently offering monies for all sorts of worthy causes with the good of the countryside at heart, you will note.

However, *if the produce of the land cannot be marketed so as to give the primary producer a fair return, all such initiatives come to nothing.*

At the end of last century, the Danish farmer was being exploited by the larger landowners and the big export wholesalers supplying the burgeoning industrial populations of Britain and Germany. They were being screwed into the ground in exactly the same way as our farmers today are being plundered by the high street supermarkets, and it's no good the NFU or anyone else moaning on about level playing fields or promoting British produce. The bottom line for them all is profit, and they don't give a damn who or where it comes from. At long last and after a decade of procrastination, legislation is to be introduced to protect farmers from unfair retailer practices and the abuse of market power. Such disgraceful tricks as the alteration in the contracted price for a farmer's milk at four days notice; cancellation of vegetable contracts to growers on flimsy excuses or because of unanticipated gluts or shortage – just some examples of the short-term treatments suffered by producers.

In order to negotiate with these vast companies to obtain the best deal available, farmers need to organise themselves into production and marketing co-operatives just as the Danes have done.

The first Danish farmers' co-operatively owned and operated dairy was founded in

Bramley Farmhouse in May 1960. A typical fell farm with its long, sloping roof to the prevailing winds and the main doors and windows looking over the farm yard at the back (see colour section for the alterations).

Hjedding in 1872, and since then the Danish farmer has rarely looked behind him. Today, wherever I look in Europe, farmers think co-operative enterprises.

A group of Spanish farmers joining together to market a rather special wine; Austrian and Slovenian farmers joining together to produce and market organic foods in both countries of the South Tyrol; the vegetable growers of Insel Reichenau in Lake Konstanz forming a co-operative to counter the competition in the vegetable trade from their arch rivals, the Dutch; in Sweden and Finland farmers who market the wood from their farms through a producer co-operative sell their timber for ten times what I get for it here.

While British farmers continue to attempt to operate as exemplars of the robust nineteenth-century self-made small capitalist entrepreneurs, and politicians 'bum' them on to do so, they will be mercilessly exploited by a system which demands cheap food whether it comes from Thailand or Argentina. Industrialists keen to keep down costs (wages), and politicians anxious to placate the unions, have conspired together (not deliberately) to provide the British public with 'cheap food' from anywhere on earth ... because the Victorians and their industrial power made it possible.

As I have mentioned earlier in this book, my first experience of farmers' co-operatives came to me when I worked on farms in Sweden 65 years ago. I never saw my boss waste a minute standing around auction rings as British farmers did, looking on and trying to assess 'wat trade was ganna be like' for his pigs, sheep, fat cattle, etc. That was the job of the marketing specialists employed by the Headquarters organisations of the various producer co-operatives. For 50 years I have watched our farmers being fleeced by dealers in a marketing set-up which can only be described as mediaeval because of pride, tradition and ignorance that there could be any other way of doing things. Indeed, whenever I have suggested these views to farmers, especially the established middle-aged ones, I am invariably admonished with, 'Hoo wad ta git a fair price widoot a hockshin ...?' The simple fact never seems to cross the minds of the NFU etc. as to how a car manufacturer decides on the production run of a proposed new model, or the employment of analysts who research the market.

Also, politicians of all political parties must bear a heavy responsibility for all that has happened since the formation of the most successful marketing operation ever set up by British farmers, in response to the depression of the 1930s, namely the MMB, in my college days, 'The sheet anchor of British Farming'. So successful was it that the political establishment took fright. To operate effectively the Board controlled the whole product.

You could only sell to the Board even though your milk might be collected by any processing contractor's lorry, and politicians imagined that farmers would operate restrictive practices and 'SCREW' the consumer; *this they never did.*

After the depression of the '30s, the 'regular' monthly milk cheque gave the producer confidence. All the Marketing Boards set up after the war had failure built into them, because you could sell some of your eggs, potatoes, or tomatoes at the farm gate, thus by-passing the price agreements negotiated by the respective Boards. They all failed with the exception of the Wool Board which, again, had a monopoly of supply and still has.

It was the weak and woolly headed thinking which allowed John Gummer to use EU competition regulations to break-up (destroy) the Milk Marketing Board. The idiocy of this policy which promised gullible farmers 'competition for their milk' (when in fact there was a glut and there should have been a cut-back in production), had disastrous repercussions. It exacerbated the quota system and in Britain, as opposed to the continent, allowed 'smart Alec' farmers to trade quotas which were in actual fact the property or gift of the EU commission. Furthermore, unleashing the 'dogs of the market' into milk sales had the opposite effect to the intention of the quota system.

It destroyed the family farm producer. Worse still, 'open borders' allowed the dairy companies to import as they wished, so those very Tory-voting big farmers now squeal and bleat about level playing-fields as a result of market forces.

Quotas destroyed those very people they were supposed to help – quota could be divorced from ownership of land and the means of production. The word 'entitlement' was misleading. The British Government for political reasons (blame Europe) were quite happy to allow the assumption that the quota was yours to do as you liked; so a whole 'industry' grew up on quota trading. Farmers nearing retirement or wanting to get out of milk production and farming, looked upon it as a pension or 'retirement windfall' – sold out or perhaps rented out their acres but retained the quota to lease out for income. Some financed new ventures – holiday cottages of converted buildings to bed and breakfast accommodation.

The Commission and some far-sighted industry watchers were dismayed and furious. It drove up the price of land, exacerbated the shortage of farms (study the countryside around you and note the properties from which the fields have gone), and the chances for new young men to 'get a start'. Bad enough to scrape and save to buy the farm but then to have to search around to buy quota to start up – frightening.

Hjedding, Denmark – the foundation of the first Danish Farmers' co-operative dairy in 1882.

In truth, 'quota' was the property and gift of the EU and when a farmer 'declined farming' it should have gone back to the Brussels 'pool' on which new men could draw and apply for. The problems created were immense and far-reaching on farmers, the structure of the countryside, demise of the family farm business, decline of rural transport, and closure of rural schools. Policies suiting the big noises of the NFU 100-strong council of big farmers were given the blessing of governments trying to ride two horses – production on the one hand and the rural environment which the public thought the subsidies were safeguarding. There has been just a little flutter of alarm at the mass 'exit' of dairy farmers these past five years to just about fifteen thousand left today.

Now we are witnessing another loop-hole in which corporate investors, royal estates, city companies and the already well-off invest their profits from, e.g., arable into milk quota or buying SFP (single farm payments) 'entitlements', because a retiring or tenant farmer can give up and walk away from the land (farm) taking the 'entitlements' with him. The purchaser, having acquired a blue chip annual payment, just looks around for any 'lot' of mediocre land, does virtually nothing with it (he may even let it out for 'summer grazing'), and draws the money, some of these clever people audaciously waving their cheques as their annual Christmas present from Brussels!

Of course, the present EU Commissioner – Mr Ciolos – is not flavour of the month with the big boys, their cheer leaders in the farming papers and free marketeers in government. At least three former commissioners have faced an uphill struggle over twenty years to stop 80% of the subsidy going to the biggest farmers. These men invariably present themselves as paragons of efficient production with subtle help from DEFRA to deride the small family farmer. Yet NFU presidents rarely admit DEFRA figures that 'average' farm income is just £25,000 a year – four fifths of it made up of EU subsidy without which the beef, dairy, and sheep sectors would be on their knees.

No good the NFU and dependent advocates of 'industrial agriculture' professing concern for new entrants/new blood in farming while we allow the bedblockers of vested interests to run away with so much money. The situation enhances my conviction that the unfair convoluted system must be replaced with a maximum single farm payment – equal to no more than the average national wage of around £20,000 a year per farm and let loop-hole seekers cry 'foul'. As the authors of 'the Manifesto for the year 2000' have written:

> The horrors rural Britain has been made to suffer in recent years are proof enough of what happens when policies are made or maintained to satisfy sectional groups. Forestry to cure the tax headaches of the wealthy; planning rules which explode some villages while condemning others to gentrification; farm support engineered by barley barons for barley barons; buses and trains devastated by subservience to the private transport lobbies – these are but a few examples.

Had not the Tory party been so addicted to its market forces dogma, coupled with an anti-European attitude, we could have negotiated a special 'dispensation' from

Brittany Ferries, set up by French farmers' co-operatives to transport vegetables to Covent Garden via Plymouth and St Malo.

Brussels and our partners to preserve the MMB. After all, it was our only functioning farmers' co-operative with member/supplier control, whereas producer (and consumer) co-operatives are to be found everywhere throughout the community. A certain French President would have stood his ground and said 'Non'. Also his fellow countryman, Monsieur Bové, told big MacDonald's business that the world is not a supermarket.

Yet the Foot and Mouth crisis caused many farmers to take their stock to the auction marts which served as collection, batching and despatching centres just as happens as normal on the continent. Thus the result in Denmark is that no animal spends more than two hours in transit from farm to slakteriet … and this was also the situation in pre-1989 Hungary.

Anyone who doubts the ability of farmers' co-operatives to get the producer a fair deal should study the history of the Co-operative movement on the continent and ask themselves, for example, who founded Brittany Ferries? In the '50s the Breton vegetable growers were dumping produce on the streets in their battles for a better deal from the French Government. To expand their markets they wanted to sell at Covent Garden, so they bought a ship to sail their produce from St Malo to Plymouth – thus French farmers acting co-operatively founded one of the most successful Ferry Companies on the Channel. Likewise the largest shareholders in Danish Seaways were for a long time the Danish Farmers' co-operatives … success speaks success.

If the politicians want to make a valuable contribution to a stable future for British farmers, they must be prepared to finance farmer/producer co-operatives throughout the country in bacon, eggs, pigmeat, mutton, beef, vegetables, milk and dairy produce, timber harvesting operations etc. etc., following the models which are so successful in Europe. And, if need be, the government has to follow the French lead – a few years ago where its young farmers were concerned – by introducing a large element of carrot and a big stick … viz. 'we will give you a generous start-up loan but you will join a co-operative, won't you?'

As I wrote these comments a few years ago, the site of a meat abattoir in the Borders was up for sale as a car park – a facility which the livestock producers of the Borders desperately need. It was John Gummer in the '90s who knew what the EEC regulations required (only 12 of our abattoirs complied at that time), but he refused to give the industry long-term loans or grants to modernise; so the facilities shrank and the Foot and Mouth crisis revealed a huge haulage operation of hapless animals being trucked about the country – spreading disease and lining the pockets of dealer farmers.

Without a radical reorganisation of marketing, the British farmer will be a drain on society – whether he is bleating about the high price of corn, the low margins destroying pig farmers, the declining incomes of the livestock industry, or the destruction or withdrawal of services for rural areas.

Worse still, we are 100 years behind the European competition in these matters. Indeed, we have allowed the supermarkets to take over many of the functions which should be under our control. Meat hygiene and quality control should be done by us – after all it's our product and the farmer suffers when there is, to quote the *Guardian*'s cartoonist Steve Bell, 'shit on the meat'.

Only by running the job ourselves can we stop such disgraceful practices as the rebranding and redating of milk by cowboy companies, or sale of broiler chickens pumped up with 50% by weight of water. Farmers and their industry get the blame for these disgraceful operations. A nation which in the nineteenth century gave birth to the Rochdale Pioneers and the CWS to protect industrial workers under the Truck Acts and adulterated foodstuffs etc. is still reluctant to protect its primary producers, the farmers, from exploitation. Also we have been arguing for over a decade about a standardised food labelling system to protect the baffled consumer *and* the producer. One is tempted to question whether this is deliberate to offload *unsuitable junk food on a public growing evermore obese by the decade.*

The Fatstock Marketing Corporation set up in the '50s was not a true co-operative, for there were shareholders whose voting strength was related to their share holdings or the volume of trade done by them. I sold my fatstock on deadweight basis and by-and-large did as well as I would have done at the auction; my stock went straight to the abattoir and I was free of the ridiculous market day ritual apparently so enjoyed by older farmers (or is it popular as an excuse for a day out and a gossip away from the missus!)

FMC failed because when the main shareholders saw an opportunity to make a fast buck they sold out. Therefore any co-operatives set up with start-up aid from government must follow continental practice to the letter … *one member one vote* . This means as in Holland that the man who takes 10 boxes of Cox's Orange Pippins to the packing station has the same say in the business as the man who drives in with four tonnes.

Here I quote from the Federation of Danish Farmers' publication about Co-operatives in that country:

'In several Western Countries there are hybrids of co-operatives/corporate companies,

where the farmers own "shares" in their company and where these "shares" are tradable. There are also co-operatives where people other than farmers own shares and capital and have influence. In Denmark the co-operatives are kept pure.'

Fortunately there are some younger farmers who realise that they do not, and will not, have time to waste standing about at auctions if they are to survive in the farming future – many of them operating as 'one man bands' or doing a part-time job (as I have done).

This is standard practice all across the continent – from northern Sweden to prosperous Bavaria – but it should be stated that the NFU has never accepted that people like me are 'farmers' and that we are a net gain to the rural economy as well as maintaining a strong rural population (they have never accepted the OECD report of 1972).

But the writing is on the wall ... the citizens of Europe are prepared to pay for landscape scenery, environmental protection and enhancement. They are not going to pay for surpluses of food and cost the taxpayer vast amounts of money – funds which we cannot afford to extend to Eastern Europe.

However, it should be noted that a discerning public conscious of health issues are demanding ever larger quantities of organic food. The Farmers' Union with their maximum production philosophies, poured scorn on those who were pushing organic three years ago.

We were told it was 'a niche market and would never catch on'. So today the British farmer, led by a Union selfishly serving the biggest arable farmers and arrogantly dismissive of the House of Lords report on 'Antibiotics in Food', finds himself 'up the creek without a paddle'.

It is a situation which an all-embracing national farmers' co-operative association would have market researched, and advised the various production sectors, e.g. the Dutch and Germans, realised the potential 15 years ago for the pink curly leafed lettuce, and promoted it. The progressive breeding for a long lean carcass in the Swedish Landrace pig 50 years ago – another example.

With production subsidies gone, the role of the family farmer must change to that of 'landscape gardener' and be paid the average minimum wage for the country of their domicile (this would not cost as much as the present CAP system). The large farmers on the best and most suitable farms can manage without aid and enjoy their 'economies of scale'.

Increasingly there are demands amongst grassland/livestock farmers for the return of ADAS (the state run agricultural advisory service), destroyed by the Thatcher government in pursuit of economies and replaced by an army of consultants all flogging you their 'advice', often heavily 'loaded' at £100 a touch; fees which many family farmers quite rightly resent when hitherto they could drop into the local office, in most market towns with an auction, and obtain advice/help with a form – see a face, see a body – all done and dusted as part of a busy market day.

Alas, *the family farmer on his 50 to 250 acres is just a confounded nuisance to bureaucracy.*

Far easier to deal with the big man and his itinerant farm secretary at the farm two or three days a week. No wonder as 'Private Eye' has revealed, 'it costs a sizeable handling charge to deal with one SFP form.' Ah! But how efficient we are aren't we? It's ALL on LINE. So the tired out hard-working farmer or his wife, are obliged to sit at a computer screen when they should be relaxing, scrolling through the 'bumf' to access the information they want, much of which should have ended up in the bin anyway. All these so-called aids may be convenient to administration but they all cost us time and waste our money.

Town-reared bureaucrats, administrators, have lost sight of the primary job of the farmer which is quite simply 'husbandry' – something a nation might be glad of in a few years time; some of us remember the war and rationing.

The prices for the produce of those smaller farms and family units would be safeguarded, along with that of the big units by the co-operatives. In order to achieve this the ESA schemes need to be vastly expanded to take in whole new areas of the country, even individual farms/parishes of the prairie countries (Lincolnshire, Cambridgeshire) – where good landscape and some traditional farming patterns still prevail, e.g. the Welsh Border Counties, parts of the Eden Valley, the Tweed Valley, the Weser Valley, Germany, or the Forest farms of Finland.

As well as the co-ops we need government to set up Organisations like the Federation of Danish Co-operatives or Sveriges Lantbruksforbund.

These bodies are crucial to ensure quality, standards, contracts, orderly marketing,

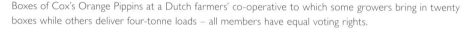

Boxes of Cox's Orange Pippins at a Dutch farmers' co-operative to which some growers bring in twenty boxes while others deliver four-tonne loads – all members have equal voting rights.

Auction companies develop a huge 'froth' if farmers attempt to organise their own marketing co-operatives – largely because of ignorance that affairs could be better organised in better ways to the benefit of everyone as noted by groups of agriculturalists who visit Britain. This picture shows the Autumn breeding sheep sales at Cockermouth.

branding, promotion etc. and product research. Schemes to slaughter locally produced livestock and livestock products deserve encouragement, but supermarkets need continuity of supply and quality maintained to the highest standards on which their customers can rely and demand, e.g. 'Danish' or 'Holland' Apples, Tomatoes etc.

'Fellbred' may be a good brand name but it is no use if it is just available in Cumbria – it has to become nationally recognised, as coming from and providing a taste of Cumbria's internationally known Lake District.

One of the problems which may well worry farmers clinging on to the auction mart system, is where would they off-load all their old draft ewes for example? There is no reason why these should not be processed at farmer-owned abattoirs, made into our own brand of dog meat under a trade name. Already the auction companies are telling farmers that the old system cannot go on where sheep were sold in batches of from two to a hundred animals at a 10% commission – they are saying that this is time consuming and uneconomic. However, mention of Farmers' Co-operatives gives many of the traditional auction companies severe palpitations.

They do not seem to realise that by acting as collecting, batching and despatching centres they would *make* their money easier and still retain all their 'special' breeding sales, their property and valuation work. No need either for farmers to lose their sacred day out and gossip while they watched their stock collected and loaded, as determined by a national computer network matching demand with supply on any given day.

But to do this Britain must be in the forefront in a microchip system of identification for the rapid recording of animal details, numbers, origins etc. This requires international co-operation and some investment on the part of EU governments to set it up and maintain it, as we must do, to protect member states against another dangerous disease outbreak.

In moving to a system of orderly marketing on co-operative lines, which is necessary to meet the dual challenges of foreign competition and the withdrawal of subsidies, the changes must not be entrusted to DEFRA and the NFU for these reasons.

The symbiotic relationship between these two bodies has been a disaster for farmers, consumers and taxpayers alike. When Thatcher sold off or privatised ADAS, the Ministry became nothing more than a subsidy 'bran-tub', devising ever more complicated regulations against fraud (F & M revealed the ineffectiveness of the system), and gold-plating – in the best British fashion – relatively simple EU decisions. Like the NFU they are stuck in a Time-Warp of production subsidies. Farmers are just a small piece of the rural jigsaw and policy to date has given them a cockeyed and selfish opinion of their importance against all the other interests in the countryside – an idea that the CAP exists as a fund whose sole purpose is to top up farmers' incomes.

As Paul Flynn, MP, has admirably described the situation, there have been no Royal Miners or Royal Marconi workers. Farmers will have to learn to co-operate for their common good and salvation, or go out. They can stack supermarket shelves, or do another job like anyone else as I had to do to live on a hill farm; no use bleating that, 'You've done nowt else but farmin' and don't want to do anything else.' Well if that's the case, get back to your farms and shut up ... but don't expect the public to bail you out.

As the NFU only represent 33% of farmers and of those more than half are 'horsiculture' farmers, they must not be allowed to organise many co-operative ventures. They have a totally reactive attitude to most proposals by government and treat with scorn the Consumer Food groups and the environmental organisations (e.g. Nitrogen sensitive zones). Only since F & M have they made any moves towards co-operatives, shown no willingness to follow the Europeans, and continue to profess themselves the best in the world. We seem incapable of learning from the competition ... it's a national failing.

With reference to my proposal that ESA farmers – now being replaced by various 'Stewardship Schemes' – should be remunerated in parallel with the average minimum wage, is not a plea for more subsidy ... indeed the very opposite.

Farmers have been on a treadmill for the past 45 years; prices have been reduced using a variety of methods too numerous to list, since the war, and replaced with deficiency payments leading through to headage payments and ultimately to counting 'bodies' – the despicable practice which played such a critical role in the spread of F & M.

This treadmill means that producers have been forced to run ever faster to stand still. This temptation must be removed for the good of farming, the countryside, and the environmental damage it causes.

The exact figures elude my memory, but back in the 1960s a New Zealand Farmers' magazine did a calculation of the number of fat lambs you would have to sell to pay for an average modest tractor, then the figure was something like 3,000. Today you would need three times as many, hence the treadmill effect. Just produce more to maintain income – apply more fertiliser so borrow more money: result is heavier crop. Present tractor/horse power can't handle crop – need/must buy bigger tractor, so more borrowed money; so the treadmill revolves again. The bankers gain; the countryside loses.

This process may parade under the guise of economic progress, or efficiency, or economies of scale – so every farmer busts a gut trying to beat his neighbour, to earn that little bit more cash to gobble up that smaller or adjoining farm, maybe, in cahoots with another neighbour. The result in the long term is obvious; a shrinking number of farmers, farm workers and rural population. Give a farmer a subsidy and against falling returns he cuts costs, fires staff and replaces his worker with a bigger machine – a familiar and regular pattern – and in the end, when the public realise that they are left with a prairie landscape or upland sheep ranches, the remaining big farmers will turn round and wave 'bye-bye' as they fly off to their bungalows in the Canary Islands saying, 'If Joe Public wants landscape he can pay for it'. Politicians, sort it out!

It is not suggested that the basic income is given without any strings. It should be sufficient to maintain a farming family in household necessities of life, and a modest form of transport in often remote areas, on condition that they farm in environmentally sensitive ways, carry out measurable, identifiable long-term good works and true, etc. etc. To this end perhaps it is time for a reinstated ADAS combined with the aims of Natural England to achieve balance between all those conflicting vested interests in 'our land' and remove all the complicated form-filling of which farmers and country people complain so bitterly.

You may think that this is a preposterous suggestion? However, consider this scenario which more and more young people and farmers' sons are contemplating. (Incidentally research has shown that the desire to follow in fathers' footsteps is weakest in the areas of the richest and biggest farmers in the south and east of Britain). Do you expect my son with a first-class honours degree in modern languages from Oxford University, and an MSc in economics from the LSE to come back to farm here for my ESA annual payment of £4,500 and the little one can make on a hill sheep farm in the Lake District?

Yet he loves the farm, and would like to do so. Or my neighbour's girls, now qualified as teachers? Do you think they are going to face a life of hardship and miserable returns by marrying a farmer just to enjoy life in the Lake District? *As visitors you enjoy the view. But we cannot live off a view …*

14 December 2001

Sorsele station where trains pass on the one thousand mile 'Inlandsbanan' – a railway maintained for timber transport, summer tourists, winter skiers and local shoppers. This 'commune' boasts one person to every 4km^2.

Thirty Six

Transport and Visitor Numbers

Some years ago the LDSPB commissioned a survey of traffic in the Lake District. Very little has come of it and certainly no 'visionary blue sky thinking' – that would involve investment and cost money! In the 1960s another NP survey discovered that many visitors came by car with a picnic and most stayed within 25 yards of their car.

Erosion of footpaths and use of them is now causing serious expensive problems. The walkers and climbers are very well catered for but there is a large group of people who don't want to fell walk or climb; just want a nice day out and look at some beautiful scenery. We could cope with more visitors as in Switzerland or France, if our transport system was worth the name.

In the last days of a rail-tour we ended up in Paris with a day to spare on our International Rail Pass. Where to go? We decided on a day out in Avignon – 740 kilometres (1,480 in total). Departing Paris at 07.40 we alighted at Avignon at 10.00 hrs, so at French speeds Penrith would be two hours from Euston giving visitors a full day in Lakeland. To reduce traffic – which everyone agrees we need to do – we could/should build a metre gauge light railway from Windermere to Keswick to join up with a reconnected CKP to Penrith. Modern railway technology can cope with gradients and such a line would remove a huge amount of traffic, would be hardly noticed in the landscape and would serve as a footpath, as you find in Greece, France, and Spain, and provide much local employment.

If London was two hours away, Penrith and Oxenholme/Windermere could be the start points for a host of *private* operators offering tours 'Mountain Goat' style all over, reducing traffic – even rendering the car a troublesome hindrance to enjoyment. In Greece in mid-October the little train to Kalvaryta was packed. In France the railway to La Rhune climbs from sea level to the equivalent height to the top of Skiddaw, 3000 ft plus. In late October the trains were packed – views out to the Bay of

Biscay and St. Jean de Luze were magnificent. This is what is needed at Keswick – people want to see a view, climb a mountain, have an afternoon tea and clear off back home. Carefully sited around the back of Skiddaw you would never see it by contrast with the footpath erosion on Catbells. A cable-car would be similarly inconspicuous and very wild-life friendly. Such birds as exist up there would love it – no disturbance.

My critics will no doubt consider such proposals as crazy fantasy. But because our railways are John Major's *legacy* it will be a miracle if anything happens. We will just muddle on with our wretched disconnected transport system. No way that day visitors from London will ever enjoy a day out in the Lakes, for the British have no conception of the benefits of a modern integrated transport system. When I leave the Eurostar at St. Pancras, I despair of what awaits me on my way home. For all the fanfares, the journey from Manchester to London is dreadfully slow and crushingly expensive. A few tasters – Marseilles to Paris, already heavily overloaded, takes under three hours, and the world record for a standard TGV from Calais to Marseilles is 3 hrs 29 mins, for 1,000 km.

Last December – hardly noted in our newspapers – the King of Spain opened the new line from Madrid to Valencia which reduced journey time from four & a quarter hours to 90 minutes. Meanwhile we in Cumbria are that little Kingdom beyond the hills! Some of us remember from army days in the '50s, as the train chuffed out of Euston, a notice on the wall – '314 miles to Carr's of Carlisle!' Good! In six hours we'll be home … It's the same distance from Carlisle to London as Madrid to Valencia!

Surely the time has come to explode the nostalgia 'that living in the countryside is cheaper'. Visions of collecting firewood and kindling sticks, picking mushrooms, brambles, crab apples etc. from the hedgerow present an idyllic existence, but disguise a much more threatening negative side to a life of cost, problems, isolation and hardship.

When country dwellers note the frequent minibuses providing half-hourly service around housing estates in our nearby market towns, few realise the sums of government money funding its way into the prosperous South East region for example – a ratio of hundreds to one; it is little wonder that Cumbria and Northumbria are greatly disadvantaged. Community bus services where available do a wonderful and a welcome link but for the young, for health, work and education – for senior citizens, affordable transport is essential. It must have been a remarkable event when a 'Ribble' bus service was introduced from Carlisle to Caldbeck. Prior to this a bus 'service' was provided by Willy Tyson with his 'charry' from Hesket–Caldbeck and points north to Wigton on market days. It is a 'help-my-neighbour-service' still provided as a good will gesture to pensioners and villagers to the present day by Willy's son.

But a Ribble bus! (The company was a subsidiary of LMS Railways who commenced services in many parts of the North West, no doubt to answer the competition to the railways by the increasing convenience of buses.) Leaving Hesket–Caldbeck around 10.00 a.m. with a return service about 3.10 p.m. (Dalston, Bridgend, the Weltons, Caldbeck), it grew in popularity well into the 1950s and eventually there was an evening bus. So if we, the teenagers, went to the cinema at 4.30 p.m., say, you saw the larger half of the main film, sat through the first feature and the news reels, and then dashed to the bus station at the end of the first film – all of course for 6*d*.!

As you'll gather, these country buses were put on after all the 'townies' had gone to work; and operated in the afternoon before the town rush hour. Nevertheless it was very valuable even if the womenfolk had to run around like scalded cats in Carlisle to do their shopping between 11.15 a.m. and 3.00 p.m. – quite an ordeal!

With war imminent another operator came onto the scene. Ernie Harkness with his garage at Skelton road ends introduced a daily service twice a day between Penrith–Skelton–Millhouse–Hesket and Caldbeck to Wigton – as well as a special run out and back from Wigton to Sebergham on Tuesday and Thursday which were market days. Very fortunate for me as I'd started at the Nelson School in Wigton in 1938. My cycle ride to catch the bus was just a mile but other friends from Sebergham, Greystoke and Fellside endured many long windy wet cycle rides to catch the bus.

The 'Manifesto 2000' is correctly very critical of those who believe 'market forces' are a panacea for rural transport. To be brutally simple there is no competition – no market and no one wants the job.

'De-regulation involves the abolition of planned bus services and the creation of a " free market". But a free market can only work where there are enough would-be consumers to create competition – this is manifestly not so in rural public transport.'

Over the last two decades efforts have been made to provide mini-bus services but all require considerable subsidy and rely very heavily on willing local volunteer drivers.

It took well over a decade of pressure by the Rail 250 group to achieve decent parking at Penrith and other stations, while parish councils, town councils, county councils, haggled with each other and the Train Operating Companies as to who should provide, who should pay. Charges are worked out nationally by the TOCs to provide an essential service, satisfy government's 'green dreams', and provide additional income for the TOCs.

Travellers from a large rural area north of Shap fells, Keswick and the west coast – a huge swathe of thinly populated country along the Eden Valley – are forced to drive to the station and park. The 'Now' card bus pass for senior citizens is much restricted by time limits and concentrates travellers onto certain trains – who then find themselves restricted by the 'peak periods' decided by the whim of the train operators to exploit every loop-hole in our crazy railway pricing chaos. Even to use the bus those residing deep in the countryside must drive into towns like Cockermouth and pay for parking. Virgin may boast to have speeded up the services, using the perfected British method of cutting out alternate 'stops'. Thus the first train out of Euston after noon to stop at Penrith is so crowded you should expect 'hard' class carriages to be re-introduced – wooden benches, cram 'em in – so progress goes backwards, into the twenty-first century!

A noble gentleman who travels to London twice a week – first class of course, and overnight expenses and allowances paid – was quoted during an interview with the local press that, 'he loves his new life in his Lake District cottage and enjoys his taxi ride over Whinlatter to Penrith', through the alien Sitka forests. No qualms about the 'native families' dispossessed by market forces – the standard and convenient excuse for laissez-faire. Isn't it strange that all these people crave the perceived country lifestyle. Something must have gone disastrously wrong with our towns. In the eighteenth and nineteenth centuries the town was 'the' place to be and be seen – with its superior quality of life in every respect.

But today these folks wish to bring with them their urban life-styles and demand the services to go with them. And I notice this tendency even in our own family living in the south of England. You just snap your fingers and expect everything just to happen, as it does south of the Humber–Mersey line.

Until you live up here and the Borders, few of our visitors or the rest of the population have the faintest conception of countryside transport problems. Why, for instance, do most of us favour 4-wheel drive vehicles (and have to pay excessive licence duty to run them!)? Rattle and rant on as you will, about 'homes for locals', 'losing our Cumbrian heritage', 'sale of Forestry Commission woodlands', 'passing the decontamination costs of a former M.O.D. site to the local council', 'traffic congestion', etc. – so long as I have acquired my patch that's okay then. Yes! They are all at it … how many former politicians ennobled as good party men – or kicked upstairs – can you think of who have moved into Lakeland?

Visiting Keswick (by train) in 1914 with my grandparents, my father observed that for wet weather days as a resort Keswick needed a 'Winter garden' or a 'Kursaal' for its visitors. One November afternoon having tea in a well-known café, I noted the rain-bedraggled visitors shopping in the pleasantly improved and pedestrianised main street. Not much has changed – there are not many places to go. With sad regularity appear letters in the local newspapers of angry disgruntled visitors who will never return thanks to extortionate charges and inadequate parking space. Having improved our town centres do we find it impossible to compliment the work by copying the Swiss approach in tourist towns – providing cheap, silent, 12-seater electric minibuses shuttling about around the shops and between car parks? They do it in Zermatt; the Poles do it in Krakow. The lovers of the Lakes are forever telling us they do want this to be a 'quiet' area. I cannot help but feel depressed by the number of enterprises driven out or turned away over the years. Keswick Pencils upped stakes and went to Workington – and perhaps received government grants for the move – and the disgraceful display of absolute power by Natural England over the Honister Enterprise just made us locals sick. In Mark Weir we lost a man who *truly* loved his Lakeland and gave his life for it. Squeezed by government cut-backs and aided by the National Park Policies with so much apparent concern for visitors especially those who support the bodies claiming that they, we, all own the Lake District so our problems can only grow worse.

The English go touring in Europe, France especially, and enthuse about the lovely market towns, their street markets, wine and beer 'fests', yet never reflect on the state of our rural market towns today compared with just 40 years ago. Authority cannot cope with or imagine the hustle and bustle congestion in central Keswick, Cockermouth,

Brampton or Kirkby Stephen. They are 'market' towns for goodness sake, to which the population come to trade, to do business, and it would not make a tanner of difference if their main streets were seething with vehicles, stall holders and traders jamming the place from 8.00 a.m. to 6.00 p.m. Instead 'control' and planning have killed the Golden Goose. For a change take a day excursion to the market towns of the Scottish Borders and feel the difference or take a tour along the Wine route of Alsace, the markets of Colmar, or Avila in Spain. The late Martin Brannon (a former chairman of the Lake District National Park Planning Board) was right – our protectors have become our tormentors.

For years the road along the side of Thirlmere has been a developing nightmare. Narrow, frequently flooded and restricted views, as you dare not take your eyes off the road. Nevertheless the old road along the west side of the lake cries out for development – so what do we propose? To close it off and make part of it a wheelchair path. From that side there are fine views of Helvellyn, Wythburn and so on.

We are so reluctant to invest, but an enlightened solution would be to make that road into the Northbound carriageway – a bit of widening, a little blasting and make the road into a standard carriageway, also incorporating a lake-view wheelchair/cycle path, plus a light-rail track. There are no farms along the western side of the lake which cannot be serviced with a short connection to the existing farm lonnings. What's needed is 'blue sky thinking' but no 'privateers' involved, and a very long-term investment. It could even include a small pay toll to defray expenses lest any Chancellor is tempted to use a sledgehammer to crack a nut. But watch out, our politicos will embroil themselves in another 'empire' mission squandering our wealth on pointless wars to justify the Great in Britain.

Presently we have an asset crying out for improvement. We are so very bad at reusing what we already have – a solution staring us in the face.

Whether we like it or not visitor numbers are likely to increase without any high-speed rail day visits, so we should be going hell for leather for underground car parks – the Germans, Swiss and Norwegians do it. No need to expand Brockhole – for goodness sake create space underground, but we already do far too much to pander to visitors. Instead they need to look for themselves as those of the 1930s had to do.

Professor Will Hutton observed: 'We need a richer national conversation in which all the phenomena that connect – insecurity, inequality, distrust of the new, disbelief that private ambitions can have public benefits and scepticism about the effectiveness of any public action – are openly talked about and resolutions sought. That requires politicians prepared to dare and citizens prepared to respond. Until then, to dream about the Lake District celebrating modernity is just that, a dream.'

At the Paris Est terminus – the French TGV awaits departure for Zurich. Germany's ICE has just arrived from Frankfurt.

'Kamping' in East Germany – they were often located beside a 'See' or lake. Note the huddle of Travants and tents as well as the elevated bathing guard's cabin.

Thirty Seven

Gypsies at Large

Whereas my father pursued his hobbies building a radio, carving furniture and making models, I decided to build my own motor caravan. Examining some of the offerings available in the early '70s, I thought it possible to construct a dismountable body on a pick-up so that the vehicle doubled as a farm light truck most of the year. The price of a motor caravan in the early 1970s was high for a single purpose vehicle only used a couple of weeks in the year, so my first effort worked but it was like a 'hen coop' on the flat body of a VW transporter. Even so, it toured the Highlands of Scotland, and went to Holland. It gave us considerable flexibility on our short holidays, as well as saving expense.

But why should we build a caravan? As children my wife and I were unable to 'travel' in Europe but with the expanding developing Common Market it was obvious that languages would be important to our son. As an 18 year old I'd gone off to Scandinavia on my own with a vocabulary of a few words, but a modest knowledge of the Cumberland dialect – thank goodness! The fjalls, mosses, mashed haver, becks and intacks, fosses and koos became the basis of conversations with my employers and friends, so at the end of three months I could listen and take part in their conversations. But in later years it was a visiting Dutch family who came to this farm over many years who impressed us. The boy only speaks one other language – his sisters three, and Henk's wife speaks three plus Russian! No one should be surprised at the cosmopolitan European attitudes of the Dutch.

The motor caravan conversion took around 18 months of spare time and evening work. I should have just bought a large van and copied a friend who takes the mattress from their bed which he secures to the inside for travelling, a simple cooker, cool box, wash basin and a 5-gallon drum of water – no need for electricity or water 'hook-ups', portable TVs or other paraphernalia for a European break! Never mind, our home-made 'hytta' as approved by an inquisitive Norwegian lady, was comfortable in the chill winds of the North Cape or the grilling heat of Spain and Portugal.

Overnight camping by the side of European route E6 (from Palermo, Sicily, to the North Cape). This is near Lyngen Fjord north of the artic circle and in the layby we had tables and a litter bin and ice cold fresh water from a spring!

The farming timetable – haymaking, shearing, lamb sales etc. – rarely allowed us more than two weeks away. Being self-contained we were not restricted to 'sites' so we could park up in the forests or whenever we were tired.

In the early 1980s there were 'official' guided tours available for Western visitors into East Germany (the DDR) – all very carefully controlled. One particular foray beyond the 'curtain' made us appreciate the relaxed lives enjoyed by Western Europeans as the EU developed. Crossing from Newcastle to Esjberg we passed a day in Lubeck, that beautiful Hanseatic city, before driving to the border. Thank goodness we'd had cakes and coffee before we started out. It took us three hours to pass customs, forms galore, examination inside and out. They scanned underneath, jumped on the floor, opened all the lockers. Did we have any dirty films? How many D-Marks and dollars did we carry? You had to write down a 'transit' route and estimate how many days – for which you paid £10 a day. Also you had to change an appropriate amount of money into Ost marks (we called it Mickey Mouse Money).

Late evening by now as we entered a very plain, drab and subdued world. Rusty road signs had not changed since 1945. Stop to ask someone the route and they turned away, frightened to speak to you. Studying our map by the inadequate street lamps of a small town we looked up and gaped as a convoy of 30 Russian missile launchers rumbled past on a night exercise!

Finally turning down a lane with a miniscule sign 'kamping' we came to the site to be directed through the jumble of hundreds of 'Trabbies' and their tents to the 'Internationale' – a large area about the size of three tennis courts in prime position by the lakeshore and with us the only occupants. Dog tired from a somewhat hair-raising journey, we'd make ourselves some cocoa and go to bed. Connecting up the gas and water I was rummaging in the locker for the 'cool box' when I became aware of a large crowd of young people watching us. Then after a while one of them ventured forward: 'Did we have any English cigarettes?' Very sad but it would have been risky indeed had we been able to supply.

Next morning we drove to the exit about 9.30 a.m. to pay and leave. No one there – it was closed! We waited but no one came, so off we went – my wife worried lest the worst might happen. But nobody cared – the state paid them so it didn't matter. As our friends in West Germany found when 'unification' happened, they would offer employment to young 'Ozzies' in their hotel. But Jean had to go and get them up and on duty in the mornings. Strangely unaccustomed to the discipline of the capitalist system.

You would be driving along an autobahn which had the appearance of an emergency air base – not much traffic but at 9.30 a.m. everyone seemed to stop – pull onto a lay-by, up went the bonnets on the 'Trabbies' (to cool the air cooled motors) and everyone toddled off into the bushes; you had to watch where you stepped! In Berlin – in Dresden – you could always see some uniformed person in my pictures.

Imagine driving from Carlisle to Glasgow and passing but one filling station – so there was always a queue. One day in a small town we stopped at a petrol station to fill up. Operating the pump I noticed the fuel was priced in D-marks. So I asked my son to pass me the camera and took a photo – not noticing a Captain of Police striding out from the office to arrest me. In the back office he demanded my film: 'Film – give!' Why? I had photographed a 'fabrik' – a petrol pump! Protesting no handover of film without the British Consul, the confrontation lasted an anxious 20 minutes with the family still sitting in the caravan at the pump – until with a wave of the arm I was signalled to 'bee off'.

Dresden has the honour of the only city where we said to our son, 'what would you like to buy?' from the 'Inter' shop where goods were cheap and we had so much 'Mickey Mouse' money to get rid of. Luckily we treated ourselves to a slap-up lunch in the Theatre Restaurant (amongst all the officials dining out) and proceeded to the Czech frontier. There was a 3-km line of vehicles waiting to pass the border. The Czechs and Hungarians were all returning from their summer 'hollies' on the Baltic coast. Again three hours to pass through; all the coach parties having a 'brew up' by the roadside as they waited. Czechoslovakia was much more relaxed and passing into Austria was like an escape – everyone talking, joking, laughing and no feeling of being observed. Made you realise how fortunate we were in the West – and today why the Eastern Europeans are so keen on the Union.

Germany remembers the 1930s crash – we have very short and insular recollections. Our farmers should realise the disaster of the Gold Standard. Many were ruined with landlords pleading with tenants to 'farm' land at nominal rents. The Germans and French are right to seek controls on the greedy spivs, casino bankers and speculators of Anglo-American capitalism. We don't need their help to destroy a Europe for whose peace, prosperity and security millions died. I am sickened and ashamed to hear our politicians hammering on about 'a deal that's best for Britain', or 'in our best interests'. Rarely a word about what is best for the community. There is an attitude of negativism about all matters European which pervades the press, the media and even the BBC. The hang-over from Empire and the out-of-date 'special relationship' with the US mean that we still have not grasped our place in a changed world.

In my first year at University in 1946 I had a young friend who had been an infantry officer in a battalion of West African troops in the Burma campaign. One day I said to him, 'Frank, how did you communicate with them?' 'Oh, no, bother – no matter where you go in this world, if you shout hard enough or loud enough in English, someone will understand!' Plus ça change …

The disappearance of the Land Settlement Association and other county council owned farms across the country was a disaster for aspiring new entrants to farming post-World-War-Two. Originally conceived to fulfill the needs of First World War veterans for 'three acres and a cow', such holdings were created by county councils often from land owned by the declining landed estates in the '30s depression. Tenants did well on them and progressed to become some of our most successful farmers. This shows a little-altered example from the Solway plain.

THIRTY EIGHT

COMMENTS FROM A LIFETIME'S EXPERIENCE

The following chapter covers general comments from experience gained during a lifetime – living, working and farming in Cumbria for well over 70 years and long before the National Park came into existence. No apologies for quoting from the views and opinions of notable writers who have frequently expressed opinions which chime with our experiences.

The Lake District is a living organism – this simple truth needs to be assimilated by all those in the community regardless of wealth, status, politics or vested interest.

In 1946 when the first proposals for a series of 'parks' were proposed by politicians – a Labour Government with vision – the idea was for opening up green space suitable for the relaxation of workers from the large industrial towns on their 'wakes week' holidays. In those days it was accepted that the campaigns and pronouncements from Princes of the Church were not questioned – they must be good. Thus the fantasy world of Wordsworth, Southey, Ruskin and Rawnsley set the pattern and emphasis on a timeless museum landscape which over 50 years has become policy in a time warp. Most farmers and locals ignored the threat and went about their business dismissing the quirks of planning growth as, 'Nowt to dee wid me'. A few, like my father, whose work as an NFU secretary in those early euphoric post-war years, came to realise the pernicious growth in the power of the planners. Men like Patrick Duff-Pennington, whose experience on the LDSPB, caused them to fight against the introduction of a string of National Parks in Scotland.

Thus, the political classes – local and national – could bask in the limelight that they had given you 'Parks' and to hell with a few natives. Many times I have been told by visitors that, 'this is a National Park' and, 'get thee hence peasant, go forth and multiply'. After all, we subsidise farmers don't we? It must be our land so we can do as we like! Today we have reached the state that hill farmers and country labourers are an endangered

Nothing too outrageous Sharon ~ something like… charming, idyllic, enormous potential, secluded rural retreat, mature gardens, stunning views, heavenly hideaway… the normal nonsense will do nicely…

A cartoon by Henry Brewis – a farmer briefing an estate agent to sell a derelict cottage.

species. Older farmers now averaging 63+ feel very much like the Australian Aborigine – strangers, and a nuisance, in our own land.

Not so many months ago I was admonished by a new incomer – a teleworking city gent – that I shouldn't have views or express any opinions about the Lake District, in which I have lived for over 80 years and as Parish Council Secretary for 25 years of that period dealing with the foibles, fantasies, dangers and inflictions of life in a 'Park'.

In the same vein at a 'conference' a couple of years ago on the perennial subject of 'homes for locals', my wife and I were asked by the well-heeled retirees and well-groomed other participants around our table group: 'Whom did we represent?' Presumably one of the 70-odd bodies, interest groups, organisations, who assume that they have a stake in the 'Park'? To which we reply – 'Ourselves! We are natives – born here and lived here some eighty odd years – so we have come to listen to what all you folks are planning to do with us.'

In his book *The Countryside in Question*, written 24 years ago, Howard Newby reminded us that 40 years of assumptions which have influenced public policy are now coming to an end. Like Swift in 1945/50, he urged an early national debate on the future of the countryside if the opportunity is not to be lost. The following extract is entitled 'Change in the Village'.

> Even an over-sensitive desire to retain the goodwill of the locals may create problems. Many newcomers value the presence of the farming population, if only because it serves as a reminder that the village remains truly rural rather than a kind of rustic suburbia. But the locals can be assigned a definite place in the scheme of things. They can be 'characters', sources of quaint bucolic humour or homespun rural philosophy on such matters as the seasons or the weather, but not expected to put forward views which intrude on the newcomer's sense of how things should be done. What are demanded are **pet locals who adorn the landscape** along with the fields and the trees.
>
> Inevitably conflicts arise from time to time. Threatened by a loss of status in their own village, the locals frequently change the rules of the competition. They base social acceptance not on the visible signs of affluence, but on length of residence. In this way they can retain their former position among those who share their judgements. Soon newcomers begin to grumble about not being accepted until they have three generations buried in the churchyard and glumly resign themselves to thirty years' residence before they will become 'part of the village'. In the pub the locals drink in the public bar, while the newcomers patronize the lounge, often modernized in a recherché rustic décor for their benefit.
>
> The clash of two cultures may also be observed at the village fete. Newcomers tend to concentrate on the wine-making and the flower-arranging; the locals divide their time between the beer tent and the equally serious business of the fruit and vegetable show, a forum in which their skills are still subject to public competition. For those newcomers who have sought the happy intimacy of rural life, the reserve (and worse) of the locals can be mystifying. But all too often the village is now two social worlds divided by common residence.
>
> Sometimes the mutual misunderstanding of locals and newcomers has its amusing side. But underlying the common incomprehension of alien ways of life there are often more serious matters at stake. Principal among these is housing. It is something over which the entire rural population – locals and newcomers – competes. Newcomers have contributed to the increasing demand for rural housing, pricing it out of the range of most locals who are on lower incomes. Similar conditions apply to privately-rented housing – letting for holiday-makers is frequently more lucrative.

Some years ago a couple of 'staycation' visitors enjoying an evening meal in a small local family hotel were unobtrusively listening to several locals enjoying a 'drink and darts' session. Cautioned one to the other, 'I think if we just sit long enough, darling, the locals might sing to us.'

To recount a naughty story: a group of locals drinking in a Bassenthwaite pub was amused by one of their number playing a tin whistle.

'What's that thoos tryin' to play Jobby?'

Another one: 'Well, thoo should knaw Willy – thoo's an 'untin man – it's John Peel …'

'Cus man,' said Willy, 'Ah could fart it better.'

'Nay, mebee thoo could,' *retorted Jobby*, 'But when thoo kum t' variations thooed shite thysell.'

To substitute my Aussie analogy some historians and sociologists may reflect on the less glorious aspects of the 'empire on which the sun never sets', as they come to the surface. The Mau Mau repression in Kenya, the concentration camps of Boer War South Africa, the expulsion of the inhabitants of Diego Garcia (to build an air base in the Indian Ocean), the North American Indians, the Chinese shipped to Malaya, exploitation in the West African colonies; nearer to home – the Irish potato famine and the Highland clearances. It is a dubious record with far reaching consequences.

In Australia the early immigrants/settlers/convicts found natives who could live in a harsh land (like the Lake District fells) and had a culture for which modern Australians have been obliged to acknowledge and apologise. But these people were in the way – so they were driven out, murdered or enslaved. Lately those who survived on the reservations endured softer treatment, plied with slow poison in their hopeless situation – alcohol.

It must be thirty years since a respected Eskdale farmer – a board member at the time – addressing a meeting of farmers at the Cockermouth NFU, announced a great breakthrough during one of the board's planning reviews: 'We have achieved an upgrade!' By chipping away – it's like Chinese torture – 'We have succeeded in moving the needs and welfare of local people from 4th on the list (bottom) to 3rd place.' Worse still, my father wrote about this situation in 1950.

Alas in those years since – despite all the concern, the hyperbole, the disappearance of the family hill farm – very little progress has been made. In 2006 a *Guardian* editorial commented, 'Governments (both Conservative and Labour) have tiptoed round one of the most sensitive issues on the political agenda, introducing a bit of new policy here (exception sites, where planning permission is given exceptionally to provide affordable housing) or a little incentive there (private developers build a proportion of affordable housing) in return for permission.' So when Deputy PM John Prescott would shake up the planning guidance rules, we were foolish to expect a little relaxation, but he made it worse. In 2006 Michael Gove was writing to the press of the Opposition Cons wishing 'to see environmental valuable green space, in both urban and rural areas, protected'. But as I write these comments, the omens are not good for the National Parks, AONB, their residents or the general public.

Some of us are old enough to remember the Lake District as it was before World War Two and its transformation into the chocolate box vision so clearly described so many times by Professor Brian McLaughlin in 'Country Crisis – the lid off the Chocolate Box'.

In the 1950s Mr G. N. Swift, Chief Officer of the Cumberland County Council, made some far reaching predictions and warnings in the 'Official Guide to Cumberland' by the CCC (priced one shilling!) He wrote, 'Beyond the greenbelts surrounding the towns there is no reason at all why people should not be encouraged to live in the countryside, whether they actually work in the villages or whether they work in neighbouring towns. The desire for the preservation of the countryside must not, if I may use a phrase which perhaps has become somewhat hackneyed, develop into a policy of "sterilization" and unnecessary restriction.' Swift could see it coming all those years ago! He was aware of the danger that much stereotyped planning, suitable for the town, may be applied to the countryside with unfortunate results because many planners, government departments and local authorities are urbanites.

Swift saw no reason to restrict what have been termed 'isolated developments' in the countryside. He observed that 'Cumberland is, in fact, dotted with isolated houses all over the place, and this traditional development cannot be eliminated and it is unreasonable in a scattered agricultural county such as this to apply a planning technique of undue concentration which may be more appropriate in densely populated counties.' He feared the very policies currently in favour and being pursued.

You cannot enthuse about creating jobs or employment in the countryside while favouring a construction industry which seeks to build as many properties as they can on sites in the community, so maximising their investment, but forcing out those very small builders or businesses who are living there. Such 'developers' only favour and push sites where all services are handy or already there. Anyone with a sharp eye driving around Cumbria can spot and name the developers by the style of house/property they put up ... And isn't it a funny thing – every one of them completed in any year always 'gets an award'. No matter who or which Body finances these awards, distributed at annual dinners, they look good in the local papers – so plaudits all round. In Britain it seems to require a Royal Prince to rattle the cages of the architects and construction establishment. As an aside, despite promises for a more relaxed approach, I see no iconic designs so far and we ought to seriously ask ourselves what we are going to leave behind us for future generations, not only in the NP but our county market towns as well.

To compound the problem, the predicted decline in home ownership (among the middle classes) has thrown the shortage of homes to rent – rural and urban – into sharp and, for many, painful focus. We can now see that politicians of both main parties turned their backs on a looming crisis ever since the end of the 'new build' competitions of Messrs. H. Wilson and H. Macmillan. Our complacent attitudes to council provision in housing and other aspects of social provision, has landed us in a disaster situation in town and countryside. Worried? About country cousins? Well – not really, for the countryside has always been there, hasn't it!?!

Those of us who have lived most of our lives in Cumbria since childhood can recall changes without number we have experienced, usually at the hands of planning officers backed up by 'old' board members or others who have been there too long and are happy to go along and not question a policy basically unaltered since 1960, pushed out by Whitehall and 'tweaked' here and there by changing governments. When two members of the board have served for 30+ and 35+ years respectively something is wrong. So often the attitude seems to be, in the words of a notable eccentric journalist, 'If we do nothing or as little as possible, then we cannot be blamed for anything.'

It is an insult to our so-called democracy, especially the young people – as opposed to my age group – because *they want something*. Despite all the protest about their worth, contributions etc. they are 'career committee men and women'. A visit to Murley Moss and a Development Control meeting will reveal certain members must always have their 'two pennyworth' – to justify their presence. No one should sit on the board for more than three years – a chairman for four – and then off forever. A rolling membership which brings in new talent, new ideas and hopefully more young members, as I say above, people who want something – homes, progress, transport etc. Again, there needs to be a major reduction of government appointees pedalling theory and policy at the expense of local people at the coalface. We have had chairmen whose main qualifications are 'that they all love the Lake District' (essential!) and 'had fond memories of their days as evacuees in the war'! How ridiculous that such appointees spawned by government are somehow superior to the experience and intellect of a small woodland owner or Family hill sheep farmer or quarry owner!

Even planning officers require rotation around the national parks lest fixed ideas become the norm. So often because there is so little change, officers learn to 'slant' presentation of applications in ways which achieve the outcomes they – the board – desire. Brown window frames, alien and almost unknown prior to 1960, but now the preferred fashion; Lakeland Slate everywhere and shining skylights reflecting in sunshine etc., are taboo! It is difficult to avoid the conclusion that Planning has nothing to do with conservation, environment or the jobs and livelihoods of those who have made Lakeland what it is over 50 years, but is exercised for the benefit of developers and the construction industry.

In conversation with a very well known and respected Estate Agent visiting us annually, over coffee we touched on that hot issue always kicked into the long grass – 'homes for locals versus wealthy incomers'. To which his response was: 'Look, we have been fiddling around for the past 45 years and "they" have no intention of resolving the problem. Original concepts of planners as helpers and facilitators have long since been filed under the heading Regulation and Development Control.'

The 1971 Sandford Report merely underlined the two objectives, preservation and promoting public enjoyment, the precursors of Lakeland enjoyment preserved in aspic. There are, here and there, hints of change, as when a farmer journalist discovered a tricky planning application near his farm went through – 'You could have knocked me down with a feather.'

Predictably the negativism towards the indigenous which has been a constant source of friction sadly seems to have brought about the latest unequal and opposite reaction with the publication by Eric Pickle's 'National Planning Policy Framework'. As Simon Jenkins, Chairman of the National Trust, has commented, it is to replace all previous regulation and encourages building wherever the market takes it.

There may be some controls in AONB's and National Parks and Greenbelts but there will be a presumption in favour of sustainable development (whatever that is) assuring 'localism' in decision making and no one pulling strings behind the safety curtain – back-handers, trade offs: 'We'll give the money for a swimming pool', etc., 'if our application goes through/is favourably received'. Nudge, nudge – accompanied by a fair wind from the local press.

Although many of us have suffered and resent the straight-jacket of the National Park's policies, like all my native born friends we do value, enjoy and love our homeland in the Lakes but hitherto authority has been unwilling to trust or respect us, despite assurances that we were born here and do not wish to make a *mess on our own doorsteps!*

Examples of undue intrusion in design, sterilization, preservation and unnecessary restriction by the board abound and must fill the 'dead' files at Murley Moss to overflowing. Herewith a few common examples.

- A farmer outside the park but close to the edge applied for a retirement bungalow and eventual farm worker's house. It was to have two spare bedrooms in the attic and a storeroom. Disallowed, because it was not of an appropriate size for a farm worker! (Such a farm worker might have won the lottery!)
- A young man married to a farmer's daughter wished to convert part of an adjoining redundant barn to a house so they could care for her ageing parents. Disallowed, so in the fullness of time the Local Authority will need to provide carers!
- A widow, not far from here, sought to convert two small buildings adjoining the existing house so that her son and daughter had a house each and mother would have been in the middle. Refusal because the farm of 36 acres was deemed non-viable. Whether or not the farm/holding was viable is a matter for the applicant's banker or financers and none of the board's business. Result: she sold the steading and cleared out into Cockermouth. A developer purchased it, put in plans for conversion of buildings into six holiday cottages, and twelve parking spaces. These were passed but he went bankrupt, fortunately, but the farmstead is presently occupied by a couple and is an untidy mess.
- Another family, 30 years ago, applied to improve the old farmhouse which was in a bad state of repair – adding a wing. The refusal so angered the applicant, who was happily able to sit and wait, that he erected the largest ugliest barn you could imagine for his lorries. It stuck out like a sore thumb but has mellowed over 25 years until no doubt a new planner appeared and applied some common sense to the matter and the house improved with the extension.

- A young man inherited a barn and four acres in a village, 30 uneconomic miles distant from the home farm. After a terrific battle over a parking space at the back, approval was given because it was proved he could go around the side entrance to his land, but in the upshot two neighbours were denied a parking space each, which would have been part of a deal. And because of the occupancy clauses mentioned later, the property took ten years to sell! Of course, there were speculators around to offer half its value on the chance that strings might be pulled. It took a snowstorm to collapse the roof of a picturesque bit of the village before restoration began, and today you would think it had always been there.

Alas, not everyone among the local young people can wait so long for a roof. People from the south of England and Europeans are just appalled that decaying properties, derelict barns, off-lying buildings in the Lune Gorge extension/amalgamation of the Lake District and Dales National Parks are just allowed to waste.

In the 1960s a well-known London business man moved to West Cumbria and established his thermometer factory. Living at Keswick he eventually became chairman of the Board (LDSPB). A wealthy man, he was not averse to rattling a lot of cages, so when a whole chapter of occupancy restrictions and control were introduced in 1972 he was highly critical that 'the Board's Policy was to preserve and reproduce all those features that happened fortuitously before planning was thought of'. He quoted Lord Scarman: 'The Protectors of the People in one generation become the abusers of the people in the next.'

The localism bill now before parliament is a straight developer's romp. Drafted by Eric Pickles and Vince Cable, the Business Secretary, it stresses business and 'national economic policy over conservation at every turn'. The word countryside appears 4 times – the words 'development and business', 340 times.

There has always been this conflict between those who seek Lakeland in Aspic and those born here who seek other employ rather than the tourism-generated low wage economy (no prospects) jobs dubbed by one teacher 'chamberpot and spanner jobs'.

Will Hutton, the famous social economist, has criticised those whose suspicion of some development has become a fetishistic obstruction to every form of modernity. Native born residents, for example, seeking jobs, double glazing in their homes, and transport to work, realise that the National Park faces a dilemma or in military terms, 'divergent objectives'. You cannot profess to create jobs and employment and have a 'quiet area'. There is limited scope and opportunity for teleworking/cottages, The villages where my generation grew up were noisy, busy, dirty, with clarty roads of horse, cow or sheep droppings! Incomers get uptight when other local residents – the Swaledale sheep – come off the common and invade their gardens.

It is a classic 'Corkey the Cockerel' situation. Some of these folk realise we have a problem and the sensible ones know that they themselves are part of the trouble.

It is my opinion that governments of both political colours have made up their minds – that as Thatcher and Blair foolishly sold off many of our urban Parks and open spaces for development, we in Lakeland are destined to become a *playground and theme park*. After all, thanks to motorways, most of Cumbria is but three hours from our five largest industrial conurbations.

Let no one delude themselves about local democracy (localism), decennial structure plans, consultations etc., etc. It is the Mandarins of the civil service departments in London who decide such long-term policy goals (if we have any) for roads, railways, schools, hospitals or power generation – and as political parties come and go their respective often inexperienced ministers can only 'tweak' and fiddle at the edges. Since 1945 Britain has been cursed by a lack of highly experienced civil servants (as opposed to the French). Regardless of your views on Europe, remember that three Agriculture Commissioners were small farmers: McSharry – Eire; Fischer – Austria; and Mrs Fisher-Bole – Denmark. In government the Danish Fisheries minister was a trawler owner. In Britain, ministers hardly have time to settle their feet under a desk before being whisked off to another Department of State – not because he has potential, rather because he or she is a good 'talker' and can pull the wool.

You don't believe me? Look at the pattern in two major disasters – Foot and Mouth and the sorry state of our transport system. I can only recall one working farmer as chairman of the board.

As Hutton observes of the Swiss and many of us know, scenery is their only asset in the same way as Iceland's only resource is cod – no wonder they chased off the English! But the Swiss make the scenery work for them – they enhance it and actively encourage people to make their living in the hills. And my friends in the Gudbrandsdalen, Norway, are encouraged to do the same ... *where I picked potatoes sixty-three years ago you find the valley's finest golf course, and fifty flats beautifully landscaped into the mountain side with a valley view.*

Honey pot towns have parking problems be they in the Alps, Italian Riviera, Keswick, Windermere or Carlisle (notorious for its total lack of vision). The Swiss and Germans build underground car parks – out of sight – at key locations. If you seek a parking place in the city of Konstaniz, well, it's deep underground in the city centre, handy for business, shopping, eating etc. However, such far-reaching schemes require investment in the long-term future – something the British are notoriously bad at, because taxes might have to be raised and no fast bucks on offer in the short term. Our Lakeland towns you would imagine seek to drive visitors away with high charges and draconian enforcement with no 'discount' encouragement to local residents. Keswick could do with four large car parks at the north, west, east and southern entry points (temporary summer season if you like), served by a minibus diagonal free bus service – through a 'hexagone' as the French call it, across the town. 'Bring 'em on bring 'em in' and we all gain. A deal to lease the local showground at certain times of year perhaps?

Some years ago the idea of a Tourist Tax was mooted. Enthusiastically supported by the then National Park Officer. It fell flat – as you would expect. The B & B/Hotel

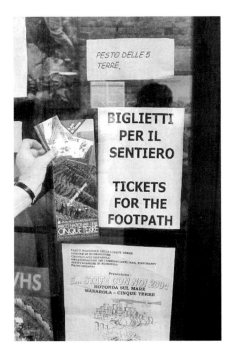

My wife buys her ticket to pass the turnstile and walk the 'Cinque Terra' path along the Ligurian Coast – which has World Heritage status.

trade were up in arms. Yet the Europeans do it. Drive in Switzerland and you pay for a car 'sticker'. To walk for two kilometres on the World Heritage Cinque Terra path on the Ligurian coast cost us 5 Euros each. Visitors never query the charge at the turnstiles, but the path runs for miles. My hotel managing friends on Insel Reichenau collect and make a return to their Local Authority for all the guests each quarter. You book a holiday in the Black Forest and there is a tourist charge covered in the small print. It seems that *the British expect* the Lake District Park *to be free*, come what may. Needless to say the resident gardeners – farmers and landowners – are expected to contribute to running the Park through the County Council tax but we are not allowed a lick from the honey pot while the tourism industry benefits. Only farmers with bed and breakfast – and not all seek this income or are able to take visitors – may gain some benefit.

It would be 'so difficult to administer' is the stock answer for no action. Yet a Tourist Tax would be so easy to administer and collect. Goodness me, where have all our practical administrators/organisers gone? The inheritors of a generation which could conceive, plan and build three harbours the size of Dover between 1942 and 1944 are now incapable of fixing anything.

What is so sad, if I go to the US I must book in advance to go down to the river in Grand Canyon. If I wish to see the Great Redwoods I am quite likely to arrive and find the park closed for some environmental reason. And to view the Kiwi bird in New Zealand I am very strictly 'controlled' – no noise, no flash etc., etc.

Funny thing, the Europeans can do it so I suggest the National Park and Local Authorities go visit and take a look.

I am fortunate in that in my outbuildings is a large loft so I can store copies of the dozens of reports, development control committee minutes, conferences and forums which one day will involve two journeys to the recycling to dump! Structure plans and consultations in pathetic progression, conferences galore, all fronted by noble mountaineers or TV personalities about 'Lakes for living and life' etc., with a £599 price tag, all well supported by a 'coterie' of Planning Officers, Local Government Officials, and a host of those lesser lights employed on that curse of modern administration, the three-year short-term contract – attending to further their CVs for their next move. Of course you would expect that those whose lives, livelihoods and lands were being discussed and futures plotted out – the farmers, small landowners and country workers – would be there in force. Sadly, they are notable by their absence.

The Goodman report a few years ago caused a measure of enthusiasm among the younger more progressive Lakeland residents as they sensed that at last someone was going to listen. Eleanor Goodman's conclusions were in line with much local thinking but it now collects cobwebs and dust in Whitehall. It was followed by a weighty 'tome' from the Commission for Rural Communities by the government's 'Rural Advocate' (Dr Stuart Burgess), which hardly broke any new ground. Then the Taylor Review, 'Living and Working in the Countryside', directed particularly on the South West and produced for yet another government department – it focussed particularly on affordable homes and job opportunities for non professionals and those in lower wage brackets.

But since then we have endured the Lehman banking collapse and the world financial crisis. Both events coincided with a steep rise in world food prices, sufficient to cause panic to the representatives of a nation which, as I pointed out earlier, assumed our industrial prowess would enable us to source food from anywhere on earth – but now only if we can pay for it.

To this end the Labour Government published two reports – 'Food 2030' and 'Food Matters' – towards a strategy for the twenty-first century; the challenges defined as 'Sustainability, Security and Health'.

Time will tell but it remains an open question whether the upland farms will be expected to play a role again in food production as they did in the last war or that the 'goods' they will provide are the fashionable requirements – clean water, carbon and climate management, recreation, as well as the more traditional industries of forestry and farming. Since the 1980s the environmental dog has wagged the farming tail. Hill farmers have become a threatened species, despite training schemes for shepherds etc. (a notable example of cosmetic tinkering). If there are no hill farms – steadings, outbuildings, barns sold off to wealthy incomers (immigrants) – no need for more shepherds? Study the *Lakeland Shepherds' Guides* for Commons throughout the area and you will observe a dramatic disappearance of owner-occupied farms, the

Tommy Winder, like my father a veteran of World War I, became a roadman but lived beside the village green and had a cow and heifer grazing on the common beside his house. Used to farm work, he often came to help out and here he is sowing oats with a fiddle drill in the 1940s.

disappearance of their hefted flocks or amalgamation with others to such an extent that from my memory of 1949 there were ten Commons Graziers on Fauld's Brow – today there are three.

Worse still, in too many cases the remaining farmers of my generation have no one to follow. The crisis is here and for years we could see the tipping point approaching, but it will require a devoted long-term effort – possibly over fifty years by the N.T., FOLD, National Park, to redress the situation. As one commoner observed, 'By 2011 the value of our native sheep and the knowledge, experience, and skill of their shepherds who tend them would have been acknowledged in a genuine partnership with Natural England, yet it worries and infuriates me that sheep are still being forced off the Commons.' But to the experts of Natural England (oozing with book learning and no experience), you can adjust the grazing density up and down by replacing or removing a few livestock here and there. You buy them down at the supermarket – batches of 25 or so of Swale hoggetts are offered as 'loss leaders'. Store bullocks to control the bracken also on offer and market forces will fix everything.

Presently, the walkers, bikers, ramblers, have taken over and to quote my neighbour when he caught up with some youths engaged in a cross-country race across his land and complained to the owner of an Outward Bound centre, 'Thoo's running thy business on my business!' Of course he wasn't invited to the Centre's Christmas party!

We are entering a very dangerous period with our emphasis on tourism, holiday cottages and leisure activities. These are all market responses with no long-term strategy; much of the dangerous expansion happened post Foot and Mouth proposed by a Ministry whose advisors could only think of 'on farm holidays' so now the area has a huge 'glut' of such property, with much of it for sale.

Cutting oats with three horses in 1936 at Brownrigg. Neighbour Willy Benn's binder and white mare with our 'Lady' and 'Tib'.

Their compensation spent, customers in short supply, alas many farmers now find the tax-man cometh. The diversification and conversions extended far beyond the National Parks from the Border to Lancaster, Whitehaven to Alston, whole villages in the Eden Valley without a single farm given over to a weekend population – but they bring trade? This is not always the case. Many shop at home before they set out; others call at supermarkets on the way, fully aware that the local store – a fond image of the sociologist – usually has to charge the highest price it can to stay in the village.

So the predicament in which our National Parks find themselves is put beautifully by the writer and broadcaster of 'One Man and His Dog' fame, Phil Drabble. 'It is easy enough to be generous with other people's goods or land, but despite their title, National Parks are neither parks nor national.'

'So part of the price we are prepared to pay to keep the countryside we love might well be to dip our hands into our pockets to pay for the privilege of enjoying ourselves there, precisely as shooting and fishing men have done for generations. The added contribution might well tip the balance from loss to profit for those at present trying in vain to scratch a living there, so helping to preserve the landscape undefiled. The something-for-nothing school who are forever whinging about their "rights" over other people's land, should realise that enjoyment of the countryside is cheap at any price, and we tend to value most what is some sacrifice to buy ...'

I am not alone with regard to a small visitor charge for our National Parks. If I go to my local town I am obliged – like all country people for whom a car is vital – to pay heavily to park even for a short time. Visiting our big cities costs us dear but Paris and Berlin offer me a weekend break plus a bundle of metro/bus tickets free.

Nevertheless, we must recognise that the Lake District is in danger of being overrun as more and more visitors come for a day, short break or holiday. As we have noted, there has been a tiresome procession of conferences, initiatives, forums, consultations etc. on 'homes for locals'. Many suggestions have been advanced but no organisation is prepared to bite the bullet. Housing Associations? Maybe – there are some good examples and it is suggested that perhaps benevolent landowners might be prepared to 'give' the land with appropriate safeguards about its future management. Too often in the past we have experienced land given for a community-worthy cause or need – taken over by a council and sold for gain without suitable protection clauses. When Thatcher decided to sell off council houses under right-to-buy legislation, how many National Park Officers or Board Chairmen resigned or threatened resignation over the issue? My friends on the board described the move as a disaster for local families trying to acquire a home. The 'council' houses in our villages disappeared within 18 months and with shrewd sitting tenants making a substantial killing. A self inflicted wound.

It is no use going along the bribery trail – permission to build x-number of houses on a site (always desirable for the Construction Groups), with y-number of houses to let. Wise men see the Pickles proposals opening the flood gates to market forces. It is the outcome of intense lobbying by the construction industry. Pickles and Cable are mere purveyors of building plots to the capitalist classes.

It is well known that the number of plots with residential planning permissions held by developers has varied between 300,000 and 350,000 every year since 2003. At current rates of construction that equals three years of housebuilding in their land banks. The proportion of planning applications approved is around 95%. The big housebuilders who have for years been colluding with government to blame the planning system for the housing shortage, cannot believe their imminent good fortune. All parties for decades have declared the need for more homes to be built so houses would become more affordable, but that's not what developers want. Restricting the supply increases profit margins. Under the 'Major' government planning rules the proportion of houses built in 'brown field sites' rose from 55% to 80% but the Pickles/Osborne relaxation will cause developers to build on the cheaper more profitable sites on virgin land. Thus Greenbelts are under threat as 'brown field' tatty difficult sites are by-passed and undeveloped to (dis)grace our towns and cities. No wonder Greenbelters are up in arms so the pressure on the national Parks and AONBs will increase from those wealthy enough to move, relocate or retire.

Despite protestations by National Parks, Historical Societies and battalions of the C. P. R. E. etc., the troika Cameron, Osborne, Pickles, are to stake their political reputations on reform of and abolition of whole swathes of planning regulation and control. This is not before time because many of us have seen the ballooning growth of the 'planning industry'. To mix metaphors the whole British economy has suffered under the embrace of a planning octopus whose tentacles have invaded the farthest boundaries and personal aspects of life in Britain. Think about the Planning bonanza over the London cross-rail link or fifteen years delay over Heathrow expansion! Strangely, hitherto, farmers have been able to erect new buildings with limited interference, perhaps as a result of lobbying by the land owning 'toffs'. Assurances that AONBs and National Parks Conservation Areas will be protected could have reverse effects on Cumbria and Lakeland by forcing the well-heeled from leafy suburbia in the green belts to move here and other protected areas, to commute by car to city jobs. Perhaps we are in for even greater pressures on our homes, villages and farms. Not the 'Highland Clearances' but the Lakeland invasion.

As the late Alan Clark famously observed, 'Every government requires someone who is prepared to be "economical with the actualité".'Not just the countryside but the small townscapes within it are also at risk from the developers. Small towns in Norfolk and Saxmundham in Suffolk have courageously resisted the invasion of supermarkets and their unrelenting pressure. Despite overwhelming opinion against them these supermarket chains can afford batteries of lawyers to wear down the opposition.

Turned down, they go away for a while, resubmit a modified plan attaching a few tempting 'goodies' (a sports ground, community hall, gallery or historic building restoration) to weaken the opposition of councillors until they break and give in lest the superstore applicant goes to appeal – the Council lose, and are faced with the applicant's costs. You cannot seek judicial review on planning grounds; only on the grounds that the Council did not follow correct procedure. Years ago the far-sighted deplored the building of a large supermarket in Penrith and its destruction of village stores Despite all the local anger and protest we enter the second decade of the twenty-first century with the opening of two more – confirming all the worst effects so admirably described by Andrew Simms in his book, *Tescopoly: How one shop came out on top and why it matters*.

Both Conservatives and Lib. Dems in opposition promised to give communities a right of appeal against planning decisions and limit the developers' rights. But government has been 'nobbled' by the construction industry, and the developers with a national newspaper currently championing their fight against Pickles, has revealed a series of stark conflicts of interest. The right to appeal against a planning decision must be hugely strengthened in favour of local opinion. All very well to protest with tongue-in-cheek about localism and increased powers or influence for local and parish councils, and some of us have noted in the past that parish or local council recommendations to the planners have just simply been ignored – we need not have wasted our time. I have attended so many 'consultations' over, for example, structure plans for the next decade, to see such meetings packed out with incomers, legal beavers, and special advisors.

At an enquiry to a structure plan in Kendal fairly recently, the Inspector was very sympathetic to people like me who cannot afford to attend day after day. However it was a revelation to note that discussion devolved into the position of commas, semi-colons, paragraphs and wording of the final presentation. To use a Yorkshire expression, a case of 'calling a spade – a bloody shovel'. In effect, a farce.

However the LDSPB and local councils should take serious note that in years to come, as the very wealthy and influential invade, these people will expect and demand the services they knew in Twickenham or Oxford.

There is also a huge loss of local knowledge as the population 'mix' changes and people of my generation, who remember (experienced) the disastrous floods, for example, in Borrowdale in 1966 *and* 1967, or Cockermouth Main Street in 1938. Can't happen again? A once in a hundred year event? Sorry, but we experienced those events!

Is it any wonder that a local pencil factory dating back to Queen Elizabeth I – its planned expansion turned down – put up the shutters and decamped to Workington. To sweeten the pill to local opinion, royalty was pulled in to declare the new factory 'open'. Continued pressure from the 'quiet area' lobby with scare stories about Alton Towers on Honister are misleading and outright selfish, putting employment at risk. But quad bike runs and mountain bike trails on Whinlatter – if anything more noisy and destructive – get the nod. Little wonder people question if it is a case of whom you know. Of course, not a squeak about the low flying jets screaming over Keswick or Honister.

Somewhere along the way the monolingual British swallowed American market forces conservatism to the letter from Reagan to Prof. Milton Friedman to Thatcher ('a rising tide lifts all boats') – and Tony Blair a capitalist wolf in sheep's clothing – so today it would appear that we have all accepted *Private equates to good, and Public means rubbish.* That is if you are not sitting at the bottom of the heap! Remember it was old Reagan who de-regulated the money markets which eventually resulted in the collapse of Lehman Bros. and the 2008 crash.

I have thought about homes for locals in the National Parks long and hard – changing my opinion several times. To ensure that the local people – young and old – working in the area are adequately housed, *local authorities must be charged with building and owning new houses for them to rent,* as was the case up to Margaret Thatcher.

And if we view the parks as national assets – which I'm sure we all do – then Central Government, the Exchequer, must adequately fund them and pick up the bill. In other words, Allerdale, Copeland, Eden, South Lakeland, must be funded and in charge of homes for rent. Developers will splutter in their coffee but they have no need to worry – they will get the work but the shifty speculators pulling strings will emigrate and good riddance!

When I put this to a member of the Commission for Rural Committees, he suggested I was putting the clock back! 'No, Jim,' I retorted, 'The people – those who are left – have seen the future and realised it doesn't work.'

You don't believe me? Then watch a few TV documentaries on housing in the rented sector and attendant scandals – there is a horror just round the corner. We are back in the era of Rachmann. At the end of WW2 Britain had the best housing stock in Europe – today we have a serious national problem. Profits being amassed from the poorest in society. In the countryside the rich buying up properties and driving out the locals. The argument is always tossed at farmers that such a situation means there must be willing sellers.

All very well to place the results of planning policy failure on farmers, but our 'politicos' would do well to remember that 40 years of declining agricultural prices relevant to profit yields and prices in industry mean that for very, very many farmers their only 'assets' for their retirement are their land and livestock – once disposed they are gone for ever. Some of the biggest farmers who appear so prosperous and create an impression with the public and politicians that all is well, are sailing very close to the rocks. Few proud farmers want to be seen to fail – but too many just melt away and the number of derelict farmsteads and land disposals in our countryside tell a sad story.

But as part of the solution to our problems in AONB's and the parks, we should actually be encouraging the wealthy retirees to 'buy up and do up', especially redundant barns surplus to modern farming. If they wish to take a risk on the property market, and invest their pensions, fine – but there are an increasing number who have paid silly prices and then invested as much again to virtually renovate the interiors to allow them to enjoy a London lifestyle. A perusal of the property sections of Cumbria papers should signal a warning that property in the 'Chocolate Box' image can go up and down. There are those who have come up here with visions of 'tele-cottages' and home working only to find the planning controls and restrictions imposed by the National Park and local councils in 'Canute' reflexes to development, cause them to sell up and clear out – there's no future.

Perversely, Pickles – Local Government Minister – is on the right lines by seeking the abolition of residency conditions and permitting 'isolated' development, i.e. houses here and there in the countryside as took place for a century before planning existed. But we have to cater for the less fortunate who are not upwardly mobile by accident of birth or opportunity.

Some of these conditions are so perverse that parish councils with a running average (over the last 25 years) of needing around twelve homes to be built, have turned down housing association schemes – initial cost, mortgage problems, low incomes, etc., resulting in stalemate.

Assurances about building a proportion of affordable homes have a hollow ring to young couples unless they are unemployed and on the 'social'. We have fiddled about with the rural housing problem for over 50 years – indeed ever since food was de-rationed and farm workers declined in importance. Then, in the 1950s, farm workers' houses became a feature of many, many farming villages. Over the years most have been sold, disposed of, or enlarged.

But there is no reason why councils cannot be empowered to *build and own good quality rentable houses of iconic design* (the buzz word of the planners), of which they and

the National Park can be proud. New designs, new materials, adoption of new energy capture, or tested small scale water power, roofing etc. instead of the traditional slate which is in danger of making our towns and villages look dull and dreary. But controls do need to be in place to curtail the invasion of supermarkets, the clutter of town streets in the park, with mountain gear floggers – or the invasion of a Main Street in Cockermouth by cafés and coffee shops.

Why have we allowed the problem to grow progressively worse despite the volumes of structure plans, reports, studies, which all fog the issue? Is it perhaps to do with a symbiotic relationship alluded to above between vested interests, developers and our planning system?

Perhaps its roots lie with our taxation of assets. For years the wealthy have moved into my home village. For instance, buying up a 'cot' (i.e. a hovel we remember in our youth in the '50s) for say £1,500 or less then; later £15,000 in the '90s – do it up and enjoy their large pensions for 20 years before exiting in a wooden box. A family 'share out' ensues of some £400,000+ amongst the grown-up children so the Chancellor collects a hefty amount of tax. So why bother about homes for a few locals?

Councils empowered with a duty to build those homes for young locals would face a frightening cost to the exchequer and local authorities as each family is a 'cost' to the Treasury – schools, bus services, medical centres or surgeries and so on for around 30 years.

Britain no can do – Jack's alright thanks! So we operate the pass-the-parcel pendulum as it swings back and forth like investment in the railways. Neither party prepared to commit lest they are caught holding the baby.

So today, a few of the opinion-formers in the county are becoming aware that we have lost a heritage. For some years now I have warned that the National Park has been at tipping point. The population of our villages are now largely incomers, some of whom, to 'identify', bury themselves recording, writing books, and some researching, about an area of which they have limited knowledge and even less experience. The population change represents a generational shift of which the National Parks have been slow to realise the implications.

As an amateur photographer of houses, villages and customs, I can best summarise what I have noticed as 'The Cotswolds have come to Cumbria'! Fast forward another decade, the National Parks and the nation will face a huge challenge and cost. The few farmers and country people remaining are in their fifties or seventies. But I do not see 'those guardians of all things rural' or Lakeland's many 'friends' turning up in task forces to do the 1001 jobs which those disappearing hard pressed farmers and villagers have done for a pittance, which the nation expects, because we pay you!

Older readers will remember the situation seventy years ago when extra 'hands' were needed on our Cumbrian and national farms to do the work. Bedford troop carrying lorries collected the 'details' (groups) of German and Italian P.O.W.s to be dropped off with their sandwiches at the farm gates of those farmers who had telephoned in to request so many prisoners to help with the work.

As you drive past 'Moota' it has a significance to those older farmers who remember the war. When branches and thorn close the footpaths; when the gorse and bracken are up to your shoulders – so pretty to look at and you remove the 'ticks' from your

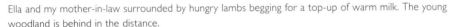

Ella and my mother-in-law surrounded by hungry lambs begging for a top-up of warm milk. The young woodland is behind in the distance.

The new hospital at Cockermouth. No increase in beds to cope with an ageing population, alas!

bared legs; when the roadside gutters are clogged; when dislodged trees surge down the Cocker and block the bridges – just think of the unseen maintenance done by generations of Cumbrian countrymen and women!

A recent report tells us what 'natives' have known and complained about for years – that country dwellers pay £100 more to the C.C. for 50% reduction in services. One wonders on which planet our politicians live to ignore a situation which the Scandinavian countries sorted out years ago.

It may be argued that the foregoing Chapter had little to do with 100 years of hill farming. But the concerns I express are *all* about hill farming, village llife, and the husbandry of those hill farmers and their families in a spectacular area.

Is the future a theme park or a World Heritage area? The former is virtually upon us now – the latter will involve a great deal of expensive 'conservation' with a comprehensive long-term strategy.

To bring back the smaller family farms to our valleys and their patterned fields; to return the hefted flocks to graze the fells, and the cattle to keep down the bracken, will be a 50–75 year undertaking far beyond the ken and the resources of those currently aware of and trying to tackle the problem with cash limited short-term 'fixes'. It is not generally realised that indigenous Lakes folk deserve the status of a 'rare breed'.

A decade has elapsed since I submitted a previous chapter to the House of Lord's Committee as part of a report on farming and the state of the countryside. Alas little of any note has happened. *The political establishment utter soothing noises, appoint Rural Czars, blame Europe for exacerbating the desperate problems of farmers and our land, but assume all will be well so long as there is food in the supermarkets and the landscape will be there, tended by a population happy to oblige.*

As this book goes to the printer's we've had yet another Government Committee's report, chaired by Ann Mackintosh MP – pointing to all the old problems – sparse population, isolated scattered communities in vast areas, poor or non-existent public transport, local people swimming against or drowning in a tide of tourism. Homes and development for the native-born unaddressed but as bad as ever and something most of us have warned, that the cost of living in these treasured areas of the countryside is much higher than in towns for which we pay disproportionate amounts of Community Charge for grudging minimal services.

Every so often 'sops' are delivered such as the new hospital in Cockermouth (which will actually have no more beds than the one it replaces!). Or grants will be given for the renewal or, for example, modernisation of village halls – after everyone has gone! Faster broadband has been promised for 90 per cent of the population but the other 10 per cent in the countryside can wait.

Parliament and the Westminster 'village' have 'received' yet another report. However politicians will continue ignoring the land and country folk ... until, as Marie Antoinette discovered, the folks revolt about the cost of bread...

A glut of holiday homes for sale in Cumbria.

The Howgill fells and the Lune gorge. Passengers riding the Pendelino trains with their eyes glued to laptop screens – some working but others no doubt watching films or playing computer games – miss out on the views of some of Britain's finest scenery from Lancaster to Carstairs.

THIRTY NINE

SUMMARY

As I write these final paragraphs we hear that beautiful area of the Lune Gorge and the Howgill fells are to become a 'park'. Despite the charade of consultation we now see that 'Fumf', the Whitehall Mandarin, has decided the area is to be 'nationalised' at no cost to the state. Disregarding unease in the Dales National Park and local concern, and bluster from Cumbria County Council, about the only question seems to be, what to call it!

A couple of days in London – the hustle and bustle, the Sardine Tube Trains, the rush, rush, rush – and it is obvious why these people seek to escape to my homeland for their pleasure, at my inconvenience.

Make no mistake, the beauty of the Howgills will change – imperceptibly at first but pernicious, and it is easy to see that yes, there will be 'controls' making us, the indigenous, feel imprisoned. Brannon and Swift all those years ago were, indeed, prescient in their predictions.

There is a desperate need for a re-appraisal of the function and purpose of a National Park. The Sandford report is of course the favoured *'gospel' to justify the growth of controls*. It was never mentioned at the time in 1948 that *we were being nationalised – and we were – without any compensation* (think railways and mine owners). Farmers received no compensation except the woolly phrase in the 1947 Agriculture Act about 'guaranteed prices and assured markets'. Marvellous what the threat of an empty stomach will do! In the 1950s as I have remarked, country people did not realise what was at stake – just getting on with their lives – and dismissed problems as the hard times of the '50s. It was unfair of Sandford and the nation to foster a fiction that the National Parks belong to us all – as Phil Drabble admirably noted.

Then, the population was around 50 million, but today it is nearer to 80 million, but the parks are not elastic and struggle to cope. Quoting laws and rights going back to pack ponies and the middle ages, various lobby groups choose to treat the countryside as their weekend playground going roughshod over residents as they please. Few restrictions have been placed on visitors beyond the 'Country Code' but the most onerous restrictions are placed on the lives, homes, farms and businesses of the remnants of the indigenous or native born inhabitants. No wonder farmers and CBLA are alarmed at the activities of Natural England and some demand the return of ADAS.

So what I am suggesting is that little Britain cannot afford the luxury of new hardwood forests today which will not 'yield' for 150 years when a refocused production policy would 'yield' in 40 years – paper for computers and IKEA furniture for houses. Furthermore, for Natural England to dispute a gold mine in Scotland or a tourist enterprise on the Honister Pass is extremely selfish. With jobs denied or destroyed we *all* pay – extra taxation, unemployment benefits, pockets of poverty and deprivation (oh yes, all there in Cumbria – just look) – because a few seek a 'quiet' area while others damage the very farms and environment generations of hill folks have created.

There are no National Parks in Ulster and a wise populace has been able to conserve the area, develop its attractions without the humbug of all the lobbyists colluding in the draconian powers now exercised by the political establishment through the agency or 'front' of Natural England.

Far too much 'power' has been divested to this Department of State whose whims and policies baffle farmers and country dwellers, treating conservation as more important than anything else. Sorry, but those who object about a few unusual but not rare plants on Honister Pass, who complain about conifers or solar power, reside in yesterday's world. With the alarming spread of oak disease, for example, across the country they may have to resign themselves to the Sitka Spruce which so far is remarkably resistant to all manner of nasties.

It cannot be emphasised too much or too often that in 1945 Britain was 60% self sufficient in food supply. This has now dropped to around 50% self sufficiency – both are magnificent achievements and a great credit to our farmers because the population has risen and all this done on a shrinking farming population and land area! The only 'negative' is that in the struggle to survive against falling prices and cash flow accountants both the CLA and the NFU have failed (both of them) to safeguard the 'family' farmers on whose work the glories of our landscape depend.

Too easy for the bodies to blame our 'gold plating' of European regulations and policies. To deride the efforts to protect their already much reduced *rural populations* by the new European Agriculture Commissioner – himself a Romanian small farmer.

As I have pointed out early on in this book, to preserve incomes farming has suffered a 'dog-eats-dog' response to market forces. A quick run through eastern, ex-communist Europe, will show you villages surrounded by large areas of abandoned land – awaiting the attentions of the International land-owing companies!

The financial crises of 2008 and 2011 reveal Britain in a perilous situation. We are a country run by the city and bankers calling the tune, laughing at incompetent politicians frightened to take remedial action. What do we expect with 18 millionaires in the cabinet? The hype is very different from the reality of the situation. It is facile to blame the 'Euro' because Wall Street requires a scapegoat and America is in quite a stew with the almighty greenback, the dollar – for half a century regarded as the world's reserve currency – in serious trouble. As well as France and Germany we in Britain have a responsibility to a strong, prosperous, peaceful Europe. I can just remember the Europe pre-1939 – the poverty, starvation, children without shoes, hopelessness – and I'm happy to celebrate 67 years of relative peace and prosperity. To allow bankers to plunge us into a catastrophe like the 1931 crash would be a crime against all those in our families worldwide who died in the Second World War. We are in danger of allowing money to rule the nation when it is merely a means to an end and ought to be our servant. All politicians are frightened to advocate the policies of Professors Keynes, Galbraith and Paul Krugman, which, stated simply, was 'in a crisis if the private sector will not create (invest in) jobs, then the public sector must do so'. I am sure you can think of many situations where useful work/jobs/industry could be created – countryside, nationwide and locally, when politicians summon the guts to outface the moneymen.

For Cameron and his coalition cabinet it is cheap and demeaning to suggest, for example, that the Greek Government 'failed to collect property taxes'. Those who live in glass houses should employ good glaziers! Which 'mobile' phone company was it that avoided/escaped millions in uncollected taxes through a cosy arrangement with a now 'retired' Treasury executive? Sorry, but as a devoted European I suggest that by resisting a 'Tobin Tax' on 'spiv' international financiers we – the British – are a large part of the problem and not the solution.

It is a national scandal that major public works projects can take a decade plus to gain approval. Yet in the National Parks we are similarly afflicted so businesses and young people just give up and move away. There are dozens of interested lobby groups, parties, organisations, who muddy the waters employing an army of solicitors, counsel, barristers, the lot, and dragging out a relatively simple process. Many many years ago two of us were deputised from the CLA to attend a meeting with the board at Brockhole over the problems created by mountain bikers on footpaths. The meeting was packed to the doors with every conceivable organisation determined to have their 'say'. We relaxed to listen to the broadsides flying back and forth – no need for us, the afflicted commoners, to say anything! In the end come 10.15 p.m., an exhausted Steele Addison summarised briefly thus: 'Ah, well I think we'll have to do something about it!' I reckon some 20 years have passed with little progress.

Some of us note that having indulged their pleasures, our visitors require all the comforts and services of the city life they have escaped – the 'après ski' after the day's fun. Pickles talks about and assumes local representation and democracy but our parish councils are increasingly packed with vocal incomers determined to run the show as they wish – never mind the 'special' nature of our National Parks or district councils.

Some years ago a senior Brussels EU Commissioner, due to retire, was asked at a Press Conference by a journalist in the know: 'If you had a choice, to which country in the Union would you retire?' A few moments of thought and to the inquisitor's surprise he said, 'Britain'. The nonplussed journalist enquired why. 'Well, in Britain events work so slowly I'd be dead before anything happened!'

I'm very sorry, but if influential articulate groups and organisations seek quiet and solitude then seek out what the Geographers call 'Mimoda country' – miles and miles of damn all; or go trek across a part of Iceland – if the wind doesn't cause you to batten down for a week! Or, for wild nature, then a tramp across Lapland in August will suit – if you can sleep for the midnight sun and the mosquitoes/midges. But if you seek a walk in warmer climes particularly along the Ligurian coast of Italy, you will very likely pass a turnstile and as Phil Drabble says, 'put your hand in your pocket'.

There are positive benefits to country living which have come with the new residents. For too long previous generations of country people have put up with minimal services from their Local Authorities because their parish councillors often took the view that if they asked for too much or too often, the 'rates' would go up. Compared with local towns such discrepancies were treated as part of life in a very rural area.

For many years the Caldbeck people disposed of their waste (there was very little – no plastics, no cans, no packaging) – the newspaper lit the fire and the tinkers and gypsies relieved you of any scrap metal. About 1938 we had a rubbish dump created in a disused very small quarry on Paddigill Brow by fencing off the front of the quarry – with not even a lock on the gate!

Even today on this farm I am obliged to take my rubbish bin to the public roadside a kilometre away, thanks to a neighbour (who worked in town and had served in the army, but was a part-time pig farmer). Said he in his broad dialect – 'Ah ast Ma Walker if thar were nee "hesh-car" aroond Sosgill?'

Answer: 'No'. Such a luxury never existed, and for years the tenant on this farm, for example, used to 'scop' (throw) his tins and bottles into the jungle wood by the farm track side (evidence: I was forever unearthing 'Camp Coffee' essence bottles!) So the neighbour went in 'ta see a fella at Cooncil. "Why were thur nee hesh-car aroond Mowerkin and Sossgill?" "Well, nebody had ivver ast for yan Mr Taylor!"' Quick as lightening my neighbour retorted: 'Aye – nin of us ivver ast for't rates demand but we still hev to pay awt syam!'

A few years later when the County Council mooted the idea that the parents of rural children should pay towards the cost of taxis and mini buses, the same man said quite rightly that it was 'they', the Authorities, who decided to transport the children to the town. Today we have housing pressure from town dwellers who move into 'catchment areas' for good country schools often to the detriment of the parish children.

Looking down from our hilltop farm located at 1000 ft onto Caldbeck in 1938, I could count six street lamps from the new electricity supply (such mind blowing modernity!) Upton Green, the School corner, the Post Office, the Smithy corner,

Churchtown and by the old Infant school. Come the 1960s – power shortages long past – and the new nationalised Electricity Boards were keen to 'sell', so villages like Lorton and no doubt Caldbeck had their street lamps doubled in number to such an extent that now at the start of the new century many parts of Rural Cumbria suffer 'light pollution'.

However, new people in the Lake District seldom realise the harsh realities of rural life. The hamlets of Fellside and Branthwaite were cut off for weeks in the winters of 1940–45.

No sooner would a track be cut through the snowdrifts by gangs of Italian Prisoners of War than the wind would blow, sweeping snow off the fields so the roads blocked up again. With the track open for a few days you stocked up quickly to prepare for the next blizzard. When I sold 'Brownrigg' in 1986 only one potential buyer asked what the winters were like 'up here at 1000ft a.s.l.' He was a Wigton based veterinary.

Where I write these lines today, we rely tenuously on a narrow back road with high banks either side and thick hedges. Just a few inches of snowfall is no problem but driven by a rising wind the fields clear and the snow is dumped in the lane. Life was better when the milk lorry used to visit the farms so the snowplough would make a pass every so often. But today we are ignored and have to wait our turn behind more important highways. Thus country people have to sit tight for days after a storm, or expensively for most of us, rely on a four-wheel drive car or vehicle.

It is in these circumstances that the National Park and local councils find themselves under pressure by those who expect the roads cleared 'pronto' so that some can travel to work. But then we find the problem identified by Swift with the birth of the National Parks – urban style solutions being imposed on rural communities. A parking problem in Buttermere many years ago was given to the late Councillor Bill Cameron: the solution – double yellow lines along the narrow roads to the village, with the objectors, the Vicar and some of the flock, carted off to Cockermouth Police Station in a police van. A problem which should have been 'sorted' with a few passing places which already existed if the council had been moved to look for, tidy up and slightly extend. Viewpoints where visitors wish to linger to take a 'snap', denied by heavy boulders along the verges. I go to Norway or Germany and find such viewpoints provided for my pleasure – not so in the Lake District.

For years remote farms and houses have had to rely on springs for water and on septic tanks for sewage. To put these services to such properties would be an impossible task. In Loweswater Valley we've had a problem with green algal bloom and the finger of blame pointed at the farmers. An expensive study, in which many outside bodies piled in to justify their funding, revealed that farmers, fertilisers and slurry were not the culprits. The number of farms has gone down markedly and livestock numbers are well below the 1960 levels. But now you have the attempt to apply the urban solution – so government is 'consulting' about proposals for all septic tanks to be registered before long under penalty of a £5,000 fine. We suspect this had nothing to do with water or lake quality – but the next move down the line will be all country property owners required to 'pay' for their septic tanks (a neat revenue earner), even though we provided them ourselves. There was a similar attempt about 30 years ago to charge us for our own spring water supplies collected off our own ground. Of course, if there's a drought we can just go 'whistle' or pay to have H2O tankered in!

New residents are often incredulous at how we were brought up with spring or well water – that a 'cosmopolitan' village like Caldbeck did not have a sewage system until the 1960s! In our childhood days every bedroom had a chamber-pot (much sought after these days for growing hyacinth bulbs). The guest bedroom possibly aspired to a commode. Otherwise it was the 'wee hoose', a two seater toilet, down the garden – the contents from a certain row of now 'des rez' cottages emptied into the beck over a picturesque bridge! On farms any 'heavy' materials would end up on the midden heap.

To go to dances, socials, Women's Institute meetings, many would start out across the field wearing wellies, to a point on the public roadside, where you changed to your shoes and hid the wellies in the hedge. You may have carried a torch (if the parish lamp – the moon – wasn't on) which you flashed time to time lest you tripped over a recumbent quiet cow. So today walkers become critical, demand metalling when paths lead them through swampy ground which dirties their white designer 'trainers'.

It is no surprise to us lifetime residents that as each year passes, the Mountain Rescue teams face an increasing load of accidents to careless, thoughtless, irresponsible visitors. There are slopes on this farm on which I would not venture in windy conditions let alone wet and storm. Despite all ostensible signs of progress in village life and services it is questionable whether in the round we are much better off. Those villages currently designated as suitable for growth (i.e. presumably able to provide all the 'urban' services necessary for the good life) seem destined to expand to become suburbs.

But if we think about Post Office closures, that was a blow at an essential village service, so we are virtually 'forced' to go to town to use those facilities which successive governments have sold off or privatised. To this day there is a forlorn post box on a wooden post at the 'Bluegate' crossroads on Fauld's Brow – it still attracts customers! It was put there in 1940 at the request of the Air Ministry and my father, so that he could post the timesheets for the crew of the *Observer Post* 'Easy One' to headquarters each week, so he didn't have a long trek to the village. Think of the village shops which disappeared with them – Embleton, Eaglesfield, Great Broughton, all gone. Yet a village like Caldbeck even had a Midland Bank branch for two days a week for a very long time after the war.

Once more the urban mind set of our planners, government departments, politicians and inspectors is revealed in a national failure to understand rural agricultural districts with all the implications for adaptation to harsh conditions, independence and self sufficiency by directing any development to large 'super' villages which become mini-towns scattered like islands in a mediaeval landscape. Admirably summarised in a letter to the *Herald* newspaper by Maggie Clowes of Appleby.

> *Sir, I read your article 'Newton Reigny appeal rejected' with utter amazement. There is surely more to this situation than appears in the article.*
>
> *Dividing a too-big house in two sounds rather sensible, particularly in view of the determination of the Government and Eden District Council to make better use of existing housing stock.*
>
> *But the reasons given for refusal are incredible. The inspector apparently stated that facilities in Newton Reigny were limited and any residents would have to make frequent car journeys to access virtually all services.*
>
> *Nearly everyone in rural Cumbria has to travel to access services; which villages have doctors, dentists, libraries, shops, post offices, banks?*
>
> *Journeys by private car were also likely to be necessary to access employment, opportunities. Surely, that's a given in this area.*
>
> *If this judgement sets a precedent, then the planners will surely reject Story's plan to build 143 houses in Appleby. With little, if any, employment opportunities in the town there are likely to be a great many private car journeys. Yours etc.*

My father came to Cumberland a hundred years ago as a 'fugitive' town boy to work in a farming village with a strong supportive base of related activities. Certainly he was an 'incomer' but he came to work in a farming community – not to retire to a rural retreat on a good pension.

The second half of his life was not only devoted to farming, but as an NFU Secretary he gave help and service to his generation of hill farmers with whom he so strongly identified.

With his hobby writing columns for local and national farming papers he always championed the cause of the grassland and hill farmers of northern Britain.

Long before the establishment of the now numerous Museums of English Rural Life he recognised that after WWI a whole way of life was changing fast. He collected relevant antiques, by-gones, furniture and artefacts which were being thrown out, as farming pulled out of the Great Depression. Succeeding generations have suddenly realised they were all gone as 'junk'.

Some looked on him as slightly eccentric at the time. Army call-up papers from 1916, ration books, petrol coupons, dipping papers, feeding stuff coupons, licences, ploughing orders, Ministry of Food leaflets and Ministry of Agriculture Growmore leaflets, records of the Barony Court pre-1900, Sports Posters, the family's farming accounts pre-1900, autumn sales slips, cream and milk sales, payment notes, the ledger of the Ivinson Mill patronised by John Peel for his Hodden grey tweed, John Peel's farm sale notice and memorabilia of the Beauty of Buttermere – my great great grandmother, whose escapades inspired novels by Melvyn Bragg, Graham Sutton and many others.

His collection included a Lewis Machine Gun (very illegal), a mantrap (lethal!), a Carlisle policeman's truncheon (nasty), grandmother's Victorian clothes and an R.O.C. Lady Observer's issue 'great coat' – all now in Tullie House.

As I have described above, we placed many of the outstanding examples of country and farmhouse furniture with the National Trust for Scotland where they are on view in several properties.

Given my time over again I would not choose to farm in a National Park but rather outside the boundary and beyond the straightjacket. Somehow we need to change our approach and attitudes to these very special areas, their individual economies and their native population. It is too easy, and it is a 'retreat' to dismiss today's problems as 'economic' which 'market forces' will fix. Across the world market forces have not 'fixed' anything – only made matters worse.

More and more countries are protecting their native or indigenous populations and their lands. We should be mindful of Professor David Bellamy's warning at a Travel Industry Award Ceremony when he urged us to visit quietly, tread lightly, and leave nothing but your footprints. To which I would add, don't dispossess us or buy us out but enjoy our landscape – go back home and return again as welcome visitors.

It is now 80 years since the great Kinder Scout trespass which brought about the National Parks and Open Access. However, the pendulum has swung too far in favour of preservation, conservation and recreation with Cumbria treated as a playground despite its position as one of our largest Agricultural counties. Indigenous Cumbrians have been mercilessly regulated, planned and controlled to the detriment of everyone. The time has come for 'controls' to be applied to other activities too. Yes! Horror and uproar, but very few readers will remember that era 1933–1953 – the depression, stagnation, food and fuel rationing, which haunted my generation.

Few readers of this book will remember the post-war East African Groundnut scheme. It became an example of a desperate nation attempting a short-term solution to increase the meagre ration of margarine by tearing up the bush of Kenya and Tanganyika. It was an expensive failure and the local population didn't matter!

There are today about a dozen huge multi-national companies which control food supply and own vast areas of land across the world. Surplus food – if there is much on offer – will go to those who can afford it. Despite a fall in our ewe flock market fluctuations do not imbue Lakeland sheep producers with a great deal of confidence. The biggest markets for 'New Zealand' today are the Asian countries.

Vested interests tell us that tourism is our most important wealth creation business – dependent of course on farmers, agriculture and rural workers in a large remote county. Short termism grabs a nuclear waste dump by a sort of 'County referendum' which the English – as opposed to the Swiss Cantons – seem unable to organise. Some of our politicians should reflect that when Chernobyl exploded it sterilised an area larger than Cumbria creating a huge no-go zone for ever. And Fukushima? ... Have we forgotten?

At long last the National Park is said to be planning 900 more homes for locals, but I am sceptical while the myth of 'private best – public rubbish' is foisted on the public. This dogma is like 'dry-rot' in a building where mycelium spreads unnoticed until the building suddenly collapses and we are all asked to rescue the 'privateers' and repair the damage.

In rural Britain, especially in the AONBs and National Parks, we need an approach similar to our Scandinavian neighbours to ensure that country people enjoy the same services and rewards as urban dwellers and so remove the push by the younger generation to outward migration. It has been common knowledge amongst teachers of country children, especially 'If they go into the sixth form you lose them'.

Indeed I was one – but returned in my thirties – earlier than many who have never returned. We go to towns large and small, Cockermouth or Carlisle, and note – for instance – buses with two or three passengers plying the housing estates hourly but ask for a minimum country bus service? 'No way' will private operators provide without a subsidy. Yet we spend billions on dubious overseas military adventures – 'Blue Streak' fireworks; Trident Missiles; Millennium Domes; Afghanistan and a 14-day Olympic 'Jolly' in Docklands.

In so many ways 'Natural England' deserves respect and support because miracles are expected of them … while politicians scatter a little money around rural Britain like confetti without doing much good.

So what of the future for our grassland, upland and fell farmers? We are experiencing the cumulative effects of BSE, organo-phosphates, F&M, bovine TB, etc., etc. – extreme weather patterns of climate change underlined by the 'long winters' of April 2012 and April 2013. None of these caused directly by farmers themselves.

From an urban population and their Westminster politicians we need a complete re-appraisal of farming and the countryside respecting what it is and accepting maximum land utilisation by, for example, commercial forests, wind turbines, solar power, polytunnels etc,. and not what the perceived image regards as a 'place to escape' – because for us it is still a tough or harsh place to live.

The misleading artificial price of land invokes questions about we older farmers 'hanging on' with suggestions we should 'move over', clear out, sell up in favour of the younger generaton … no suggestion by the NFU and smooth soothing comments from national and local politicians about the creation of Scandinavian style cooperation or a British equivalent of Credit Agricole in France or the Reiffeisen banks of Germany and eastern Europe.

We are persistently reminded that the CAP takes 40 per cent of the EU budget, but have we rich Europeans and particularly the prodigal British forgotten the havoc, starvation, scarcity and poverty some of my generation experienced between 1939 and 1951?

My father and I worked all our lives, making a frugal living to hand over to the next generation a farm, debt and mortgage free and, to quote the old sailors, 'without any [financial] monkeys in the rigging'. Eventually, when the city rat race becomes too stressful, my son will return to the farm which like me, is his life. But it does not pay.

Few give a thought as to where you find the banker prepared to grant a lifetime loan of a million or so to a young man in his thirties to buy a farm and another half million to stock and run it ... it used to be said that there are three ways into farming: Patrimony, Matrimony and Alimony! But there needs to be change. If our addiction to market forces is paramount then we must be prepared to ease the load on our grassland ,livestock, hill and upland farmers ... because when the crunch comes, Britain will need potato chips, not Microchips!

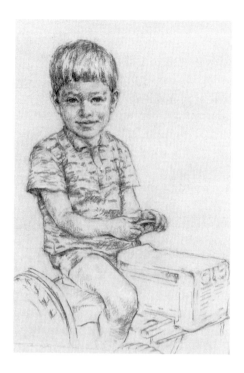

The future of farming? Our son, aged four, in a charcoal etching by the late Ronald Dickinson, the notable Cumbrian artist. As a school boy, John was keen to train as a Veterinary Surgeon but sciences could not be combined with languages. He studied French at the British Institute in Paris, German at the University of Konstanz and he taught himself basic Spanish before graduating from Oxford in Modern Languages. He gained his Master's degree in European Studies at the London School of Economics.

Remembering my own days as a student embarking on a career, we have always welcomed young people interested in farming to come and work here and gain experience. This is Nicole from Bavaria, the last in a long line of students who have come to us over the years. Her mother – ever proud of her Scottish roots and Lancashire upbringing – married Peter from the Sudeten Land of the Czech Republic and went on to live in Germany. Nicole studied veterinary science at Hanover University, gained her doctorate and lectured at Berlin University. Today she is on the research staff for an international pharmaceutical company.

Forty

We are the Survivors

We very much respect Mr Bridge of Bisley who penned these lines, for they describe the world enjoyed by the writers of our book over the last 100 years.

+ We were born before television, penicillin, polio shots, frozen foods, Xerox, contact lenses, videos, Frisbees, freebies and the Pill.
+ We lived before radar, credit cards, split atoms, laser beams and ball point pens, before dish washers, tumble dryers, electric blankets, air conditioners, drip-dry clothes and before man walked on the moon.
+ We got married first and then lived together – how quaint can you be?
+ We thought 'fast food' was what you ate in Lent.
+ A 'Big Mac' was an oversized raincoat and crumpet we had for tea.
+ We existed before house husbands, computer dating, dual careers; when a meaningful relationship meant getting along with your cousins and sheltered accommodation was where you waited for a bus.
+ We were before day care centres, group homes and disposable nappies.
+ We had never heard of FM radio, tape decks, artificial hearts, word processors, yoghurt and men wearing earrings.
+ For us 'time sharing' meant togetherness, a chip was a piece of wood or fried potato, hardware meant nuts and bolts and software wasn't a word.
+ Before 1940 'Made in Japan' meant junk; the term 'making out' referred to how you did in your exams; a stud was something that fastened a collar to a shirt and 'going all the way' meant staying on a double-decker bus until it reached the depot.
+ Pizzas, McDonalds and instant coffee were unheard of.
+ In our day cigarette-smoking was fashionable; grass was mown, coke was kept in a coal house; a joint was a piece of meat you had on Sundays, and pot was something you cooked it in.
+ Rock music was a grandmother's lullaby; El Dorado was an ice cream; a gay person was the life and soul of the party.
+ There were three grades of toilet paper: *Radio Times*, *Daily Despatch*, *Daily Herald*.
+ A money box was called a penny gas meter.
+ People had their toilet outside the home and ate their meals inside the home.
+ Transportable lightweight baths could be used in any room of the home.
+ A porn shop was a pawn shop; and a handkerchief was a coat sleeve. Footwear

was constructed of leather, iron and wood, a disc jockey was a National Hunt rider with a back injury.

- The recycling unit was known as the rag and bone man.
- An alarm was known as a knocker-up.
- The NHS was known as the doctor's bill, 6*d*. a week.
- Debt and illegitimacy were secrets, Macdonald only had a farm.
- Central heating was an oven place or firebrick, wrapped in a blanket.
- A duvet was your dad's overcoat.
- A kitchen unit was known as a slopstone.
- The Top Ten used to be known as the Ten Commandments.
- We who were born before 1940 must be a hardy bunch when you think of the ways in which the world has changed and the adjustments we have had to make. No wonder we are so confused and there is a generation gap!